Data Analysis and Decision Making

Revised 3rd Edition

by Albright, Winston and Zappe

NELSON / E D U C A T I O N

ISBN-13: 978-0-17-647793-6
ISBN-10: 0-17-647793-4

Consists of Selected Chapters
from:

*Data Analysis & Decision Making
with Microsoft® Excel,*
Revised 3rd Edition
ISBN 10: 0-324-66244-0,
© 2009/2006

Contents

Normal, Binomial, Poisson, and Exponential Distributions

© Photodisc/Getty Images

CHALLENGING CLAIMS OF *The Bell Curve*

One of the most controversial books of the past decade is *The Bell Curve* (Herrnstein and Murray, 1994). The authors are the late Richard Herrnstein, a psychologist, and Charles Murray, an economist, both of whom had extensive training in statistics. The book is a scholarly treatment of differences in intelligence, measured by IQ, and its effect on socioeconomic status (SES). The authors argue, by appealing to many past studies and presenting many statistics and graphs, that there are significant differences in IQ among different groups of people, and that these differences are at least partially responsible for differences in SES. Specifically, their basic claims are that (1) there is a quantity, intelligence, that can be measured by an IQ test; (2) the distribution of IQ scores is essentially a symmetric bell-shaped curve; (3) IQ scores are highly correlated with various indicators of success; (4) IQ is determined predominantly by genetic factors and less so by environmental factors; and (5) African Americans score significantly lower—about 15 points lower—on IQ than whites.

Although the discussion of this latter point takes up a relatively small part of the book, it has generated by far the most controversy. Many criticisms of the authors' racial thesis have been based on emotional arguments. However, it can also be criticized on entirely statistical grounds, as Barnett (1995) has done.[1] Barnett never states that the analysis by Herrnstein and Murray is *wrong*. He merely states that (1) the assumptions behind some of the analysis are at best questionable, and (2) some of the crucial details are not made as explicit as they should have been. As he states, "The issue is not that *The Bell Curve* is demonstrably wrong, but that it falls so far short of being demonstrably right. The book does not meet the burden of proof we might reasonably expect of it."

For example, Barnett takes issue with the claim that the genetic component of IQ is, in the words of Herrnstein and Murray, "unlikely to be smaller than 40 percent or higher than 80 percent." Barnett asks what it would mean if genetics made up, say, 60 percent of IQ. His only clue from the book is in an endnote, which implies this definition: If a large population of genetically identical newborns grew up in randomly chosen environments, and their IQs were measured once they reached adulthood, then the variance of these IQs would be 60 percent less than the variance for the entire population. The key word is *variance*. As Barnett notes, however, this statement implies that the corresponding drop in *standard deviation* is only 37 percent. That is, even if all members of the population were exactly the same genetically, differing environments would create a standard deviation of IQs 63 percent as large as the standard deviation that exists today. If this is true, it is hard to argue, as Herrnstein and Murray have done, that environment plays a minor role in determining IQ.

Because the effects of different racial environments are so difficult to disentangle from genetic effects, Herrnstein and Murray try at one point to bypass environmental influences on IQ by matching blacks and whites from similar environments. They report that blacks in the top decile of SES have an average IQ of 104, but that whites within that decile have an IQ 1 standard deviation higher. Even assuming that they have their facts straight, Barnett criticizes the vagueness of their claim. What standard deviation are they referring to: the standard deviation of the entire population or the standard deviation of only the people in the upper decile of SES? The latter is certainly much smaller than the former. Should we assume that the "top-decile blacks" are in the top decile of the black population or of the overall population? If the latter, then the matched comparison between blacks and whites is flawed because the wealthiest 10 percent of whites have far more wealth than the wealthiest 10 percent of blacks. Moreover, even if the reference is to the pooled national population, the matching is imperfect. It is possible that the blacks in this pool could average around the ninth percentile, whereas the whites could average around the fourth percentile, with a significant difference in income between the two groups.

The problem is that Herrnstein and Murray never state these details explicitly. Therefore, we have no way of knowing—without collecting and analyzing all of the data ourselves—whether their results are essentially correct. As Barnett concludes his article, "I believe that *The Bell Curve*'s statements about race would have been better left unsaid even if they were definitely true. And they are surely better left unsaid when, as we have seen, their meaning and accuracy [are] in doubt." ■

[1] Arnold Barnett is a professor in operations research at MIT's Sloan School of Management and specializes in data analyses about issues of health and safety.

6.1 INTRODUCTION

In the previous chapter we discussed probability distributions in general. In this chapter we investigate several specific distributions that commonly occur in a variety of business applications. The first of these is a continuous distribution called the *normal* distribution, which is characterized by a symmetric bell-shaped curve and is the cornerstone of statistical theory. The second distribution is a discrete distribution called the *binomial* distribution. It is relevant when we sample from a population with only two types of members or when we perform a series of independent, identical "experiments" with only two possible outcomes. The other two distributions we will discuss briefly are the *Poisson* and *exponential* distributions. These are often used when we are counting events of some type through time, such as arrivals to a bank. In this case, the Poisson distribution, which is discrete, describes the *number* of arrivals in any period of time, whereas the exponential distribution, which is continuous, describes the *times* between arrivals.

The main goals in this chapter are to present the properties of these distributions, give some examples of when they apply, and see how to perform calculations involving them. Regarding this last objective, analysts have traditionally used special tables to look up probabilities or values for the distributions in this chapter. However, we will see how these tasks can be simplified with the statistical functions available in Excel. Given the availability of these Excel functions, the traditional tables are no longer necessary.

We cannot overemphasize the importance of these distributions. Almost all of the statistical results we will learn in later chapters are based on either the normal distribution or the binomial distribution. The Poisson and exponential distributions play a less important role in this book, but they are nevertheless extremely important in many management science applications. Therefore, it is essential that you become familiar with these distributions before proceeding.

6.2 THE NORMAL DISTRIBUTION

The single most important distribution in statistics is the normal distribution. It is a *continuous* distribution and is the basis of the familiar symmetric bell-shaped curve. The normal distribution is defined by its mean and standard deviation. By changing the mean, we can shift the normal curve to the right or left. By changing the standard deviation, we can make the curve more or less spread out. Therefore, there are really many normal distributions, not just a single normal distribution.

6.2.1 Continuous Distributions and Density Functions

We first take a moment to discuss continuous probability distributions in general. In the previous chapter we discussed discrete distributions, characterized by a list of possible values and their probabilities. The same idea holds for continuous distributions such as the normal distribution, but the mathematics becomes more complex. Now instead of a list of possible values, there is a *continuum* of possible values, such as all values between 0 and 100 or all values greater than 0. Instead of assigning probabilities to each individual value in the continuum, we "spread" the total probability of 1 over this continuum. The key to this spreading is called a *probability density function,* which acts like a histogram. The higher the value of the density function, the more likely this region of the continuum is.

Probability Density Function

A **probability density function,** usually denoted by $f(x)$, specifies the probability distribution of a continuous random variable X. The higher $f(x)$ is, the more likely x is. Also, the total area between the graph of $f(x)$ and the horizontal axis, which represents the total probability, is equal to 1. Finally, $f(x)$ is nonnegative for all possible values of X.

As an example, consider the density function—*not* a normal density function—shown in Figure 6.1. It indicates that all values in the continuum from 25 to 100 are possible, but that the values near 70 are most likely. (This density function might correspond to scores on an exam.) To be a bit more specific, because the height of the density at 70 is approximately twice the height of the curve at 84 or 53, a value near 70 is approximately twice as likely as a value near 84 or a value near 53. In this sense, the height of the density function indicates *relative* likelihoods.

Figure 6.1

A Skewed Density Function

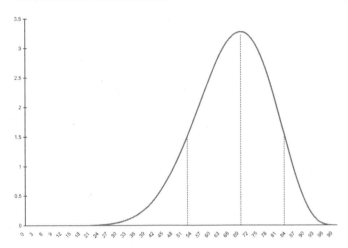

For continuous distributions, probabilities are areas under the density function. These probabilities can often be calculated with special Excel functions. They can be calculated even more easily with the RISKview add-in, which we discuss in Chapter 16.

To find probabilities from a density function, we need to calculate areas under the curve. For example, the area of the designated region in Figure 6.2 represents the probability of a score between 65 and 75. Also, the area under the *entire* curve is 1 because the total probability of all possible values is always 1. Unfortunately, this is about as much as we can say without calculus. Integral calculus is necessary to find areas under curves. Fortunately, statistical tables have been constructed to find such areas for a number of well-known density functions, including the normal. Even better, Excel functions have been developed to find these areas—without the need for bulky tables. We take advantage of these Excel functions as we study the normal distribution (and other distributions).

Figure 6.2

Probability as the Area Under the Density

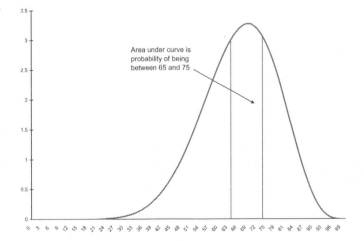

Area under curve is probability of being between 65 and 75

What about the mean and standard deviation (or variance) of a continuous distribution? As before, the mean is a measure of central tendency of the distribution, and the standard deviation (or variance) measures the variability of the distribution. Again, however, calculus is generally required to calculate these quantities. We will simply list their values (which *were* obtained through calculus) for the normal distribution and any other continuous distributions where we need them. By the way, the mean for the density in Figure 6.1 is slightly *less* than 70—it is always to the left of the peak for a left-skewed distribution and to the right of the peak for a right-skewed distribution—and the standard deviation is approximately 15.

6.2.2 The Normal Density

The normal distribution is a continuous distribution with possible values ranging over the *entire* number line—from "minus infinity" to "plus infinity." However, only a relatively small range has much chance of occurring. The normal density function is actually quite complex, in spite of its "nice" bell-shaped appearance. For the sake of completeness, we list the formula for the normal density function in equation (6.1). Here, μ and σ are the mean and standard deviation of the distribution.

Normal Probability Density Function

$$f(x) = \frac{1}{\sqrt{2\pi}\sigma} e^{-(x-\mu)^2/(2\sigma^2)} \quad \text{for } -\infty < x < +\infty \qquad (6.1)$$

The curves in Figure 6.3 illustrate several normal density functions for different values of μ and σ. The mean μ can be any number: negative, positive, or zero. As we see, the effect of increasing or decreasing the mean μ is to shift the curve to the right or the left. On the other hand, the standard deviation σ must be a *positive* number. It controls the spread of the normal curve. When σ is small, the curve is more peaked; when σ is large, the curve is more spread out. For shorthand, we use the notation $N(\mu, \sigma)$ to refer to the normal distribution with mean μ and standard deviation σ. For example, $N(-2, 1)$ refers to the normal distribution with mean -2 and standard deviation 1.

Figure 6.3

Several Normal
Density Functions

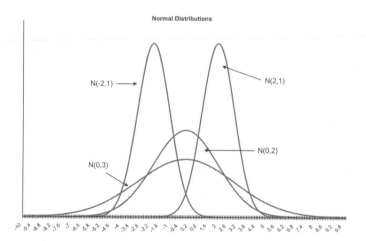

6.2.3 Standardizing: *Z*-Values

There are infinitely many normal distributions, one for each pair μ and σ. We single out one of these for special attention, the *standard normal* distribution. The **standard normal** distribution has mean 0 and standard deviation 1, so we can denote it by $N(0,1)$. It is also referred to as the **Z distribution.** Suppose the random variable X is normally distributed with mean μ and standard deviation σ. We define the random variable Z by equation (6.2). This operation is called *standardizing*. That is, to **standardize** a variable, we subtract its mean and then divide the difference by the standard deviation. When X is normally distributed, the standardized variable is $N(0, 1)$.

Standardizing a Normal Random Variable

$$Z = \frac{X - \mu}{\sigma}$$

(6.2)

One reason for standardizing is to measure variables with different means and/or standard deviations on a single scale. For example, suppose several sections of a college course are taught by different instructors. Because of differences in teaching methods and grading procedures, the distributions of scores in these sections might differ, possibly by a wide margin. However, if each instructor calculates his or her mean and standard deviation and then calculates a Z-value for each student, the distributions of the Z-values should be approximately the same in each section.

It is also easy to interpret a Z-value. It is the number of standard deviations to the right or the left of the mean. If Z is positive, the original value (in this case, the original score) is to the *right* of the mean; if Z is negative, the original score is to the *left* of the mean. For example, if the Z-value for some student is 2, then this student's score is 2 standard deviations above the mean. If the Z-value for another student is -0.5, then this student's score is 0.5 standard deviation below the mean. We illustrate Z-values in the following example.

EXAMPLE | **6.1 STANDARDIZING RETURNS FROM MUTUAL FUNDS**

The annual returns for 30 mutual funds appear in Figure 6.4. (See the file **Standardizing.xlsx**.) Find and interpret the Z-values of these returns.

Objective To use Excel to standardize annual returns of various mutual funds.

Solution

The 30 annual returns appear in column B of Figure 6.4. Their mean and standard deviation are calculated in cells B4 and B5 with the AVERAGE and STDEV functions. The corresponding Z-values are calculated in column C by entering the formula

=**(B8-Mean)/Stdev**

in cell C8 and copying it down column C.

There is an equivalent way to calculate these Z-values in Excel. We do this in column D, using Excel's STANDARDIZE function directly. To use this function, enter the formula

=**STANDARDIZE(B8,Mean,Stdev)**

in cell D8 and copy it down column D.

The Z-values in Figure 6.4 range from a low of -1.80 to a high of 2.19. Specifically, the return for stock 1 is about 1.80 standard deviations below the mean, whereas the return for fund 17 is about 2.19 standard deviations above the mean. As we will see shortly, these values are typical: Z-values are usually in the range from -2 to $+2$ and values beyond -3 or $+3$ are very uncommon. (Recall the *empirical* rules that we first discussed in Chapter 3.) Also, the Z-values automatically have mean 0 and standard deviation 1, as we see in cells C5 and C6 by using the AVERAGE and STDEV functions on the Z-values in column C (or D).

Figure 6.4

Mutual Fund Returns and Z-Values

	A	B	C	D	E	F	G	H
1	Standardizing mutual fund returns							
2								
3	Summary statistics from returns below			Calculated two different ways - the second with the Standardize function				
4	Mean	0.091						
5	Stdev	0.047						
6								
7	Fund	Annual return	Z value	Z value		Range names used		
8	1	0.007	-1.8047	-1.8047		Annual_return	=Data!$B$8:$B$37	
9	2	0.080	-0.2363	-0.2363		Mean	=Data!$B$4	
10	3	0.082	-0.1934	-0.1934		Stdev	=Data!$B$5	
11	4	0.123	0.6875	0.6875				
12	5	0.022	-1.4824	-1.4824				
13	6	0.054	-0.7949	-0.7949				
14	7	0.109	0.3867	0.3867				
15	8	0.097	0.1289	0.1289				
16	9	0.047	-0.9453	-0.9453				
17	10	0.021	-1.5039	-1.5039				
18	11	0.111	0.4297	0.4297				
19	12	0.180	1.9121	1.9121				
20	13	0.157	1.4180	1.4180				
21	14	0.134	0.9238	0.9238				
22	15	0.140	1.0528	1.0528				
23	16	0.107	0.3438	0.3438				
24	17	0.193	2.1914	2.1914				
25	18	0.156	1.3965	1.3965				
26	19	0.095	0.0859	0.0859				
27	20	0.039	-1.1172	-1.1172				
28	21	0.034	-1.2246	-1.2246				
29	22	0.064	-0.5801	-0.5801				
30	23	0.071	-0.4297	-0.4297				
31	24	0.079	-0.2578	-0.2578				
32	25	0.088	-0.0645	-0.0645				
33	26	0.077	-0.3008	-0.3008				
34	27	0.125	0.7305	0.7305				
35	28	0.094	0.0645	0.0645				
36	29	0.078	-0.2793	-0.2793				
37	30	0.066	-0.5371	-0.5371				

6.2.4 Normal Tables and Z-Values[2]

A common use for Z-values and the standard normal distribution is in calculating probabilities and percentiles by the "traditional" method. This method is based on a table of the standard normal distribution found in many statistics textbooks. Such a table is given in Figure 6.5. The body of the table contains probabilities. The left and top margins contain possible values. Specifically, suppose we want to find the probability that a standard normal random variable is less than 1.35. We locate 1.3 along the left and 0.05—for the second decimal in 1.35—along the top, and then read into the table to find the probability 0.9115. In words, the probability is about 0.91 that a standard normal random variable is less than 1.35.

Alternatively, if we are given a probability, we can use the table to find the value with this much probability to the left of it under the standard normal curve. We call this a *percentile* calculation. For example, if the probability is 0.75, we can find the 75th percentile by locating the probability in the table closest to 0.75 and then reading to the left and up. With interpolation, the required value is approximately 0.675. In words, the probability of being to the left of 0.675 under the standard normal curve is approximately 0.75.

[2]If you intend to rely on Excel functions for normal calculations, you can skip this subsection.

Figure 6.5 Normal Probabilities

z	0.00	0.01	0.02	0.03	0.04	0.05	0.06	0.07	0.08	0.09
0.0	0.5000	0.5040	0.5080	0.5120	0.5160	0.5199	0.5239	0.5279	0.5319	0.5359
0.1	0.5398	0.5438	0.5478	0.5517	0.5557	0.5596	0.5636	0.5675	0.5714	0.5753
0.2	0.5793	0.5832	0.5871	0.5910	0.5948	0.5987	0.6026	0.6064	0.6103	0.6141
0.3	0.6179	0.6217	0.6255	0.6293	0.6331	0.6368	0.6406	0.6443	0.6480	0.6517
0.4	0.6554	0.6591	0.6628	0.6664	0.6700	0.6736	0.6772	0.6808	0.6844	0.6879
0.5	0.6915	0.6950	0.6985	0.7019	0.7054	0.7088	0.7123	0.7157	0.7190	0.7224
0.6	0.7257	0.7291	0.7324	0.7357	0.7389	0.7422	0.7454	0.7486	0.7517	0.7549
0.7	0.7580	0.7611	0.7642	0.7673	0.7704	0.7734	0.7764	0.7794	0.7823	0.7852
0.8	0.7881	0.7910	0.7939	0.7967	0.7995	0.8023	0.8051	0.8078	0.8106	0.8133
0.9	0.8159	0.8186	0.8212	0.8238	0.8264	0.8289	0.8315	0.8340	0.8365	0.8389
1.0	0.8413	0.8438	0.8461	0.8485	0.8508	0.8531	0.8554	0.8577	0.8599	0.8621
1.1	0.8643	0.8665	0.8686	0.8708	0.8729	0.8749	0.8770	0.8790	0.8810	0.8830
1.2	0.8849	0.8869	0.8888	0.8907	0.8925	0.8944	0.8962	0.8980	0.8997	0.9015
1.3	0.9032	0.9049	0.9066	0.9082	0.9099	0.9115	0.9131	0.9147	0.9162	0.9177
1.4	0.9192	0.9207	0.9222	0.9236	0.9251	0.9265	0.9279	0.9292	0.9306	0.9319
1.5	0.9332	0.9345	0.9357	0.9370	0.9382	0.9394	0.9406	0.9418	0.9429	0.9441
1.6	0.9452	0.9463	0.9474	0.9484	0.9495	0.9505	0.9515	0.9525	0.9535	0.9545
1.7	0.9554	0.9564	0.9573	0.9582	0.9591	0.9599	0.9608	0.9616	0.9625	0.9633
1.8	0.9641	0.9649	0.9656	0.9664	0.9671	0.9678	0.9686	0.9693	0.9699	0.9706
1.9	0.9713	0.9719	0.9726	0.9732	0.9738	0.9744	0.9750	0.9756	0.9761	0.9767
2.0	0.9772	0.9778	0.9783	0.9788	0.9793	0.9798	0.9803	0.9808	0.9812	0.9817
2.1	0.9821	0.9826	0.9830	0.9834	0.9838	0.9842	0.9846	0.9850	0.9854	0.9857
2.2	0.9861	0.9864	0.9868	0.9871	0.9875	0.9878	0.9881	0.9884	0.9887	0.9890
2.3	0.9893	0.9896	0.9898	0.9901	0.9904	0.9906	0.9909	0.9911	0.9913	0.9916
2.4	0.9918	0.9920	0.9922	0.9925	0.9927	0.9929	0.9931	0.9932	0.9934	0.9936
2.5	0.9938	0.9940	0.9941	0.9943	0.9945	0.9946	0.9948	0.9949	0.9951	0.9952
2.6	0.9953	0.9955	0.9956	0.9957	0.9959	0.9960	0.9961	0.9962	0.9963	0.9964
2.7	0.9965	0.9966	0.9967	0.9968	0.9969	0.9970	0.9971	0.9972	0.9973	0.9974
2.8	0.9974	0.9975	0.9976	0.9977	0.9977	0.9978	0.9979	0.9979	0.9980	0.9981
2.9	0.9981	0.9982	0.9982	0.9983	0.9984	0.9984	0.9985	0.9985	0.9986	0.9986
3.0	0.9987	0.9987	0.9987	0.9988	0.9988	0.9989	0.9989	0.9989	0.9990	0.9990
3.1	0.9990	0.9991	0.9991	0.9991	0.9992	0.9992	0.9992	0.9992	0.9993	0.9993
3.2	0.9993	0.9993	0.9994	0.9994	0.9994	0.9994	0.9994	0.9995	0.9995	0.9995
3.3	0.9995	0.9995	0.9995	0.9996	0.9996	0.9996	0.9996	0.9996	0.9996	0.9997
3.4	0.9997	0.9997	0.9997	0.9997	0.9997	0.9997	0.9997	0.9997	0.9997	0.9998

We can perform the same kind of calculations for *any* normal distribution if we first standardize. As an example, suppose that X is normally distributed with mean 100 and standard deviation 10. We will find the probability that X is less than 115 and the 85th percentile of this normal distribution. To find the probability that X is less than 115, we first standardize the value 115. The corresponding Z-value is

$Z = (115 - 100)/10 = 1.5$

Now we look up 1.5 in the table (1.5 row, 0.00 column) to obtain the probability 0.9332. For the percentile question we first find the 85th percentile of the standard normal distribution. Interpolating, we obtain a value of approximately 1.037. Then we set this value equal to a standardized value:

$Z = 1.037 = (X - 100)/10$

Finally, we solve for X to obtain 110.37. In words, there is a probability 0.85 of being to the left of 110.37 in the $N(100, 10)$ distribution.

There are some obvious drawbacks to using the standard normal table for probability calculations. The first is that there are holes in the table—we often have to interpolate. A second drawback is that the standard normal table takes different forms in different textbooks. These differences are rather minor, but they can easily cause confusion. Finally, the table requires us to perform calculations. For example, we might have to standardize. More importantly, we often have to use the symmetry of the normal distribution to find probabilities that are not in the table. As an example, to find the probability that Z is less than -1.5, we must go through some mental gymnastics. First, by symmetry this is the same as the probability that Z is greater than 1.5. Then, because only left-tail probabilities are tabulated, we must find the probability that Z is less than 1.5 and subtract this probability from 1. The chain of reasoning is

$$P(Z < -1.5) = P(Z > 1.5) = 1 - P(Z < 1.5) = 1 - 0.9332 = 0.0668$$

This is not too difficult, given a bit of practice, but it is easy to make a mistake. Spreadsheet functions make the whole procedure much easier and less prone to errors.

6.2.5 Normal Calculations in Excel

Two types of calculations are typically made with normal distributions: finding probabilities and finding percentiles. Excel makes each of these fairly simple. The functions used for normal probability calculations are NORMDIST and NORMSDIST. The main difference between these is that the one with the "S" (for standardized) applies only to $N(0, 1)$ calculations, whereas NORMDIST applies to *any* normal distribution. On the other hand, percentile calculations, where we supply a probability and require a value, are often called *inverse* calculations. Therefore, the Excel functions for these are named NORMINV and NORMSINV. Again, the "S" in the second of these indicates that it applies only to the standard normal distribution.

The NORMDIST and NORMSDIST functions give left-tail probabilities, such as the probability that a normally distributed variable is *less than* 35. The syntax for these functions is

=NORMDIST(x,μ,σ,1)

and

=NORMSDIST(x)

Here, x is a number we supply, and μ and σ are the mean and standard deviation of the normal distribution. The last argument "1" in the NORMDIST function is used to obtain the *cumulative* normal probability, the only kind we'll ever need. (This 1 is a bit of a nuisance to remember, but it's necessary.) Note that NORMSDIST takes only one argument (because μ and σ are known to be 0 and 1), so it is easier to use—when it applies.

The NORMINV and NORMSINV functions return values for user-supplied probabilities. For example, if we supply the probability 0.95, these functions return the 95th percentile. Their syntax is

=NORMINV(p,μ,σ)

and

=NORMSINV(p)

where p is a probability we supply. These are analogous to the NORMDIST and NORMSDIST functions (except there is no fourth argument "1" in the NORMINV function).

We illustrate these Excel functions in the following example.[3]

---

[3]Actually, we already illustrated the NORMSDIST function; it was used to create the body of Figure 6.5. In other words, you can use it to build your own normal probability table!

EXAMPLE | 6.2 BECOMING FAMILIAR WITH NORMAL CALCULATIONS IN EXCEL

Use Excel to calculate the following probabilities and percentiles for the standard normal distribution: (a) $P(Z < -2)$, (b) $P(Z > 1)$, (c) $P(-0.4 < Z < 1.6)$, (d) the 5th percentile, (e) the 75th percentile, and (f) the 99th percentile. Then for the $N(75, 8)$ distribution, find the following probabilities and percentiles: (a) $P(X < 70)$, (b) $P(X > 73)$, (c) $P(75 < X < 85)$, (d) the 5th percentile, (e) the 60th percentile, and (f) the 97th percentile.

Objective To calculate probabilities and percentiles for standard normal and nonstandard normal random variables in Excel.

Solution

The solution appears in Figure 6.6. (See the file **Normal Calculations.xlsx**.) The $N(0, 1)$ calculations are in rows 7 through 14; the $N(75, 8)$ calculations are in rows 23 through 30. For your convenience, the formulas used in column B are spelled out in column D (as labels). Note that the standard normal calculations use the normal functions with the "S" in the middle; the rest use the normal functions without the "S"—and require more arguments.

Figure 6.6 Normal Calculations with Excel Functions

	A	B	C	D	E	F	G	H	I
1	**Normal probability calculations**								
2									
3	**Examples with standard normal**								
4									
5	**Probability calculations**								
6	Range	Probability		Formula					
7	Less than -2	0.0228		=NORMSDIST(-2)					
8	Greater than 1	0.1587		=1-NORMSDIST(1)					
9	Between -.4 and 1.6	0.6006		=NORMSDIST(1.6)-NORMSDIST(-0.4)					
10									
11	**Percentiles**								
12	5th	-1.645		=NORMSINV(0.05)					
13	75th	0.674		=NORMSINV(0.75)					
14	99th	2.326		=NORMSINV(0.99)					
15									
16	**Examples with nonstandard normal**								
17				Range names used:					
18	Mean	75		Mean	=Normal!$B$18				
19	Stdev	8		Stdev	=Normal!$B$19				
20									
21	**Probability calculations**								
22	Range	Probability		Formula					
23	Less than 70	0.2660		=NORMDIST(70,Mean,Stdev,1)					
24	Greater than 73	0.5987		=1-NORMDIST(73,Mean,Stdev,1)					
25	Between 75 and 85	0.3944		=NORMDIST(85,Mean,Stdev,1)-NORMDIST(75,Mean,Stdev,1)					
26									
27	**Percentiles**								
28	5th	61.841		=NORMINV(0.05,Mean,Stdev)					
29	60th	77.027		=NORMINV(0.6,Mean,Stdev)					
30	97th	90.046		=NORMINV(0.97,Mean,Stdev)					

Note the following for normal *probability* calculations:

- For "less than" probabilities, use NORMDIST or NORMSDIST directly. (See rows 7 and 23.)

- For "greater than" probabilities, subtract the NORMDIST or NORMSDIST function from 1. (See rows 8 and 24.)

- For "between" probabilities, subtract the two NORMDIST or NORMSDIST functions. For example, in row 9 the probability of being between -0.4 and 1.6 is the probability of being less than 1.6 minus the probability of being less than -0.4.

The percentile calculations are even more straightforward. In most percentile problems we want to find the value with a certain probability to the *left* of it. In this case we use the NORMINV or NORMSINV function with the specified probability as the first argument. See rows 12 through 14 and 28 through 30. ■

There are a couple of variations of percentile calculations. First, suppose we want the value with probability 0.05 to the *right* of it. This is the same as the value with probability 0.95 to the left of it, so we use NORMINV or NORMSINV with probability argument 0.95. For example, the value with probability 0.4 to the right of it in the $N(75, 8)$ distribution is 77.027. (See cell B29 in Figure 6.6.)

As a second variation, suppose we want to find an interval of the form $-x$ to x, for some positive number x, with (1) probability 0.025 to the left of $-x$, (2) probability 0.025 to the right of x, and (3) probability 0.95 between $-x$ and x. This is a very common problem in statistical inference. In general, we want a probability (such as 0.95) to be in the middle of the interval so that half of the remaining probability (0.025) is in each of the tails. (See Figure 6.7.) Then the required x can be found with NORMINV or NORMSINV, using probability argument 0.975, because there must be a total probability of 0.975 to the left of x.

For example, if the relevant distribution is the standard normal, then the required value of x is 1.96, found with the function NORMSINV(0.975). Similarly, if we want probability 0.90 in the middle and probability 0.05 in each tail, the required x is 1.645, found with the function NORMSINV(0.95). Remember these two numbers, 1.96 and 1.645. They occur frequently in statistical applications.

Figure 6.7

Typical Normal
Probabilities

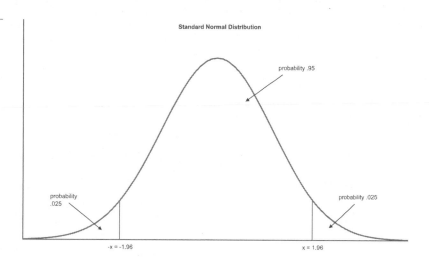

6.2.6 Empirical Rules Revisited

Chapter 3 introduced three empirical rules that apply to many data sets. Namely, about 68% of the data fall within 1 standard deviation of the mean, about 95% fall within 2 standard deviations of the mean, and almost all fall within 3 standard deviations of the mean. For these rules to hold with real data, the distribution of the data must be at least approximately symmetric and bell shaped. Let's look at these rules more closely.

Let X be normally distributed with mean μ and standard deviation σ. To perform a probability calculation on X, we can first standardize X and then perform the calculation on the standardized variable Z. Specifically, we will find the probability that X is within k standard deviations of its mean for $k = 1$, $k = 2$, and $k = 3$. In general, this probability is $P(\mu - k\sigma < X < \mu + k\sigma)$. But by standardizing the values $\mu - k\sigma$ and $\mu + k\sigma$, we obtain the equivalent probability $P(-k < Z < k)$, where Z has a $N(0, 1)$ distribution. This latter probability can be calculated in Excel with the formula

$$=\text{NORMSDIST}(k) - \text{NORMSDIST}(-k)$$

The normal distribution is the basis for the empirical rules introduced in Chapter 3.

By substituting the values 1, 2, and 3 for k, we find the following probabilities:

$P(-1 < Z < 1) = 0.6827$
$P(-2 < Z < 2) = 0.9545$
$P(-3 < Z < 3) = 0.9973$

As we see, there is virtually no chance of being beyond 3 standard deviations from the mean, the chances are about 19 out of 20 of being within 2 standard deviations of the mean, and the chances are about 2 out of 3 of being within 1 standard deviation of the mean. These probabilities are the basis for the empirical rules in Chapter 3. These rules more closely approximate reality as the histograms of observed data become more bell shaped.

6.3 APPLICATIONS OF THE NORMAL DISTRIBUTION

In this section we apply the normal distribution to a variety of business problems.

EXAMPLE 6.3 PERSONNEL TESTING AT ZTEL

The personnel department of ZTel, a large communications company, is reconsidering its hiring policy. Each applicant for a job must take a standard exam, and the hire or no-hire decision depends at least in part on the result of the exam. The scores of all applicants have been examined closely. They are approximately normally distributed with mean 525 and standard deviation 55.

The current hiring policy occurs in two phases. The first phase separates all applicants into three categories: automatic accepts, automatic rejects, and "maybes." The automatic accepts are those whose test scores are 600 or above. The automatic rejects are those whose test scores are 425 or below. All other applicants (the "maybes") are passed on to a second phase where their previous job experience, special talents, and other factors are used as hiring criteria. The personnel manager at ZTel wants to calculate the percentage of applicants who are automatic accepts or rejects, given the current standards. She also wants to know how to change the standards to automatically reject 10% of all applicants and automatically accept 15% of all applicants.

Objective   To determine test scores that can be used to accept or reject job applicants at ZTel.

Solution

Let X be the test score of a typical applicant. Then the distribution of X is $N(525, 55)$. If we find a probability such as $P(X \leq 425)$, we can interpret this as the probability that a typical applicant is an automatic reject, or we can interpret it as the percentage of *all* applicants who are automatic rejects. Given this observation, the solution to ZTel's problem appears in Figure 6.8. (See the file **Personnel Decisions.xlsx**.) The probability that a typical applicant is automatically accepted is 0.0863, found in cell B10 with the formula

$$=1-\text{NORMDIST(B7,Mean,Stdev,1)}$$

Figure 6.8

Calculations for
Personnel Example

	A	B	C	D	E	F
1	Personnel Decisions					
2				Range names used:		
3	Mean of test scores	525		Mean	=Model!$B$3	
4	Stdev of test scores	55		Stdev	=Model!$B$4	
5						
6	Current Policy					
7	Automatic accept point	600				
8	Automatic reject point	425				
9						
10	Percent accepted	8.63%		=1-NORMDIST(B7,Mean,Stdev,1)		
11	Percent rejected	3.45%		=NORMDIST(B8,Mean,Stdev,1)		
12						
13	New Policy					
14	Percent accepted	15%				
15	Percent rejected	10%				
16						
17	Automatic accept point	582		=NORMINV(1-B14,Mean,Stdev)		
18	Automatic reject point	455		=NORMINV(B15,Mean,Stdev)		

Similarly, the probability that a typical applicant is automatically rejected is 0.0345, found in cell B11 with the formula

$$=\text{NORMDIST(B8,Mean,Stdev,1)}$$

Therefore, ZTel automatically accepts about 8.6% and rejects about 3.5% of all applicants under the current policy.

To find new cutoff values that reject 10% and accept 15% of the applicants, we need the 10th and 85th percentiles of the $N(525, 55)$ distribution. These are 455 and 582 (rounded to the nearest integer), respectively, found in cells B17 and B18 with the formulas

$$=\text{NORMINV(1-B14,Mean,Stdev)}$$

and

$$=\text{NORMINV(B15,Mean,Stdev)}$$

To accomplish its objective, ZTel needs to raise the automatic rejection point from 425 to 455 and lower the automatic acceptance point from 600 to 582. ■

EXAMPLE | **6.4 QUALITY CONTROL AT PAPERSTOCK COMPANY**

The PaperStock Company runs a manufacturing facility that produces a paper product. The fiber content of this product is supposed to be 20 pounds per 1000 square feet. (This is typical for the type of paper used in grocery bags, for example.) Because of random variations in the inputs to the process, however, the fiber content of a typical 1000-square-foot roll varies according to a $N(\mu, \sigma)$ distribution. The mean fiber content (μ) can be controlled—that is, it can be set to any desired level by adjusting an instrument on the machine. The variability in fiber content, as measured by the standard deviation σ, is 0.1 pound when the process is "good," but it sometimes increases to 0.15 pound when the machine goes "bad." A given roll of this product must be rejected if its actual fiber content is less than 19.8 pounds or greater than 20.3 pounds. Calculate the probability that a given roll is rejected, for a setting of $\mu = 20$, when the machine is "good" and when it is "bad."

Objective To determine the machine settings that result in paper of acceptable quality at PaperStock Company.

Solution

Let X be the fiber content of a typical roll. The distribution of X will be either $N(20, 0.1)$ or $N(20, 0.15)$, depending on the status of the machine. In either case, the probability that the roll must be rejected can be calculated as shown in Figure 6.9. (See the file **Paper Machine Settings.xlsx**.) The formula for rejection in the "good" case appears in cell B12:

$$=NORMDIST(B8,Mean,Stdev\_good,1)+(1-NORMDIST(B9,Mean,Stdev\_good,1))$$

Figure 6.9 Calculations for Paper Quality Example

	A	B	C	D	E	F	G	H	I	J
1	Paper Machine Settings			Range names used:						
2				Mean	=Model!$B$3					
3	Mean	20		Stdev_bad	=Model!$B$5					
4	Stdev in good case	0.1		Stdev_good	=Model!$B$4					
5	Stdev in bad case	0.15								
6										
7	Reject region									
8	Lower limit	19.8								
9	Upper limit	20.3								
10										
11	Probability of reject									
12	in good case	0.024		=NORMDIST(B8,Mean,Stdev_good,1)+(1-NORMDIST(B9,Mean,Stdev_good,1))						
13	in bad case	0.114		=NORMDIST(B8,Mean,Stdev_bad,1)+(1-NORMDIST(B9,Mean,Stdev_bad,1))						
14										
15	Data table of rejection probability as a function of the mean and good standard deviation									
16				Standard deviation						
17		0.024	0.1	0.11	0.12	0.13	0.14	0.15		
18		19.7	0.841	0.818	0.798	0.779	0.762	0.748		
19		19.8	0.500	0.500	0.500	0.500	0.500	0.500		
20		19.9	0.159	0.182	0.203	0.222	0.240	0.256		
21	Mean	20	0.024	0.038	0.054	0.072	0.093	0.114		
22		20.1	0.024	0.038	0.054	0.072	0.093	0.114		
23		20.2	0.159	0.182	0.203	0.222	0.240	0.256		
24		20.3	0.500	0.500	0.500	0.500	0.500	0.500		
25		20.4	0.841	0.818	0.798	0.779	0.762	0.748		

It is the sum of two probabilities: the probability of being to the left of the lower limit and the probability of being to the right of the upper limit. These probabilities of rejection are represented graphically in Figure 6.10. A similar formula for the "bad" case appears in cell B13, using Stdev_bad in place of Stdev_good.

Figure 6.10

Rejection Regions for Paper Quality Example

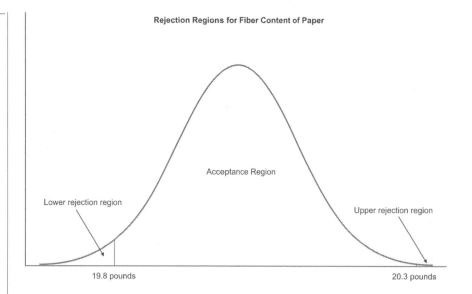

Rejection Regions for Fiber Content of Paper

Acceptance Region

Lower rejection region

Upper rejection region

19.8 pounds

20.3 pounds

To form this data table, enter the formula =B12 in cell B17, highlight the range B17:H25, and create a data table with row input cell B4 and column input cell B3.

We see that the probability of a rejected roll in the "good" case is 0.024; in the "bad" case it is 0.114. That is, when the standard deviation increases by 50% from 0.1 to 0.15, the percentage of rolls rejected more than quadruples, from 2.4% to 11.4%.

It is certainly possible that the true process mean and "good" standard deviation will not always be equal to the values we've assumed in cells B3 and B4. Therefore, it is useful to see how sensitive the rejection probability is to these two parameters. We do this with a two-way data table, as shown in Figure 6.9. The tabulated values show that the probability of rejection varies greatly even for small changes in the key inputs. In particular, a combination of a badly centered mean and a large standard deviation can make the probability of rejection very large. ∎

EXAMPLE **6.5 ANALYZING AN INVESTOR'S AFTER-TAX PROFIT**

Howard Davis invests $10,000 in a certain stock on January 1. By examining past movements of this stock and consulting with his broker, Howard estimates that the annual return from this stock, X, is normally distributed with mean 10% and standard deviation 4%. Here X (when expressed as a decimal) is the profit Howard receives per dollar invested. It means that on December 31, his $10,000 will have grown to $10,000(1 + X)$ dollars. Because Howard is in the 33% tax bracket, he will then have to pay the Internal Revenue Service 33% of his profit. Calculate the probability that Howard will have to pay the IRS at least $400. Also, calculate the dollar amount such that Howard's after-tax profit is 90% certain to be less than this amount; that is, calculate the 90th percentile of his after-tax profit.

Objective   To determine the after-tax profit Howard Davis can be 90% certain of earning.

Solution

Howard's before-tax profit is $10,000X$ dollars, so the amount he pays the IRS is $0.33(10,000X)$, or $3300X$ dollars. We want the probability that this is at least $400. Because

$3300X > 400$ is the same as $X > 4/33$, the probability of this outcome can be found as in Figure 6.11. (See the file **Tax on Stock Return.xlsx.**) It is calculated with the formula

$$=1\text{-NORMDIST(400/(Amount\_invested*Tax\_rate),Mean,Stdev,1)}$$

in cell B8. As we see, Howard has about a 30% chance of paying at least \$400 in taxes.

To answer the second question, note that the after-tax profit is 67% of the before-tax profit, or $6700X$ dollars, and we want its 90th percentile. If this percentile is x, then we know that $P(6700X < x) = 0.90$, which is the same as $P(X < x/6700) = 0.90$. In words, we want the 90th percentile of the X distribution to be $x/6700$. From cell B10 of Figure 6.11, we see that the 90th percentile is 15.13%, so the required value of x is \$1,013. Note that the *mean* after-tax profit is \$670 (67% of the mean before-tax profit of 0.10 multiplied by \$10,000). Of course, Howard might get lucky and make more than this, but he is 90% certain that his after-tax profit will be no greater than \$1013. ∎

Figure 6.11 Calculations for Taxable Returns Example

	A	B	C	D	E	F	G	H	I
1	Tax on Stock Return								
2				Range names used:					
3	Amount invested	\$10,000		Amount_invested	=Model!\$B\$3				
4	Mean	10%		Mean	=Model!\$B\$4				
5	Stdev	4%		Stdev	=Model!\$B\$5				
6	Tax rate	33%		Tax_rate	=Model!\$B\$6				
7									
8	Probability he pays at least \$400 in taxes	0.298		=1-NORMDIST(400/(Amount_invested*Tax_rate),Mean,Stdev,1)					
9									
10	90th percentile of stock return	15.13%		=NORMINV(0.9,Mean,Stdev)					
11	90th percentile of after-tax return	\$1,013		=(1-Tax_rate)*Amount_invested*B10					

It is sometimes tempting to model every continuous random variable with a normal distribution. This can be dangerous for at least two reasons. First, not all random variables have a *symmetric* distribution. Some are skewed to the left or the right, and for these the normal distribution can be a poor approximation. The second problem is that many random variables in real applications must be *nonnegative,* and the normal distribution allows the possibility of negative values. The following example shows how assuming normality can get us into trouble if we aren't careful.

EXAMPLE

6.6 PREDICTING FUTURE DEMAND FOR MICROWAVE OVENS AT HIGHLAND COMPANY

The Highland Company is a retailer that sells microwave ovens. The company wants to model its demand for microwaves over the next 12 years. Using historical data as a guide, it assumes that demand in year 1 is normally distributed with mean 5000 and standard deviation 1500. It assumes that demand in every subsequent year is normally distributed with mean equal to the *actual* demand from the previous year and standard deviation 1500. For example, if demand in year 1 turns out to be 4500, then the *mean* demand in year 2 is 4500. This assumption appears plausible because it leads to correlated demands. For example, if demand is high one year, it will tend to be high the next year. Investigate the ramifications of this model, and suggest models that might be more realistic.

Objective To construct and analyze a spreadsheet model for microwave oven demand over the next 12 years using Excel's NORMINV function, and to show how "normal" models can lead to nonsensical outcomes unless we are careful.

Solution

The best way to analyze this model is with simulation, much as we did in Chapter 5. To do this, we must be able to simulate normally distributed random numbers in Excel. We can do this with the NORMINV function. Specifically, to generate a normally distributed number with mean μ and standard deviation σ, we use the formula

$=$**NORMINV(RAND(),μ,σ)**

Because this formula uses the RAND function, it generates a *different* random number each time it is used—and each time the spreadsheet recalculates.[4]

The spreadsheet in Figure 6.12 shows a simulation of yearly demands over a 12-year period. (See the file **Oven Demand Simulation.xlsx**.) To simulate the demands in row 15, we enter the formula

Figure 6.12 One Set of Demands for Model 1 in the Microwave Example

	A	B	C	D	E	F	G	H	I	J	K	L	M
1	Normal model for multiperiod demand												
2													
3	Assumptions of a tentative model												
4													
5	Demand in year 1 (normally distributed)												
6	Mean	5000											
7	Stdev	1500											
8													
9	Demand in other years (normally distributed)												
10	Mean	actual demand in previous year											
11	Stdev	1500											
12													
13	Simulated demands												
14	Year	1	2	3	4	5	6	7	8	9	10	11	12
15	Demand	5266	7657	7420	8094	9099	11674	7245	7191	8420	8638	9702	7275
16													

Time series of demand

$=$**NORMINV(RAND(),B6,B7)**

in cell B15. Then we enter the formula

$=$**NORMINV(RAND(),B15,\$B\$11)**

[4] To see why this formula makes sense, note that the RAND function in the first argument generates a uniformly distributed random value between 0 and 1. Therefore, the effect of the function is to generate a random *percentile* from the normal distribution.

in cell C15 and copy it across row 15. (Note how the mean demand in any year is the *simulated* demand from the previous year.) As the accompanying time series graph of these demands indicates, the model seems to be performing well.

However, the simulated demands in Figure 6.12 are only one set of possible demands. Remember that each time the spreadsheet recalculates, all of the random numbers change.[5] Figure 6.13 shows a different set of random numbers generated by the *same* formulas. Clearly, the model is not working well in this case—some demands are negative, which makes no sense. The problem is that if the actual demand is low in one year, there is a fair chance that the next normally distributed demand will be negative. You can check (by recalculating many times) that the demand sequence is *usually* all positive, but every now and then you'll get a nonsense sequence as in Figure 6.13. We need a new model!

One way to modify the model is to let the standard deviation and mean move together. That is, if the mean is low, then the standard deviation will also be low. This minimizes the chance that the *next* random demand will become negative. Besides, this type of model is probably more realistic. If demand in one year is low, there is likely to be less variability in next year's demand. Figure 6.14 illustrates one way to model this changing standard deviation.

Figure 6.13   Another Set of Demands for Model 1 in the Microwave Example

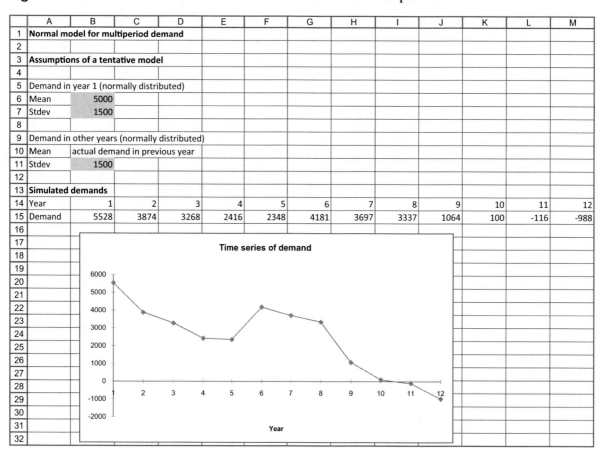

[5]The usual way to get Excel to recalculate is to press the F9 key. However, this makes all of the data tables in the workbook recalculate, which can take forever. Because there is a data table in another sheet of the **Oven Demand Simulation.xlsx** file, we suggest a different way to recalculate. Simply position the cursor on any blank cell and press the Delete key.

Figure 6.14 Generated Demands for Model 2 in Microwave Example

	A	B	C	D	E	F	G	H	I	J	K	L	M
1	Normal model for multiperiod demand												
2													
3	Assumptions of a "safer" model												
4													
5	Demand in year 1 (normally distributed)												
6	Mean	5000											
7	Stdev	1500											
8													
9	Demand in other years (normally distributed)												
10	Mean	actual demand in previous year											
11	Stdev	1500 times ratio of previous year's actual demand to year 1's mean demand											
12													
13	Simulated demands												
14	Year	1	2	3	4	5	6	7	8	9	10	11	12
15	Demand	6521	6255	8239	6856	9638	7045	7122	4877	7212	10681	5211	4211
16													

Time series of demands

We let the standard deviation of demand in any year (after year 1) be the original standard deviation, 1500, multiplied by the ratio of the expected demand for this year to the expected demand in year 1. For example, if demand in some year is 500, then the expected demand next year is 500, and the standard deviation of next year's demand is reduced to 1500(500/5000) = 150. The only change to the spreadsheet model is in row 15, where we enter

=NORMINV(RAND(),B15,$B$7*B15/$B$6)

in cell C15 and copy it across row 15. Now the chance of a negative demand is practically negligible because this would require a value more than 3 standard deviations below the mean.

The model in Figure 6.14 is still not foolproof. By recalculating many times, we can still generate a negative demand now and then. To be even safer, we can "truncate" the demand distribution at some nonnegative value such as 250, as shown in Figure 6.15. Now we generate a random demand as in the previous model, but if this randomly generated value is below 250, we set the demand equal to 250. This is done by entering the formulas

=MAX(NORMINV(RAND(),B8,B9),D5)

and

=MAX(NORMINV(RAND(),B17,$B$9*B17/$B$8),$D$5)

in cells B17 and C17 and copying this latter formula across row 17. Whether this is the way the demand process works for Highland's microwaves is an open question, but at least we have prevented demands from ever becoming negative—or even falling below 250. Moreover, this type of truncation is a common way of modeling when we want to use a normal distribution but for physical reasons cannot allow the random quantities to become negative.

Figure 6.15 Generated Demands for a Truncated Model in Microwave Example

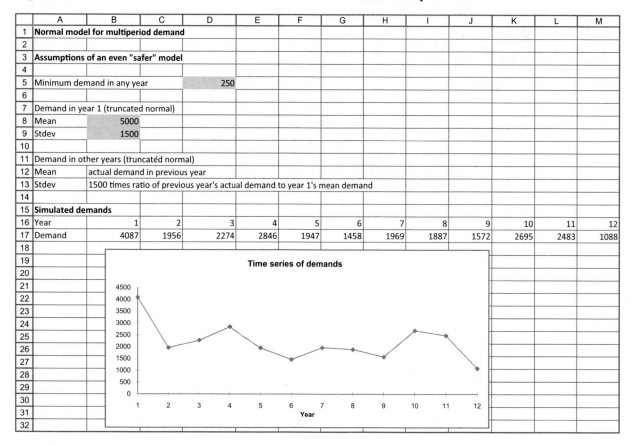

	A	B	C	D	E	F	G	H	I	J	K	L	M
1	Normal model for multiperiod demand												
2													
3	Assumptions of an even "safer" model												
4													
5	Minimum demand in any year			250									
6													
7	Demand in year 1 (truncated normal)												
8	Mean	5000											
9	Stdev	1500											
10													
11	Demand in other years (truncated normal)												
12	Mean	actual demand in previous year											
13	Stdev	1500 times ratio of previous year's actual demand to year 1's mean demand											
14													
15	Simulated demands												
16	Year	1	2	3	4	5	6	7	8	9	10	11	12
17	Demand	4087	1956	2274	2846	1947	1458	1969	1887	1572	2695	2483	1088
18													
19													
20													
21													
22													
23													
24													
25													
26													
27													
28													
29													
30													
31													
32													

Before leaving this example, we challenge your intuition. In the final model in Figure 6.15, the demand in any year (say, year 6) is, aside from the truncation, normally distributed with a mean and standard deviation that depend on the previous year's demand. Does this mean that if we recalculate many times and keep track of the year 6 demand each time, the resulting histogram of these year 6 demands will be normally distributed? Perhaps surprisingly, the answer is a clear "no." We show the evidence in Figures 6.16 and 6.17. In Figure 6.16 we use a data table to obtain 400 replications of demand in year 6 (in column B). Then we use StatTools's histogram procedure to create a histogram of these simulated demands in Figure 6.17. It is clearly skewed to the right and *nonnormal*.

What causes this distribution to be nonnormal? It is *not* the truncation. Truncation has a relatively minor effect because most of the demands don't need to be truncated anyway. The real reason is that the distribution of year 6 demand is only normal *conditional* on the demand in year 5. That is, if we fix the demand in year 5 at any level and then replicate year 6 demand many times, the resulting histogram *is* normally shaped. But we don't fix the year 5 demand. It varies from replication to replication, and this variation causes the skewness in Figure 6.17. Admittedly, the reason for this skewness is not obvious from an intuitive standpoint, but simulation makes it easy to demonstrate.

Figure 6.16

Replication of Demand in Year 6

	A	B	C	D	E
36	Replication	Demand			
37		4476		Average	4916
38	1	1635		Stdev	3956
39	2	8229			
40	3	3582			
41	4	11282			
42	5	2845			
43	6	3942			
44	7	5700			
45	8	12273			
433	396	8919			
434	397	4587			
435	398	10003			
436	399	5012			
437	400	3944			

Figure 6.17 Histogram of Year 6 Demands

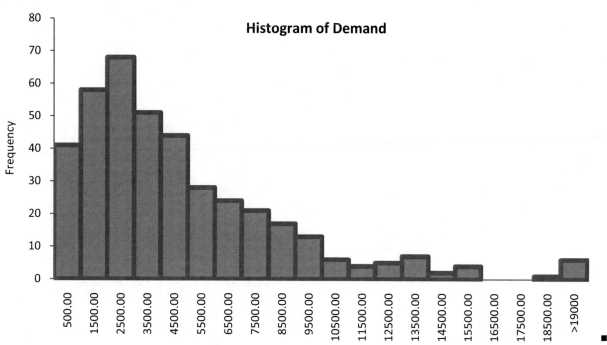

PROBLEMS

Level A

1. The grades on the midterm examination given in a large managerial statistics class are normally distributed with mean 75 and standard deviation 9. The instructor of this class wants to assign an A grade to the top 10% of the scores, a B grade to the next 10% of the scores, a C grade to the next 10% of the scores, a D grade to the next 10% of the scores, and an F grade to all scores below the 60th percentile of this distribution. For each possible letter grade, find the lowest acceptable score within the established range. For example, the lowest acceptable score for an A is the score at the 90th percentile of this normal distribution.

2. Suppose it is known that the distribution of purchase amounts by customers entering a popular retail store is approximately normal with mean $25 and standard deviation $8.
  a. What is the probability that a randomly selected customer spends less than $35 at this store?
  b. What is the probability that a randomly selected customer spends between $15 and $35 at this store?
  c. What is the probability that a randomly selected customer spends more than $10 at this store?
  d. Find the dollar amount such that 75% of all customers spend no more than this amount.
  e. Find the dollar amount such that 80% of all customers spend at least this amount.
  f. Find two dollars amounts, equidistant from the mean of $25, such that 90% of all customer purchases are between these values.

3. A machine used to regulate the amount of a certain chemical dispensed in the production of a particular type of cough syrup can be set so that it discharges an average of μ milliliters (ml) of the chemical in each bottle of cough syrup. The amount of chemical placed into each bottle of cough syrup is known to have a normal distribution with a standard deviation of 0.250 ml. If this machine discharges more than 2 ml of the chemical when preparing a given bottle of this cough syrup, the bottle is considered to be unacceptable by industry standards. Determine the setting for μ so that no more than 1% of the bottles of cough syrup prepared through the use of this machine will be rejected.

4. The weekly demand for Ford car sales follows a normal distribution with mean 50,000 cars and standard deviation 14,000 cars.
  a. There is a 1% chance that Ford will sell more than what number of cars during the next year?
  b. What is the probability that Ford will sell between 2.4 and 2.7 million cars during the next year?

5. Warren Dinner has invested in nine different investments. The returns on the different investments are probabilistically independent, and each return follows a normal distribution with mean $500 and standard deviation $100.
  a. There is a 1% chance that the total return on the nine investments is less than what value? (Use the fact that the sum of independent normal random variables is normally distributed, with mean equal to the sum of the individual means, and variance equal to the sum of the individual variances.)
  b. What is the probability that Warren's total return is between $4000 and $5200?

6. Scores on an exam appear to follow a normal distribution with $\mu = 60$ and $\sigma = 20$. The instructor wishes to give a grade of D to students scoring between the 10th and 30th percentiles on the exam. For what range of scores should a D be given?

7. Suppose the weight of a typical American male follows a normal distribution with $\mu = 180$ lb and $\sigma = 30$ lb. Also, suppose 91.92% of all American males weigh more than I weigh.
  a. What fraction of American males weigh more than 225 pounds?
  b. How much do I weigh?

8. Assume that the length of a typical televised baseball game, including all the commercial timeouts, is normally distributed with mean 2.45 hours and standard deviation 0.37 hour. Consider a televised baseball game that begins at 2:00 in the afternoon. The next regularly scheduled broadcast is at 5:00.
  a. What is the probability that the game will cut into the next show, that is, go past 5:00?
  b. If the game is over before 4:30, another half-hour show can be inserted into the 4:30–5:00 slot. What is the probability of this occurring?

9. The amount of a soft drink that goes into a typical 12-ounce can varies from can to can. It is normally distributed with an adjustable mean μ and a fixed standard deviation of 0.05 ounce. (The adjustment is made to the filling machine.)
  a. If regulations require that cans have at least 11.9 ounces, what is the smallest mean μ that can be used so that at least 99.5% of all cans meet the regulation?
  b. If the mean setting from part **a** is used, what is the probability that a typical can has at least 12 ounces?

Level B

10. The manufacturer of a particular bicycle model has the following costs associated with the management of this product's inventory. In particular, the company currently maintains an inventory of 1000 units of this bicycle model at the beginning of each year. If X units are demanded each year and X is less than 1000, the excess supply, $1000 - X$ units, must be stored until next year at a cost of $50 per unit. If X is greater than 1000 units, the excess demand, $X - 1000$ units, must be produced separately at an extra cost of $80 per unit. Assume that the annual demand (X) for this bicycle model is normally distributed with mean 1000 and standard deviation 75.
    a. Find the expected annual cost associated with managing potential shortages or surpluses of this product. (*Hint*: Use simulation to approximate the answer. An exact solution using probability arguments is beyond the level of this book.)
    b. Find two annual total cost levels, equidistant from the expected value found in part **a**, such that 95% of all costs associated with managing potential shortages or surpluses of this product are between these values. (Continue to use simulation.)
    c. Comment on this manufacturer's annual production policy for this bicycle model in light of your findings in part **b**.

11. Matthew's Bakery prepares peanut butter cookies for sale every morning. It costs the bakery $0.25 to bake each peanut butter cookie, and each cookie is sold for $0.50. At the end of the day, leftover cookies are discounted and sold the following day at $0.10 per cookie. The daily demand (in dozens) for peanut butter cookies at this bakery is known to be normally distributed with mean 50 and standard deviation 15. The manager of Matthew's Bakery is trying to determine how many dozen peanut butter cookies to make each morning to maximize the product's contribution to bakery profits. Use simulation to find a very good, if not optimal, production plan.

12. Suppose that a particular production process fills detergent in boxes of a given size. Specifically, this process fills the boxes with an amount of detergent (in ounces) that is adequately described by a normal distribution with mean 50 and standard deviation 0.5.
    a. Simulate this production process for the filling of 500 boxes of detergent. Compute the mean and standard deviation of your simulated sample weights. How do your sample statistics compare to the theoretical population parameters in this case? How well do the empirical rules apply in describing the variation in the weights of the detergent in your simulated detergent boxes?
    b. A box of detergent is rejected by quality control personnel if it is found to contain less than

49 ounces or more than 51 ounces of detergent. Given these quality standards, what proportion of all boxes are rejected? What step(s) could the supervisor of this production process take to reduce this proportion to 1%?

13. It is widely known that many drivers on interstate highways in the United States do not observe the posted speed limit. Assume that the actual rates of speed driven by U.S. motorists are normally distributed with mean μ mph and standard deviation 5 mph. Given this information, answer each of the following independent questions.
    a. If 40% of all U.S. drivers are observed traveling at 65 mph or more, what is the mean μ?
    b. If 25% of all U.S. drivers are observed traveling at 50 mph or less, what is the mean μ?
    c. Suppose now that the mean μ and standard deviation σ of this distribution are both unknown. Furthermore, it is observed that 40% of all U.S. drivers travel at less than 55 mph and 10% of all U.S. drivers travel at more than 70 mph. What must μ and σ be?

14. The lifetime of a certain manufacturer's washing machine is normally distributed with mean 4 years. Only 15% of all these washing machines last at least 5 years. What is the standard deviation of the lifetime of a washing machine made by this manufacturer?

15. You have been told that the distribution of regular unleaded gasoline prices over all gas stations in Indiana is normally distributed with mean $2.95 and standard deviation $0.075, and you have been asked to find two dollar values such that 95% of all gas stations charge somewhere between these two values. Why is each of the following an acceptable answer: between $2.776 and $3.081, or between $2.802 and $3.097? Can you find any other acceptable answers? Which of the many possible answers would you prefer if you are asked to obtain the *shortest* interval?

16. When we create box plots, we place the sides of the "box" at the first and third quartiles, and the difference between these (the length of the box) is called the interquartile range (IQR). A mild outlier is then defined as an observation that is between 1.5 and 3 IQRs from the box, and an extreme outlier is defined as an observation that is more than 3 IQRs from the box.
    a. If the data are normally distributed, what percentage of values will be mild outliers? What percentage will be extreme outliers? Why don't the answers depend on the mean and/or standard deviation of the distribution?
    b. Check your answers in part **a** with simulation. Simulate a large number of normal random numbers (you can choose any mean and standard deviation), and count the number of mild and extreme outliers with appropriate IF functions. Do these match, at least approximately, your answers to part **a**?

17. A fast-food restaurant sells hamburgers and chicken sandwiches. On a typical weekday the demand for hamburgers is normally distributed with mean 313 and standard deviation 57; the demand for chicken sandwiches is normally distributed with mean 93 and standard deviation 22.

  a. How many hamburgers must the restaurant stock to be 98% sure of not running out on a given day?

  b. Answer part **a** for chicken sandwiches.

  c. If the restaurant stocks 400 hamburgers and 150 chicken sandwiches for a given day, what is the probability that it will run out of hamburgers or chicken sandwiches (or both) that day? Assume that the demand for hamburgers and the demand for chicken sandwiches are probabilistically independent.

  d. Why is the independence assumption in part **c** probably not realistic? Using a more realistic assumption, do you think the probability requested in part **c** would increase or decrease?

18. Suppose that the demands for a company's product in weeks 1, 2, and 3 are each normally distributed. The means are 50, 45, and 65. The standard deviations are 10, 5, and 15. Assume that these three demands are probabilistically independent. This means that if you observe one of them, it doesn't help you to predict the others. Then it turns out that total demand for the 3 weeks is also normally distributed. Its mean is the sum of the individual means, and its variance is the sum of the individual variances. (Its standard deviation, however, is not the sum of the individual standard deviations; square roots don't work that way.)

  a. Suppose that the company currently has 180 units in stock, and it will not be receiving any more shipments from its supplier for at least 3 weeks. What is the probability that it will stock out during this 3-week period?

  b. How many units should the company currently have in stock so that it can be 98% certain of not stocking out during this 3-week period? Again, assume that it won't receive any more shipments during this period.

6.4 THE BINOMIAL DISTRIBUTION

The normal distribution is undoubtedly the most important probability distribution in statistics. Not far behind in order of importance is the *binomial* distribution. The binomial distribution is a discrete distribution that can occur in two situations: (1) whenever we sample from a population with only two types of members (males and females, for example), and (2) whenever we perform a sequence of identical experiments, each of which has only two possible outcomes.

Imagine any experiment that can be repeated many times under identical conditions. It is common to refer to each repetition of the experiment as a *trial*. We assume that the outcomes of successive trials are probabilistically independent of one another and that each trial has only two possible outcomes. We label these two possibilities generically as success and failure. In any particular application the outcomes might be Democrat/Republican, defective/nondefective, went bankrupt/remained solvent, and so on. The probability of a success on each trial is p, and the probability of a failure is $1 - p$. The number of trials is n.

Binomial Distribution

Consider a situation in which there are n independent, identical trials, where the probability of a success on each trial is p and the probability of a failure is $1 - p$. Define X to be the random number of successes in the n trials. Then X has a **binomial** distribution with parameters n and p.

For example, the binomial distribution with parameters 100 and 0.3 is the distribution of the number of successes in 100 trials when the probability of success is 0.3 on each trial. A simple example that you can keep in mind throughout this section is the number of heads you would see if you flipped a coin n times. Assuming the coin is well balanced, the relevant distribution is binomial with parameters n and $p = 0.5$. This coin-flipping example is often used to illustrate the binomial distribution because of its simplicity, but we will see that the binomial distribution also applies to many important business situations.

To understand how the binomial distribution works, consider the coin-flipping example with $n = 3$. If X represents the number of heads in three flips of the coin, then the possible values of X are 0, 1, 2, and 3. We can find the probabilities of these values by considering the eight possible outcomes of the three flips: (T,T,T), (T,T,H), (T,H,T), (H,T,T), (T,H,H), (H,T,H), (H,H,T), and (H,H,H). Because of symmetry (the well-balanced property of the coin), each of these eight possible outcomes must have the same probability, so each must have probability 1/8. Next, note that one of the outcomes has $X = 0$, three outcomes have $X = 1$, three outcomes have $X = 2$, and one outcome has $X = 3$. Therefore, the probability distribution of X is

$$P(X = 0) = 1/8, P(X = 1) = 3/8, P(X = 2) = 3/8, P(X = 3) = 1/8$$

This is a special case of the binomial distribution, with $n = 3$ and $p = 0.5$. In general, where n can be any positive integer and p can be any probability between 0 and 1, there is a rather complex formula for calculating $P(X = k)$ for any integer k from 0 to n. Instead of presenting this formula, we will discuss how to calculate binomial probabilities in Excel. We do this with the BINOMDIST function. The general form of this function is

=BINOMDIST(*k,n,p,cum*)

The middle two arguments are as stated previously: the number of trials n and the probability of success p on each trial. The first parameter k is an integer number of successes that we specify. The last parameter, *cum*, is either 0 or 1. It is 1 if we want the probability of *less than or equal to* k successes, and it is 0 if we want the probability of *exactly* k successes. We illustrate typical binomial calculations in the following example.

EXAMPLE | **6.7 BATTERY LIFE EXPERIMENT**

Suppose 100 identical batteries are inserted in identical flashlights. Each flashlight takes a single battery. After 8 hours of continuous use, we assume that a given battery is still operating with probability 0.6 and has failed with probability 0.4. Let X be the number of successes in these 100 trials, where a success means that the battery is still functioning. Find the probabilities of the following events: (a) exactly 58 successes, (b) no more than 65 successes, (c) less than 70 successes, (d) at least 59 successes, (e) greater than 65 successes, (f) between 55 and 65 successes (inclusive), (g) exactly 40 failures, (h) at least 35 failures, and (i) less than 42 failures. Then find the 95th percentile of the distribution of X.

Objective To use Excel's BINOMDIST and CRITBINOM functions for calculating binomial probabilities and percentiles in the context of batteries in flashlights.

Solution

Figure 6.18 shows the solution to all of these problems. (See the file **Binomial Calculations.xlsx**.) The probabilities requested in parts (a) through (f) all involve the number of successes X. The key to these is the wording of phrases such as "no more than," "greater than," and so on. In particular, we have to be careful to distinguish between probabilities such as $P(X < k)$ and $P(X \leq k)$. The latter includes the possibility of having $X = k$ and the former does not.

Figure 6.18 Typical Binomial Calculations

	A	B	C	D	E	F	G	H	I	J
1	Binomial Probability Calculations									
2				Range names used:						
3	Number of trials	100		NTrials	=BinomCalcs!$B$3					
4	Probability of success on each trial	0.6		PSuccess	=BinomCalcs!$B$4					
5										
6	Event	Probability		Formula						
7	Exactly 58 successes	0.0742		=BINOMDIST(58,NTrials,PSuccess,0)						
8	No more than 65 successes	0.8697		=BINOMDIST(65,NTrials,PSuccess,1)						
9	Less than 70 successes	0.9752		=BINOMDIST(69,NTrials,PSuccess,1)						
10	At least 59 successes	0.6225		=1-BINOMDIST(58,NTrials,PSuccess,1)						
11	Greater than 65 successes	0.1303		=1-BINOMDIST(65,NTrials,PSuccess,1)						
12	Between 55 and 65 successes (inclusive)	0.7386		=BINOMDIST(65,NTrials,PSuccess,1)-BINOMDIST(54,NTrials,PSuccess,1)						
13										
14	Exactly 40 failures	0.0812		=BINOMDIST(40,NTrials,1-PSuccess,0)						
15	At least 35 failures	0.8697		=1-BINOMDIST(34,NTrials,1-PSuccess,1)						
16	Less than 42 failures	0.6225		=BINOMDIST(41,NTrials,1-PSuccess,1)						
17										
18	Finding the 95th percentile (trial and error)									
19	Trial values	CumProb								
20	65	0.8697		=BINOMDIST(A20,NTrials,PSuccess,1)						
21	66	0.9087		(Copy down)						
22	67	0.9385								
23	68	0.9602								
24	69	0.9752								
25	70	0.9852								
26				Formula in cell A27:						
27	68	0.95		=CRITBINOM(NTrials,PSuccess,B27)						

With this in mind, we can translate the probabilities requested in (a) through (f) to the following:

a. $P(X = 58)$

b. $P(X \leq 65)$

c. $P(X < 70) = P(X \leq 69)$

d. $P(X \geq 59) = 1 - P(X < 59) = 1 - P(X \leq 58)$

e. $P(X > 65) = 1 - P(X \leq 65)$

f. $P(55 \leq X \leq 65) = P(X \leq 65) - P(X < 55) = P(X \leq 65) - P(X \leq 54)$

Note how we have converted each of these so that it includes only terms of the form $P(X = k)$ or $P(X \leq k)$ (for suitable values of k). These are the types of probabilities that can be handled directly by the BINOMDIST function. The answers appear in the range B7:B12, and the corresponding formulas are shown (as labels) in column D.

The probabilities requested in (g) through (i) involve *failures* rather than successes. But because each trial results in either a success or a failure, the number of failures is also binomially distributed, with parameters n and $1 - p = 0.4$. So in rows 14 through 16, we calculate the requested probabilities in exactly the same way, except that we substitute 1-PSuccess for PSuccess in the third argument of the BINOMDIST function.

Finally, to calculate the 95th percentile of the distribution of X, we proceed by trial and error. For each value k from 65 to 70, we have calculated the probability $P(X \leq k)$ in column B with the BINOMDIST function. Note that there is no value k such that $P(X \leq k) = 0.95$ exactly. We see that $P(X \leq 67)$ is slightly less than 0.95, and $P(X \leq 68)$ is slightly greater than 0.95. Therefore, the meaning of the "95th percentile" is a bit ambiguous. If we want the largest value k such that $P(X \leq k) \leq 0.95$, then this k is 67. If instead we want the smallest value k such that $P(X \leq k) \geq 0.95$, then this value is 68. The latter interpretation is the one usually accepted for binomial percentiles.

In fact, Excel has another built-in function, CRITBINOM, for finding this value of k. We illustrate it in row 27 of Figure 6.18. Now we enter the requested probability, 0.95, in cell B27 and the formula

=CRITBINOM(NTrials,PSuccess,B27)

in cell A27. It returns 68, the smallest value k such that $P(X \leq k) \geq 0.95$ for this binomial distribution. ∎

6.4.1 Mean and Standard Deviation of the Binomial Distribution

It can be shown that the mean and standard deviation of a binomial distribution with parameters n and p are given by the following equations.

$$E(X) = np \tag{6.3}$$

$$\text{Stdev}(X) = \sqrt{np(1-p)} \tag{6.4}$$

The formula for the mean is quite intuitive. For example, if you observe 100 trials, each with probability of success 0.6, your best guess for the number of successes is clearly $100(0.6) = 60$. The standard deviation is less obvious but still very useful. It indicates how far the actual number of successes might deviate from the mean. In this case the standard deviation is $\sqrt{100(0.6)(0.4)} = 4.90$.

Fortunately, the empirical rules discussed in Chapter 3 also apply, at least approximately, to the binomial distribution. That is, there is about a 95% chance that the actual number of successes will be within 2 standard deviations of the mean, and there is almost no chance that the number of successes will be more than 3 standard deviations from the mean. So for this example, it is very likely that the number of successes will be in the range of approximately 50 to 70, and it is very unlikely that there will be fewer than 45 or more than 75 successes.

This reasoning is extremely useful. It gives us a rough estimate of the number of successes we are likely to observe. Suppose we randomly sample 1000 parts from an assembly line and, based on historical performance, we know that the percentage of parts with some type of defect is about 5%. Translated into a binomial model, we assume that each of the 1000 parts, independently of the others, has some type of defect with probability 0.05. Would we be surprised to see, say, 75 parts with a defect? The mean is $1000(0.05) = 50$ and the standard deviation is $\sqrt{1000(0.05)(0.95)} = 6.89$. Therefore, the number of parts with defects is 95% certain to be within $50 \pm 2(6.89)$, or approximately from 36 to 64. Because 75 is slightly beyond 3 standard deviations from the mean, it is highly unlikely that we would observe 75 (or more) parts with defects.

6.4.2 The Binomial Distribution in the Context of Sampling

We now discuss how the binomial distribution applies to sampling from a population with two types of members. Let's say these two types are men and women, although in applications they might be Democrats versus Republicans, users of our product versus nonusers, and so on. We will assume that the population has N members, of whom N_M are men and N_W are women (where $N_M + N_W = N$). If we sample n of these randomly, we are typically interested in the composition of the sample. We might expect that the number of men in the sample is binomially distributed with parameters n and $p = N_M/N$, the fraction of men in the population. However, this depends on how the sampling is performed.

If sampling is done **without replacement**, then each member of the population can be sampled only once. That is, once a person is sampled, his or her name is struck from the list and cannot be sampled again. If sampling is done **with replacement**, then it is possible, although maybe not likely, to select a given member of the population any number of times. Most real-world sampling is performed *without* replacement. There is no point in obtaining information from the same person more than once. However, *the binomial model applies only to sampling with replacement.* Because the composition of the remaining population keeps changing as the sampling progresses, the binomial model can provide only an approximation if sampling is done without replacement. If there is no replacement, the value of *p*, the proportion of men in this case, does *not* stay constant, a requirement of the binomial model. The appropriate distribution for sampling without replacement is called the **hypergeometric** distribution, a distribution we will not discuss in detail here.

If *n* is small relative to *N*, however, the binomial distribution is a very good approximation to the hypergeometric distribution and can be used even if sampling is performed without replacement. A rule of thumb is that if *n* is no greater than 10% of *N*, that is, no more than 10% of the population is sampled, then the binomial model can be used safely. Of course, most national polls sample considerably less than 10% of the population. In fact, they often sample only a few thousand people from the hundreds of millions in the entire population. The bottom line is that in most real-world sampling contexts, the binomial model is perfectly adequate.

6.4.3 The Normal Approximation to the Binomial

If n is large and p is not too close to 0 or 1, the binomial distribution is bell shaped and can be approximated well by the normal distribution.

If we graph the binomial probabilities, we see an interesting phenomenon—namely, the graph begins to look symmetric and bell shaped when *n* is fairly large and *p* is not too close to 0 or 1. An example is illustrated in Figure 6.19 with the parameters $n = 30$ and $p = 0.4$. Generally, if $np > 5$ and $n(1 - p) > 5$, the binomial distribution can be approximated well by a normal distribution with mean np and standard deviation $\sqrt{np(1 - p)}$.

One practical consequence of the normal approximation to the binomial is that the empirical rules can be applied. That is, when the binomial distribution is approximately symmetric and bell shaped, we know the chances are about 2 out of 3 that the number of successes will be within 1 standard deviation of the mean. Similarly, there is about a 95% chance that the number of successes will be within 2 standard deviations of the mean, and the number of successes will almost surely be within 3 standard deviations of the mean. Here, the mean is np and the standard deviation is $\sqrt{np(1 - p)}$.

Figure 6.19

Bell-shaped
Binomial
Distribution

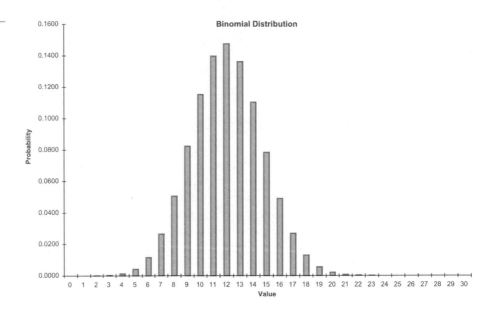

6.5 APPLICATIONS OF THE BINOMIAL DISTRIBUTION

The binomial distribution finds many applications in the business world and elsewhere. We discuss a few typical applications in this section.

EXAMPLE	6.8 Is This Mutual Fund Really a Winner?

An investment broker at the Michaels & Dodson Company claims that he has found a real winner. He has tracked a mutual fund that has beaten a standard market index in 37 of the past 52 weeks. Could this be due to chance, or has he *really* found a winner?

Objective   To determine the probability of a mutual fund outperforming a standard market index at least 37 out of 52 weeks.

Solution

The broker is no doubt tracking a lot of mutual funds, and he is probably reporting on the best of these. Therefore, we will check whether the best of *many* mutual funds could do at least this well purely by chance. To do this, we first specify what we mean by "purely by chance." This means that each week, a given fund has a 50–50 chance of beating the market index, independently of performance in other weeks. In other words, the number of weeks where a given fund outperforms the market index is binomially distributed with $n = 52$ and $p = 0.5$. With this in mind, cell B6 of Figure 6.20 shows the probability that a given fund does at least as well—beats the market index at least 37 out of 52 weeks—as the reported fund. (See the **Beating the Market.xlsx** file.) Because $P(X \geq 37) = 1 - P(X \leq 36)$, the relevant formula is

=1-BINOMDIST(B3-1,B4,0.5,1)

Obviously, this probability, 0.00159, is quite small. A single fund isn't likely to beat the market this often purely by chance.

However, the probability that the *best* of many mutual funds does at least this well is much larger. To calculate this probability, let's assume that 400 funds are being tracked, and let Y be the number of these that beat the market at least 37 of 52 weeks. Then Y is also binomially distributed, with parameters $n = 400$ and $p = 0.00159$, the probability calculated previously. We want to know whether *any* of the 400 funds beats the market at least 37 of 52 weeks, so we calculate $P(Y \geq 1) = 1 - P(Y = 0)$. We do this in cell B9 with the formula

=1-BINOMDIST(0,B8,B6,1)

(Can you see why the fourth argument could be 0 *or* 1?) The resulting probability is nearly 0.5—that is, there is nearly a 50–50 chance that at least one of 400 funds will do as well as the reported fund. This certainly casts doubt on the broker's claim that he has found a real winner. Perhaps his star fund just got lucky and will perform no better than average in succeeding weeks.

To see how the probability in cell B9 depends on the level of success of the reported fund (the value in cell B3) and the number of mutual funds being tracked (in cell B8), we create a two-way data table in the range B13:G18. (The formula in cell B13 is =B9, the row input cell is B3, and the column input cell is B8.) As we saw, beating the market 37 times out of 52 is no big deal with 400 funds, but beating it 40 times out of 52, even with 600 funds, is something worth reporting. The probability of this happening purely by chance is only 0.038, or less than 1 out of 25.

Figure 6.20

Binomial Calculations for Investment Example

	A	B	C	D	E	F	G
1	Beating the market						
2							
3	Weeks beating market index	37					
4	Total number of weeks	52					
5							
6	Probability of doing at least this well by chance	0.00159		=1-BINOMDIST(B3-1,B4,0.5,1)			
7							
8	Number of mutual funds	400					
9	Probability of at least one doing at least this well	0.471		=1-BINOMDIST(0,B8,B6,1)			
10							
11	Two-way data table of the probability in B9 as a function of values in B3 and B8						
12			Number of weeks beating the market index				
13		0.471	36	37	38	39	40
14	Number of mutual funds	200	0.542	0.273	0.113	0.040	0.013
15		300	0.690	0.380	0.164	0.060	0.019
16		400	0.790	0.471	0.213	0.079	0.025
17		500	0.858	0.549	0.258	0.097	0.031
18		600	0.904	0.616	0.301	0.116	0.038

The next example requires a normal calculation to find a probability p, which is then used in a binomial calculation.

EXAMPLE
6.9 Analyzing Daily Sales at Diggly Wiggly Supermarket

Customers at the Diggly Wiggly Supermarket spend varying amounts. Historical data show that the amount spent per customer is normally distributed with mean $85 and standard deviation $30. If 500 customers shop in a given day, calculate the mean and standard deviation of the number who spend at least $100. Then calculate the probability that at least 30% of all customers spend at least $100.

Objective To use the normal *and* binomial distributions to calculate the typical number of customers who spend at least $100 per day and the probability that at least 30% of all 500 daily customers spend at least $100.

Solution

Both questions involve the number of customers who spend at least $100. Because the amounts spent are normally distributed, the probability that a typical customer spends at least $100 is found with the NORMDIST function. This probability, 0.309, appears in cell B7 of Figure 6.21. (See the file **Supermarket Spending.xlsx**.) We calculate it with the formula

=1-NORMDIST(100,B4,B5,1)

This probability is then used as the parameter p in a binomial model. The mean and standard deviation of the number who spend at least $100 are calculated in cells B13 and B14 as np and $\sqrt{np(1-p)}$, using $n = 500$, the number of shoppers, and $p = 0.309$. The expected number who spend at least $100 is slightly greater than 154, and the standard deviation of this number is slightly greater than 10.

Figure 6.21 Calculations for Supermarket Example

	A	B	C	D	E	F
1	**Supermarket spending**					
2						
3	Amount spent per customer (normally distributed)					
4	Mean	$85				
5	StDev	$30				
6						
7	Probability that a customer spends at least $100	0.309		=1-NORMDIST(100,B4,B5,1)		
8						
9						
10	Number of customers	500				
11						
12	Mean and stdev of number who spend at least $100					
13	Mean	154.27		=B10*B7		
14	StDev	10.33		=SQRT(B10*B7*(1-B7))		
15						
16	Probability at least 30% spend at least $100	0.676		=1-BINOMDIST(0.3*B10-1,B10,B7,1)		

To answer the second question, note that 30% of 500 customers is 150 customers. Then the probability that at least 30% of the customers spend at least $100 is the probability that a binomially distributed random variable, with $n = 500$ and $p = 0.309$, is at least 150. We calculate this binomial probability, which turns out to be about 2/3, in cell B16 with the formula

=1-BINOMDIST(0.3*B10-1,B10,B7,1)

Note that the first argument calculates to 149. This is because the probability of *at least* 150 customers is 1.0 minus the probability of less than or equal to 149 customers. ∎

EXAMPLE | **6.10 OVERBOOKING BY AIRLINES**

This example presents a simplified version of calculations used by airlines when they overbook flights. They realize that a certain percentage of ticketed passengers will cancel at the last minute. Therefore, to avoid empty seats, they sell more tickets than there are seats, hoping that just about the right number of passengers show up. We will assume that the no-show rate is 10%. In binomial terms, we are assuming that each ticketed passenger, independently of the others, shows up with probability 0.90 and cancels with probability 0.10.

For a flight with 200 seats, the airline wants to find how sensitive various probabilities are to the number of tickets it issues. In particular, it wants to calculate (a) the probability that more than 205 passengers show up, (b) the probability that more than 200 passengers show up, (c) the probability that at least 195 seats will be filled, and (d) the probability that at least 190 seats will be filled. The first two of these are "bad" events from the airline's perspective; they mean that some customers will be bumped from the flight. The last two events are "good" in the sense that the airline wants most of the seats to be occupied.

Objective To assess the benefits and drawbacks of issuing various numbers of tickets on an airline flight with 200 seats.

Solution

To solve the airline's problem, we use the BINOMDIST function and a data table. The solution appears in Figure 6.22. (See the file **Airline Overbooking.xlsx**.) We first enter a possible number of tickets issued in cell B6 and, for this number, calculate the required probabilities in row 10. For example, the formulas in cells B10 and D10 are

=1-BINOMDIST(205,NTickets,1-PNoShow,1)

and

=1-BINOMDIST(194,NTickets,1-PNoShow,1)

Figure 6.22

Binomial Calculations for Overbooking Example

	A	B	C	D	E	F
1	Airline overbooking			Range names used:		
2				NTickets	=Overbooking!$B$6	
3	Number of seats	200		PNoShow	=Overbooking!$B$4	
4	Probability of no-show	0.1				
5						
6	Number of tickets issued	215				
7						
8	Required probabilities					
9		More than 205 show up	More than 200 show up	At least 195 seats filled	At least 190 seats filled	
10		0.001	0.050	0.421	0.820	
11						
12	Data table showing sensitivity of probabilities to number of tickets issued					
13	Number of tickets issued	More than 205 show up	More than 200 show up	At least 195 seats filled	At least 190 seats filled	
14		0.001	0.050	0.421	0.820	
15	206	0.000	0.000	0.012	0.171	
16	209	0.000	0.001	0.064	0.384	
17	212	0.000	0.009	0.201	0.628	
18	215	0.001	0.050	0.421	0.820	
19	218	0.013	0.166	0.659	0.931	
20	221	0.064	0.370	0.839	0.978	
21	224	0.194	0.607	0.939	0.995	
22	227	0.406	0.802	0.981	0.999	
23	230	0.639	0.920	0.995	1.000	
24	233	0.822	0.974	0.999	1.000	

Note that the condition "more than" requires a slightly different calculation than "at least." The probability of more than 205 is 1.0 minus the probability of less than or equal to 205, whereas the probability of at least 195 is 1.0 minus the probability of less than or equal to 194. Also, note that we are treating a "success" as a passenger who shows up. Therefore, the third argument of each BINOMDIST function is 1.0 minus the no-show probability.

To see how sensitive these probabilities are to the number of tickets issued, we create a one-way data table at the bottom of the spreadsheet. It is *one-way* because there is only one *input,* the number tickets issued, even though four output probabilities are tabulated. (To create the data table, list several possible numbers of tickets issued along the side in column A and create links to the probabilities in row 10 in row 14. That is, enter the formula =B10 in cell B14 and copy it across row 14. Then form a data table using the range A14:E24, no row input cell, and column input cell B6.)

The results are as expected. As the airline issues more tickets, there is a larger chance of having to bump passengers from the flight, but there is also a larger chance of filling most seats. In reality, the airline has to make a trade-off between these two, taking its various costs and revenues into account. ∎

The following is another simplified example of a real problem that occurs every time we watch election returns on TV. This problem is of particular interest in light of the highly unusual events that took place during election night television coverage of the U.S. presidential election in 2000, where the networks declared Gore an early winner in at least one state that he eventually lost. The basic question is how soon the networks can declare one of the candidates the winner, based on early voting returns. Our example is somewhat unrealistic because it ignores the possibility that early tabulations might be biased one way or the other. For example, the earliest reporting precincts might be known to be more heavily in favor of the Democrat than the population in general. Nevertheless, the example explains why the networks are able to make conclusions based on such seemingly small amounts of data.

EXAMPLE	6.11 PROJECTING ELECTION WINNERS FROM EARLY RETURNS

We assume that there are N voters in the population, of whom N_R will vote for the Republican and N_D will vote for the Democrat. The eventual winner will be the Republican if $N_R > N_D$ and will be the Democrat otherwise, but we won't know which until all of the votes are tabulated. (To simplify the example, we assume there are only two candidates and that the election will *not* end in a tie.) Let's suppose that a small percentage of the votes have been counted and the Republican is currently ahead 540 to 460. On what basis can the networks declare the Republican the winner, especially when there are millions of voters in the population?

Objective To use a binomial model to determine whether early returns reflect the eventual winner of an election between two candidates.

Solution

Let $n = 1000$ be the total number of votes that have been tabulated. If X is the number of Republican votes so far, $X = 540$. Now we pose the following question. If the Democrat were going to be the eventual winner, that is, $N_D > N_R$, and we randomly sampled 1000 voters from the population, how likely is it that at least 540 of these voters would be in favor of the Republican? If this is very *unlikely,* then the only reasonable conclusion is that the Democrat will *not* be the eventual winner. This is the reasoning the networks use to declare the Republican the winner.

We use a binomial model to see how unlikely the event "at least 540 out of 1000" is, assuming that the Democrat will be the eventual winner. We need a value for p, the probability that a typical vote is for the Republican. This probability should be the proportion of voters in the entire population who favor the Republican. All we know is that this probability is less than 0.5, because we have assumed that the Democrat will eventually win. In Figure 6.23, we show how the probability of at least 540 out of 1000 varies with values of p less than, but close to, 0.5. (See the file **Election Returns.xlsx**.)

We enter a trial value of 0.49 for p in cell B3 and then calculate the required probability in cell B9 with the formula

$=$**1-BINOMDIST(B6-1,B5,B3,1)**

Then we use this to create the data table at the bottom of the spreadsheet. This data table tabulates the probability of the given lead (at least 540 out of 1000) for various values of p less than 0.5. As shown in the last few rows, even if the eventual outcome were going to be a virtual tie—with the Democrat slightly ahead—there would still be very little chance of the Republican being at least 80 votes ahead so far. But because the Republican *is* currently ahead by 80 votes, the networks feel safe in declaring the Republican the winner.

Figure 6.23
Binomial
Calculations for
Voting Example

	A	B	C	D	E	F
1	Election returns					
2						
3	Population proportion for Republican	0.49				
4						
5	Votes tabulated so far	1000				
6	Votes for Republican so far	540				
7						
8	Binomial probability of at least this many votes for Republican					
9		0.0009		=1-BINOMDIST(B6-1,B5,B3,1)		
10						
11	Data table showing sensitivity of this probability to population proportion for Republican					
12	Population proportion for Republican	Probability				
13		0.0009				
14	0.490	0.0009				
15	0.492	0.0013				
16	0.494	0.0020				
17	0.496	0.0030				
18	0.498	0.0043				
19	0.499	0.0052				

The final example in this section challenges the two assumptions of the binomial model. So far, we have assumed that the outcomes of successive trials (1) have the same probability p of success and (2) are probabilistically independent. There are many situations where either or both of these assumptions are questionable. For example, consider successive items from a production line, where each item either meets specifications (a success) or doesn't (a failure). If the process deteriorates over time, at least until it receives maintenance, then the probability p of success could slowly decrease. Even if p remains constant, defective items could come in bunches (because of momentary inattentiveness on the part of a worker, say), which would invalidate the independence assumption.

If an analyst believes that the binomial assumptions are invalid, then an alternative model must be specified that reflects reality more closely. This is not easy—all kinds of *nonbinomial* assumptions can be imagined. Furthermore, even when we make such assumptions, there are probably no simple formulas to use, such as the BINOMDIST formulas we have been using. Simulation might be the only alternative, as we illustrate in the following example.

EXAMPLE | **6.12 STREAK SHOOTING IN BASKETBALL**

Do basketball players shoot in streaks? This question has been debated by thousands of basketball fans, and it has even been studied statistically by several academic researchers. Most fans believe the answer is "yes," arguing that players clearly alternate between hot streaks where they can't miss and cold streaks where they can't hit the broad side of a barn. This situation does not fit a binomial model where, say, a "450 shooter" has a 0.450 probability of making each shot and a 0.550 probability of missing, independently of other shots. If the binomial model does not apply, what model might be appropriate, and how could it be used to calculate a probability such as the probability of making at least 13 shots out of 25 attempts?[6]

---

[6]There are obviously a lot of extenuating circumstances surrounding any shot: the type of shot (layup versus jump shot), the type of defense, the score, the time left in the game, and so on. For this example we focus on a pure jump shooter who is more or less unaffected by the various circumstances in the game.

Objective To formulate a nonbinomial model of basketball shooting, and to use it to find the probability of a 0.450 shooter making at least 13 out of 25 shots.

Solution

This problem is quite open-ended. There are numerous alternatives to the binomial model that could capture the "streakiness" most fans believe in, and the one we suggest here is by no means definitive. We challenge you to develop others.

The model we propose assumes that this shooter makes 45% of his shots in the long run. The probability that he makes his first shot in a game is 0.45. In general, consider his nth shot. If he has made his last k shots, we assume the probability of making shot n is $0.45 + kd_1$. On the other hand, if he has missed his last k shots, we assume the probability of making shot n is $0.45 - kd_2$. Here, d_1 and d_2 are small values (0.01 and 0.02, for example) that indicate how much the shooter's probability of success increases or decreases depending on his current streak. The model implies that the shooter gets better the more shots he makes and worse the more he misses.

To implement this model, we use simulation as shown in Figure 6.24. (See the file **Basketball Simulation.xlsx**.) Actually, we first do a "baseline" binomial calculation in cell B9, using the parameters $n = 25$ and $p = 0.450$. The formula in cell B9 is

=1-BINOMDIST(12,B7,B3,1)

If the player makes each shot with probability 0.45, independently of the other shots, then the probability that he will make over half of his 25 shots is 0.306—about a 30% chance.

The simulation in the range A17:D41 shows the results of 25 random shots according to the *nonbinomial* model we have assumed. Column B indicates the length of the current streak, where a negative value indicates a streak of misses and a positive value indicates a streak of makes. Column C indicates the probability of a make on the current shot, and column D contains 1's for makes and 0's for misses. Here are step-by-step instructions for developing this range.

1 **First shot.** Enter the formulas

=B3

and

=IF(RAND()<C17,1,0)

in cells C17 and D17 to determine the outcome of the first shot.

2 **Second shot.** Enter the formulas

=IF(D17=0,-1,1)

=IF(B18<0,$B$3+B18*$B$5,$B$3+B18*$B$4)

and

=IF(RAND()<C18,1,0)

in cells B18, C18, and D18. The first of these indicates that by the second shot, the shooter will have a streak of one make or one miss. The second formula is the important one. It indicates how the probability of a make changes depending on the current streak. The third formula simulates a make or a miss, using the probability in cell C18.

Figure 6.24 Simulation of Basketball Shooting Model

	A	B	C	D	E	F	G	H	I
1	Basketball shooting simulation								
2									
3	Long-run average	0.45							
4	Increment d1 after a make	0.015							
5	Increment d2 after a miss	0.015							
6									
7	Number of shots	25							
8									
9	Binomial probability of at least 13 out of 25	0.306							
10									
11	Summary statistics from simulation below				Compare these	Fraction of reps with at least 13 from table below			
12	Number of makes	12				0.304			
13	At least 13 makes?	0							
14									
15	Simulation of makes and misses using nonbinomial model					Data table to replicate 25 shots many times			
16		Shot	Streak	P(make)	Make?		Rep	At least 13?		
17		1	NA	0.45	0			0		
18		2	-1	0.435	1		1	0		
19		3	1	0.465	0		2	0		
20		4	-1	0.435	1		3	0		
21		5	1	0.465	0		4	1		
22		6	-1	0.435	0		5	1		
23		7	-2	0.42	0		6	0		
24		8	-3	0.405	1		7	1		
25		9	1	0.465	1		8	0		
26		10	2	0.48	0		9	0		
27		11	-1	0.435	1		10	1		
28		12	1	0.465	1		11	1		
29		13	2	0.48	1		12	1		
30		14	3	0.495	0		13	0		
31		15	-1	0.435	1		14	1		
32		16	1	0.465	0		15	1		
33		17	-1	0.435	0		16	1		
34		18	-2	0.42	1		17	1		
35		19	1	0.465	0		18	0		
36		20	-1	0.435	0		19	0		
37		21	-2	0.42	1		20	0		
38		22	1	0.465	0		21	0		
39		23	-1	0.435	0		22	1		
40		24	-2	0.42	1		23	0		
41		25	1	0.465	1		24	1		
42							25	0		
43							26	0		
265							248	1		
266							249	0		
267							250	0		

③ **Length of streak on third (and succeeding) shots.** Enter the formula

=IF(AND(B18<0,D18=0),B18-1, IF(AND(B18<0,D18=1),1,

IF(AND(B18>0,D18=0),−1,B18+1)))

in cell B19 and copy it down column B. This nested IF formula checks for all four combinations of the previous streak (negative or positive, indicated in cell B18) and the most recent shot (make or miss, indicated in cell D18) to see whether the current streak continues by one or a new streak starts.

4 **Results of remaining shots.** The logic for the formulas in columns C and D is the same for the remaining shots as for shot 2, so copy the formulas in cells C18 and D18 down their respective columns.

5 **Summary of 25 shots.** Enter the formulas

=SUM(D17:D41)
　　and

=IF(B12>=13,1,0)

in cells B12 and B13 to summarize the results of the 25 simulated shots. In particular, the value in cell B13 is 1 only if at least 13 of the shots are successes.

What about the *probability* of making at least 13 shots with this nonbinomial model? So far, we have simulated one set of 25 shots and have reported whether at least 13 of the shots are successes. We need to replicate this simulation many times and report the fraction of the replications where at least 13 of the shots are successes. We do this with a data table in columns F and G.

To create this table, enter the replication numbers 1 through 250 (you could use any number of replications) in column F. Then put a link to B13 in cell G17 by entering the formula = B13 in this cell. Essentially, we are recalculating this value 250 times, each with different random numbers. To do this, highlight the range F17:G267, and create a data table with no row input cell and *any blank cell* (such as F17) as the column input cell. This causes Excel to recalculate the basic simulation 250 times, each time with different random numbers. Finally, enter the formula

=AVERAGE(G18:G267)

in cell F12 to calculate the fraction of the replications with at least 13 makes out of 25 shots.

After finishing all of this, you'll note that the spreadsheet is "live" in the sense that if you press the F9 recalculation key, all of the simulated quantities change—new random numbers. In particular, the estimate in cell F12 of the probability of at least 13 makes out of 25 shots changes. It is sometimes less than the binomial probability in cell B9 and sometimes greater. In general, the two probabilities are roughly the same. The bottom line? Even if the world doesn't behave exactly as the binomial model indicates, probabilities of various events can often be approximated fairly well by binomial probabilities—which saves us the trouble of developing and working with more complex models! ■

PROBLEMS

Level A

19. In a typical month, an insurance agent presents life insurance plans to 40 potential customers. Historically, one in four such customers chooses to buy life insurance from this agent. Based on the relevant binomial distribution, answer the following questions:

a. What is the probability that exactly 5 customers will buy life insurance from this agent in the coming month?

b. What is the probability that no more than 10 customers will buy life insurance from this agent in the coming month?

c. What is the probability that at least 20 customers will buy life insurance from this agent in the coming month?

d. Determine the mean and standard deviation of the number of customers who will buy life insurance from this agent in the coming month.

e. What is the probability that the number of customers who buy life insurance from this agent in the coming month will lie within 2 standard deviations of the mean?

f. What is the probability that the number of customers who buy life insurance from this agent in the coming month will lie within 3 standard deviations of the mean?

20. Continuing the previous exercise, use the normal approximation to the binomial to answer each of the questions posed in parts **a** through **f**. How well does the normal approximation perform in this case? Explain.

21. Many vehicles used in space travel are constructed with redundant systems to protect flight crews and their valuable equipment. In other words, backup systems are included within many vehicle components so that if one or more systems fail, backup systems will assure the safe operation of the given component and thus the entire vehicle. For example, consider one particular component of the U.S. space shuttle that has n duplicated systems (i.e., one original system and $n - 1$ backup systems). Each of these systems functions, independently of the others, with probability 0.98. This shuttle component functions successfully provided that *at least* one of the n systems functions properly.

   a. Find the probability that this shuttle component functions successfully if $n = 2$.

   b. Find the probability that this shuttle component functions successfully if $n = 4$.

   c. What is the minimum number n of duplicated systems that must be incorporated into this shuttle component to ensure at least a 0.9999 probability of successful operation?

22. Suppose that a popular hotel for vacationers in Orlando, Florida, has a total of 300 identical rooms. Like many major airline companies, this hotel has adopted an overbooking policy in an effort to maximize the usage of its available lodging capacity. Assume that each potential hotel customer holding a room reservation, independently of other customers, cancels the reservation or simply does not show up at the hotel on a given night with probability 0.15.

   a. Find the largest number of room reservations that this hotel can book and still be at least 95% sure that everyone who shows up at the hotel will have a room on a given night.

   b. Given that the hotel books the number of reservations found in answering part **a**, find the probability that at least 90% of the available rooms will be occupied on a given night.

   c. Given that the hotel books the number of reservations found in answering part **a**, find the probability that at most 80% of the available rooms will be occupied on a given night.

   d. How does your answer to part **a** change as the required assurance rate increases from 95% to 97%? How does your answer to part **a** change as the required assurance rate increases from 95% to 99%?

   e. How does your answer to part **a** change as the cancellation rate varies between 5% and 25% (in increments of 5%)? Assume now that the required assurance rate is held fixed at 95%.

23. A production process manufactures items with weights that are normally distributed with mean 15 pounds and standard deviation 0.1 pound. An item is considered to be defective if its weight is less than 14.8 pounds or greater than 15.2 pounds. Suppose that these items are currently produced in batches of 1000 units.

   a. Find the probability that at most 5% of the items in a given batch will be defective.

   b. Find the probability that at least 90% of the items in a given batch will be acceptable.

   c. How many items would have to be produced in a batch to guarantee that a batch consists of no more than 1% defective items?

24. Past experience indicates that 30% of all individuals entering a certain store decide to make a purchase. Using (a) the binomial distribution and (b) the normal approximation to the binomial, find that probability that 10 or more of the 30 individuals entering the store in a given hour will decide to make a purchase. Compare the results obtained using the two different approaches. Under what conditions will the normal approximation to this binomial probability become even more accurate?

25. Suppose that the number of ounces of soda put into a Pepsi can is normally distributed with $\mu = 12.05$ ounces and $\sigma = 0.03$ ounce.

   a. Legally, a can must contain at least 12 ounces of soda. What fraction of cans will contain at least 12 ounces of soda?

   b. What fraction of cans will contain less than 11.9 ounces of soda?

   c. What fraction of cans will contain between 12 and 12.08 ounces of soda?

   d. One percent of all cans will weigh more than what value?

   e. Ten percent of all cans will weigh less than what value?

   f. Pepsi controls the mean weight in a can by setting a timer. For what mean should the timer be set so that only 1 in 1000 cans will be underweight?

   g. Every day Pepsi produces 10,000 cans. The government inspects 10 randomly chosen cans each day. If at least two are underweight, Pepsi is fined $10,000. Given that $\mu = 12.05$ ounces and $\sigma = 0.03$ ounce, what is the probability that Pepsi will be fined on a given day?

26. Suppose that 52% of all registered voters prefer John Kerry to George Bush. (You may substitute the names of the current presidential candidates!)

   a. In a random sample of 100 voters, what is the probability that the sample will indicate that Kerry will win the election (that is, there will be more votes in the sample for Kerry)?

   b. In a random sample of 100 voters, what is the probability that the sample will indicate that Bush will win the election?

c. In a random sample of 100 voters, what is the probability that the sample will indicate a dead heat (50–50)?

d. In a random sample of 100 voters, what is the probability that between 40 and 60 (inclusive) voters will prefer Kerry?

27. Assume that, on average, 95% of all ticket-holders show up for a flight. If a plane seats 200 people, how many tickets should be sold to make the chance of an overbooked flight as close as possible to 5%?

28. Suppose that 60% of all people prefer Coke to Pepsi. We randomly choose 500 people and ask them if they prefer Coke to Pepsi. What is the probability that our survey will (erroneously) indicate that Pepsi is preferred by more people than Coke?

29. A firm's office contains 150 PCs. The probability that a given PC will not work on a given day is 0.05.

a. On a given day what is the probability that exactly one computer will not be working?

b. On a given day what is the probability that at least two computers will not be working?

c. What assumptions do your answers in parts **a** and **b** require?

30. Suppose that 4% of all tax returns are audited. In a group of *n* tax returns, consider the probability that at most two returns are audited. How large must *n* be before this probability will be less than 0.01?

31. Suppose that the height of a typical American female is normally distributed with $\mu = 64$ inches and $\sigma = 4$ inches. We observe the height of 10 American females.

a. What is the probability that exactly half the women will be under 58 inches tall?

b. Let *X* be the number of the 10 women who are under 58 inches tall. Determine the mean and standard deviation of *X*.

32. Consider a large population of shoppers, each of whom spends a certain amount during their current shopping trip; the distribution of these amounts is normally distributed with mean $55 and standard deviation $15. We randomly choose 25 of these shoppers. What is the probability that at least 15 of them spend between $45 and $75?

Level B

33. Many firms utilize sampling plans to control the quality of manufactured items ready for shipment. To illustrate the use of a sampling plan, suppose that a particular company produces and ships electronic computer chips in lots, each consisting of 1000 chips. This company's sampling plan specifies that quality control personnel will randomly sample 50 chips from each lot and accept the lot for shipping if the number of defective chips is less than 5. The lot will be rejected if the number of defective chips is 5 or more.

a. Find the probability of accepting a lot as a function of the actual fraction of defective chips. In particular, let the actual fraction of defective chips in a given lot equal any of 0.02, 0.04, 0.06, 0.08, 0.10, 0.12, 0.14, 0.16, 0.18. Then compute the lot acceptance probability for each of these lot defective fractions.

b. Construct a graph showing the probability of lot acceptance for each of the 9 lot defective fractions. Interpret your graph.

34. Continuing the previous exercise, repeat parts **a** and **b** under a revised sampling plan that calls for accepting a given lot if the number of defective chips found in the random sample of 50 chips is *not greater than* 5. Summarize any notable differences between the two graphs you have constructed in completing part **b** of this and the previous exercise.

35. Comdell Computer receives computer chips from Chipco. Each batch sent by Chipco is inspected as follows: 35 chips are tested and the batch passes inspection if at most one defective chip is found in the set of 35 tested chips. Past history indicates an average of 1% of all chips produced by Chipco are defective. Comdell has received 10 batches this week. What is the probability that at least 9 of the batches will pass inspection?

36. A standardized test consists entirely of multiple-choice questions, each with 5 possible choices. You want to ensure that a student who randomly guesses on each question will obtain an expected score of zero. How would you accomplish this?

37. In the current tax year, suppose that 5% of the millions of individual tax returns are fraudulent. That is, they contain errors that were purposely made to cheat the government.

a. Although these errors are often well concealed, let's suppose that a thorough IRS audit will uncover them. If a random 250 tax returns are audited, what is the probability that the IRS will uncover at least 15 fraudulent returns?

b. Answer the same question as in part **a**, but this time assume there is only a 90% chance that a given fraudulent return will be spotted as such if it is audited.

38. Suppose you work for a survey research company. In a typical survey, you mail questionnaires to 150 companies. Of course, some of these companies might decide not to respond. We'll assume that the nonresponse rate is 45%; that is, each company's probability of not responding, independently of the others, is 0.45. If your company requires at least 90 responses for a "valid" survey, find the probability that it will get this many. Use a data table to see how your answer varies as a function of the nonresponse rate (for a reasonable range of response rates surrounding 45%).

39. Continuing the previous problem, suppose your company does this survey in two "waves." It mails the 150 questionnaires and waits a certain period for the responses. As before, assume that the nonresponse rate is 45%. However, after this initial period, your company follows up (by telephone, say) on the nonrespondents, asking them to please respond. Suppose that the nonresponse rate on this second "wave" is 70%; that is, each original nonrespondent now responds with probability 0.3, independently of the others. Your company now wants to find the probability of obtaining at least 110 responses total. It turns out that this is a very difficult probability to calculate directly. So instead, approximate it with simulation.

40. A person claims that she is a fortune teller. Specifically, she claims that she can predict the direction of the change (up or down) in the Dow Jones Industrial Average for the next 10 days (such as U, U, D, U, D, U, U, D, D, D). (You can assume that she makes all 10 predictions right now, although that won't affect your answer to the question.) Obviously, you are skeptical, thinking that she is just guessing, so you'll be surprised if her predictions are accurate. Which would surprise you more: (1) she predicts at least 8 out of 10 correctly, or (2) she predicts at least 6 out of 10 correctly on each of 4 separate occasions? Answer by assuming that (1) she really is guessing and (2) each day the Dow is equally likely to go up or down.

6.6 THE POISSON AND EXPONENTIAL DISTRIBUTIONS

The final two distributions in this chapter are called the *Poisson* and *exponential* distributions. In most statistical applications, including those in the rest of this book, these distributions play a much less important role than the normal and binomial distributions. For this reason we will not analyze them in as much detail. However, in many applied management science models, the Poisson and exponential distributions are as important as any other distributions, discrete or continuous. For example, much of the study of probabilistic inventory models, queuing models, and reliability models relies heavily on these two distributions.

6.6.1 The Poisson Distribution

The **Poisson distribution** is a discrete distribution. It usually applies when we are interested in the *number* of events occurring within a specified period of time or space. Its possible values are all of the nonnegative integers: 0, 1, 2, and so on—there is no upper limit. Even though there is an infinite number of possible values, this causes no real problems because the probabilities of all sufficiently large values are essentially 0.

The Poisson distribution is characterized by a single parameter, usually labeled λ (Greek lambda), which must be positive. By adjusting the value of λ, we are able to produce different Poisson distributions, all of which have the same basic shape as in Figure 6.25. That is, they first increase, then decrease. It turns out that λ is easy to interpret. It is both the mean and the variance of the Poisson distribution. Therefore, the standard deviation is $\sqrt{\lambda}$.

Figure 6.25

Typical Poisson Distribution

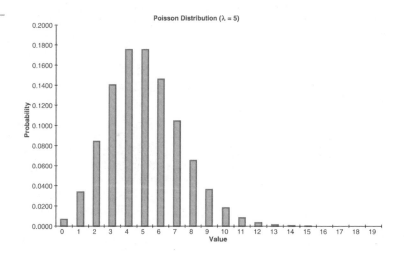

Typical Examples of the Poisson Distribution

1. A bank manager is studying the arrival pattern to the bank. Then the events are customer arrivals, the number of arrivals in an hour is Poisson distributed, and λ represents the expected number of arrivals per hour.

2. An engineer is interested in the lifetime of a type of battery. A device that uses this type of battery is operated continuously. When the first battery fails, it is replaced by a second; when the second fails, it is replaced by a third, and so on. The events are battery failures, the number of failures that occur in a month is Poisson distributed, and λ represents the expected number of failures per month.

3. A retailer is interested in the number of units of a product demanded in a particular unit of time such as a week. Then the events are customer demands, the number of units demanded in a week is Poisson distributed, and λ is the expected number of units demanded per week.

4. In a quality control setting, the Poisson distribution is often relevant for describing the number of defects in some unit of space. For example, when paint is applied to the body of a new car, any minor blemish is considered a defect. Then the number of defects on the hood, say, might be Poisson distributed. In this case, λ is the expected number of defects per hood.

These examples are representative of the many situations where the Poisson distribution has been applied. For the obvious reason, the parameter λ is often called a rate—arrivals per hour, failures per month, and so on. If we change the unit of time, we simply modify the rate accordingly. For example, if the number of arrivals to a bank in a single hour is Poisson distributed with rate $\lambda = 30$, then the number of arrivals in a half-hour period is Poisson distributed with rate $\lambda = 15$.

We can use Excel to calculate Poisson probabilities much as we did with binomial probabilities. The relevant function is the POISSON function. It takes the form

=POISSON(*k*,λ,*cum*)

The third argument *cum* works exactly as in the binomial case. If it is 0, the function returns $P(X = k)$; if it is 1, the function returns $P(X \leq k)$. As examples, if $\lambda = 5$, POISSON(7,5,0) returns the probability of exactly 7, POISSON(7,5,1) returns the probability of less than or equal to 7, and 1-POISSON(3,5,1) returns the probability of greater than 3.

The following example shows how a manager or consultant might use the Poisson distribution.

EXAMPLE | 6.13 MANAGING INVENTORY OF TELEVISIONS AT KRIEGLAND

Kriegland is a department store that sells various brands of color television sets. One of the manager's biggest problems is to decide on an appropriate inventory policy for stocking television sets. On the one hand, he wants to have enough in stock so that customers receive their requests right away, but on the other hand, he does not want to tie up too much money in inventory that sits on the storeroom floor.

Most of the difficulty results from the unpredictability of customer demand. If this demand were constant and known, the manager could decide on an appropriate inventory policy fairly easily. But the demand varies widely from month to month in a random manner. All the manager knows is that the historical average demand per month is approximately 17. Therefore, he decides to call in a consultant. The consultant immediately suggests using a probability model. Specifically, she attempts to find the probability distribution of demand in a typical month. How might she proceed?

Objective To model the probability distribution of monthly demand for color television sets with a particular Poisson distribution.

Solution

Let *X* be the demand in a typical month. The consultant knows that there are many possible values of *X*. For example, if historical records show that monthly demands have always been between 0 and 40, the consultant knows that almost all of the probability should be assigned to the values 0 through 40. However, she does not relish the thought of finding 41 probabilities, $P(X = 0)$ through $P(X = 40)$, that sum to 1 and reflect historical frequencies. Instead, she discovers from the manager that the histogram of demands from previous months is shaped much like the graph in Figure 6.25. That is, it rises to some peak, then falls.

Figure 6.26 Poisson Calculations for Television Example

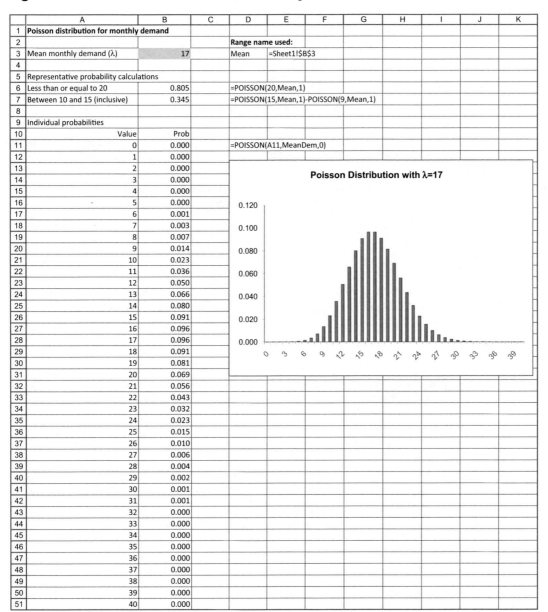

	A	B	C	D	E	F	G	H	I	J	K
1	Poisson distribution for monthly demand										
2				Range name used:							
3	Mean monthly demand (λ)	17		Mean	=Sheet1!$B$3						
4											
5	Representative probability calculations										
6	Less than or equal to 20	0.805		=POISSON(20,Mean,1)							
7	Between 10 and 15 (inclusive)	0.345		=POISSON(15,Mean,1)-POISSON(9,Mean,1)							
8											
9	Individual probabilities										
10	Value	Prob									
11	0	0.000		=POISSON(A11,MeanDem,0)							
12	1	0.000									
13	2	0.000									
14	3	0.000									
15	4	0.000									
16	5	0.000									
17	6	0.001									
18	7	0.003									
19	8	0.007									
20	9	0.014									
21	10	0.023									
22	11	0.036									
23	12	0.050									
24	13	0.066									
25	14	0.080									
26	15	0.091									
27	16	0.096									
28	17	0.096									
29	18	0.091									
30	19	0.081									
31	20	0.069									
32	21	0.056									
33	22	0.043									
34	23	0.032									
35	24	0.023									
36	25	0.015									
37	26	0.010									
38	27	0.006									
39	28	0.004									
40	29	0.002									
41	30	0.001									
42	31	0.001									
43	32	0.000									
44	33	0.000									
45	34	0.000									
46	35	0.000									
47	36	0.000									
48	37	0.000									
49	38	0.000									
50	39	0.000									
51	40	0.000									

Poisson Distribution with λ=17

Knowing that a Poisson distribution has this same basic shape, the consultant decides to model the monthly demand with a Poisson distribution. To choose a particular Poisson distribution, all she has to do is choose a value of λ, the mean demand per month. Because the historical average is approximately 17, she chooses $\lambda = 17$. Now she can test the Poisson model by calculating probabilities of various events and asking the manager whether these probabilities are a reasonable approximation to reality.

For example, the Poisson probability that monthly demand is less than or equal to 20, $P(X \leq 20)$, is 0.805 [using the Excel function POISSON(20,17,1)], and the probability that demand is between 10 and 15 inclusive, $P(10 \leq X \leq 15)$, is 0.345 [using POISSON(15,17,1)-POISSON(9,17,1)]. Figure 6.26 illustrates various probability calculations and shows the graph of the individual Poisson probabilities. (See the file **Poisson Demand Distribution.xlsx**.)

If the manager believes that these probabilities and other similar probabilities are reasonable, then the *statistical* part of the consultant's job is finished. Otherwise, she must try a different Poisson distribution—a different value of λ—or perhaps a different type of distribution altogether. ∎

6.6.2 The Exponential Distribution

Suppose that a bank manager is studying the pattern of customer arrival at her branch location. As indicated previously in this section, the number of arrivals in an hour at a facility such as a bank is often well described by a Poisson distribution with parameter λ, where λ represents the expected number of arrivals per hour. An alternative way to view the uncertainty in the arrival process is to consider the *times* between customer arrivals. The most common probability distribution used to model these times, often called *interarrival times,* is the *exponential* distribution.

In general, the *continuous* random variable X has an **exponential** distribution with parameter λ (with $\lambda > 0$) if the probability density function for X has the form $f(x) = \lambda e^{-\lambda}x$ for $x > 0$. This exact form is not as important as the shape of the graph it implies, as shown in Figure 6.27. Because this density function decreases continually from left to right, its most likely value is $x = 0$. Alternatively, if we collect many observations from an exponential distribution and draw a histogram of the observed values, then we expect it to resemble the smooth curve shown in Figure 6.27, with the tallest bars to the left. The mean and standard deviation of this distribution are easy to remember. They are both equal to the *reciprocal* of the parameter λ. For example, an exponential distribution with parameter $\lambda = 0.1$ has mean and standard deviation both equal to 10.

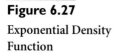

Figure 6.27

Exponential Density Function

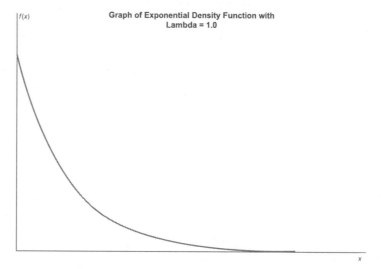

As with the normal distribution, we usually want probabilities to the left or right of a given value. For any exponential distribution, we can calculate the probability to the left of a given value $x > 0$ with Excel's EXPONDIST function. In particular, this function takes the form

=EXPONDIST(x, λ, 1)

For example, if $x = 0.5$ and $\lambda = 5$ (so that the mean equals $1/5 = 0.2$), then the probability of being less than 0.5 can be found with the formula

=EXPONDIST(0.5, 5, 1)

This returns the probability 0.918. Of course, the probability of being greater than 0.5 is then $1 - 0.918 = 0.082$.

Returning to the bank manager's analysis of customer arrival data, when the times between arrivals are exponentially distributed, we sometimes hear that "arrivals occur according to a Poisson process." This is because there is a close relationship between the exponential distribution, which measures *times* between events such as arrivals, and the Poisson distribution, which counts the *number* of events in a certain length of time. The details of this relationship are beyond the level of this book, so we will not explore the topic further. It is sufficient for our purposes to say, for example, that if customers arrive at a facility according to a Poisson process with rate 6 per hour, then we know the corresponding times between arrivals are exponentially distributed with mean $1/\lambda = 1/6$ hour.

PROBLEMS

Level A

41. The annual number of industrial accidents occurring in a particular manufacturing plant is known to follow a Poisson distribution with mean 12.
  a. What is the probability of observing exactly 12 accidents at this plant during the coming year?
  b. What is the probability of observing no more than 12 accidents at this plant during the coming year?
  c. What is the probability of observing at least 15 accidents at this plant during the coming year?
  d. What is the probability of observing between 10 and 15 accidents (inclusive) at this plant during the coming year?
  e. Find the smallest integer k such that we can be at least 99% sure that the annual number of accidents occurring at this plant will be less than k.

42. Suppose that the number of customers arriving each hour at the only checkout counter in a local pharmacy is approximately Poisson distributed with an expected arrival rate of 20 customers per hour.
  a. Find the probability that exactly 10 customers arrive at this checkout counter in a given hour.
  b. Find the probability that at least 5 customers arrive at this checkout counter in a given hour.
  c. Find the probability that no more than 25 customers arrive at this checkout counter in a given hour.

  d. Find the probability that between 10 and 30 customers (inclusive) arrive at this checkout counter in a given hour.
  e. Find the largest integer k such that we can be at least 95% sure that the number of customers arriving at this checkout counter in a given hour will be greater than k.
  f. Recalling the relationship between the Poisson and exponential distributions, find the probability that the time between two successive customer arrivals is more then 4 minutes. Find the probability that it is less than 2 minutes.

43. Suppose the number of points scored by the Indiana University basketball team in 1 minute follows a Poisson distribution with $\lambda = 1.5$. In a 10-minute span of time, what is the probability that Indiana University scores exactly 20 points? (Use the fact that if the rate per minute is λ, then the rate in t minutes is λt.)

44. Suppose that the times between arrivals at a bank during the peak period of the day are exponentially distributed with a mean of 45 seconds. If you just observed an arrival, what is the probability that you will need to wait for more than a minute before observing the next arrival? What is the probability you will need to wait at least 2 minutes?

Level B

45. Consider a Poisson random variable X with parameter $\lambda = 2$.

  a. Find the probability that X is within 1 standard deviation of its mean.

  b. Find the probability that X is within 2 standard deviations of its mean.

  c. Find the probability that X is within 3 standard deviations of its mean.

  d. Do the empirical rules we learned previously seem to be applicable in working with the Poisson distribution where $\lambda = 2$? Explain why or why not.

  e. Repeat parts **a through d** for the case of a Poisson random variable where $\lambda = 20$.

46. Based on historical data, the probability that a major league pitcher pitches a no-hitter in a game is about 1/1300.

  a. Use the binomial distribution to determine the probability that in 650 games 0, 1, 2, or 3 no-hitters will be pitched. (Find the separate probabilities of these four events.)

  b. Repeat part **a** using the Poisson approximation to the binomial. This approximation says that if n is large and p is small, a binomial distribution with parameters n and p is approximately Poisson with $\lambda = np$.

6.7 FITTING A PROBABILITY DISTRIBUTION TO DATA WITH @RISK[7]

The normal, binomial, Poisson, and exponential distributions are four of the most commonly used distributions in real applications. However, many other discrete and continuous distributions are also used. These include the uniform, triangular, Erlang, lognormal, gamma, Weibull, and others. How do we know which to choose for any particular application? Often we can answer this by seeing which of several potential distributions fits a given set of data most closely. Essentially, we compare a histogram of the data with the theoretical probability distributions available and see which gives the best fit.

@RISK, one of the Palisade add-ins in the Decision Tools suite, makes this fairly easy, as we illustrate in the following example. (Many other features of the @RISK add-in are discussed in depth in Chapters 16 and 17.)

EXAMPLE | **6.14 ASSESSING A DISTRIBUTION OF SUPERMARKET CHECKOUT TIMES**

A supermarket has collected checkout times on over 100 customers. (See the file **Checkout Times.xlsx.**) As shown in Figure 6.28, the times vary from 40 seconds to 279 seconds, with the mean and median right around 2 minutes.

Figure 6.28

Supermarket
Checkout Times

	A	B	C	D	E	F	G
1	Customer	Time			*Summary measures for selected variables*		
2	1	131				Time	
3	2	101			Count	113.000	
4	3	178			Mean	159.239	
5	4	246			Median	155.000	
6	5	207			Standard deviation	52.609	
7	6	155			Minimum	40.000	
8	7	95			Maximum	279.000	
9	8	105					
10	9	168					
11	10	92					
12	11	112					
13	12	163					
111	110	138					
112	111	279					
113	112	90					
114	113	155					

---

[7]In the previous edition, we showed how to do this with Palisade's stand-alone program BestFit. Because @RISK incorporates all the functionality of BestFit, and because BestFit is not included in the current version of the Palisade suite, we now illustrate the procedure with @RISK.

The supermarket manager would like to check whether these data are normally distributed or whether some other distribution fits them better. How can he tell?

Objective   To use @RISK to determine which probability distribution fits the given data best.

Solution

To open @RISK, go to the Windows Start button, find the Palisade group, and click on @RISK. If Excel is already open, this opens @RISK on top of it. If Excel isn't it open, this launches Excel and @RISK. You will know @RISK is open when you see the @RISK tab and the associated ribbon in Figure 6.29. For now, we are interested only in the Distribution Fitting item. From here, we can go in one of two ways. We can test the fit of a *given* distribution, or we can find the best-fitting distribution from a number of candidates. We illustrate both.

Figure 6.29   @RISK Ribbon

Because the supermarket manager wants to know whether the data could come from a normal distribution, we check this possibility first. To do so, select Fit Manager from the Distribution Fitting dropdown. The first step is to define a data set, as we have in Figure 6.30. The second step is to click on the Distributions to Fit tab and select the Normal distribution, as shown in Figure 6.31. To see how well a normal distribution fits the data, all you need to do is click on the Fit button. This produces the output shown in Figure 6.32, with a normal curve superimposed on the histogram of the data. A visual examination of this graph is often sufficient to tell whether the fit is any "good." (We would judge this fit to be "fair," but not great.)

@RISK provides several numerical measures of the goodness of fit, which you can find by clicking on the dropdown next to Fit Ranking at the top left in the figure. We won't pursue the technical details, but we will simply mention that each test value measures "goodness of fit" in a slightly different way. For each of these measures, the larger the test value is, the *worse* the fit is. They can then be used to compare fits; the distribution with the lowest test values is the winner.

Figure 6.30

Defining a Data Set

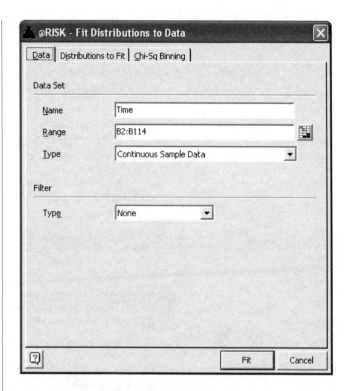

Figure 6.31

Selecting the Distribution(s) to Fit

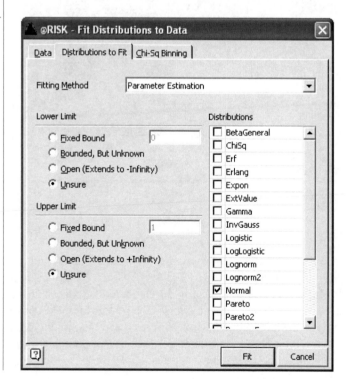

We next see which of several possible distributions fit the data best. To do this, get back into Fit Manager and click on the Distributions to Fit tab. (See Figure 6.33.) On the left we have made some "reasonable" choices about the checkout data. We have specified that the lowest possible checkout time is 0 but we are not sure about the upper limit on the checkout times. When we make such choices, the set of possible distributions that are checked on the right changes. For example, the selected list here contains only distributions with a lower limit of 0. (Note that the normal distribution does *not* satisfy these conditions.) We can then uncheck any distributions we do not want included in the search for the best fit. (You might want to uncheck distributions you've never heard of, for instance!)

Figure 6.32

Normal Fit to the Data

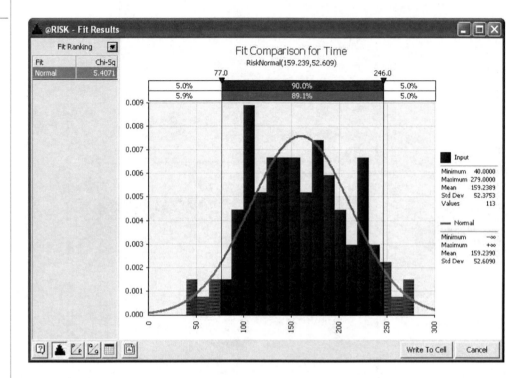

Once these candidate distributions have been specified and we click on Fit, @RISK performs a numerical algorithm to find the best-fitting distribution from each selected distribution family (the best Gamma of all Gamma distributions, for example) and displays them in ranked order, from best to worst. The best fit for these data is the BetaGeneral distribution, as shown in Figure 6.34. (The BetaGeneral family includes skewed distributions, although this one appears symmetric.) We can also click on any of the "runner up" distributions to see how well they fit. For example, the Triangular fit is shown in Figure 6.35. Obviously, this fit is not nearly as good as the BetaGeneral fit.

Figure 6.33
Selecting
Distributions to Fit

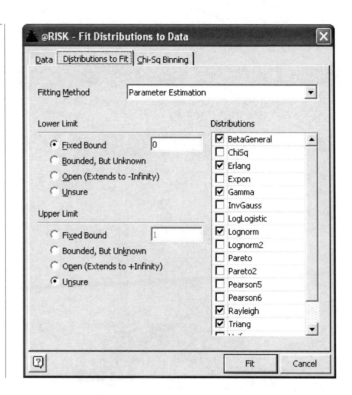

Figure 6.34 BetaGeneral Fit to the Data

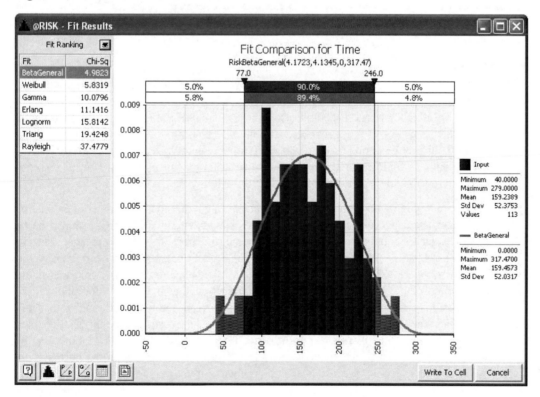

Figure 6.35 Triangular Fit to the Data

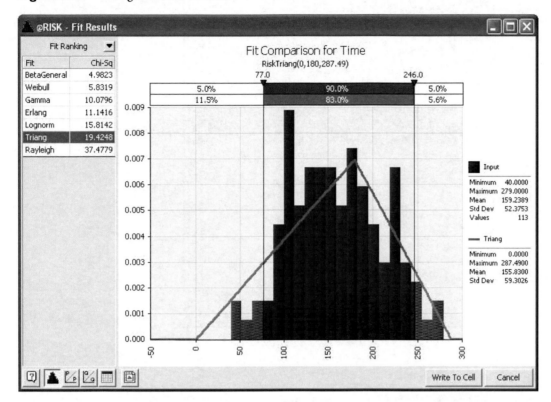

It is not always easy to "eyeball" these graphs and judge which fit is best. This is the reason for the goodness-of-fit measures. Comparing Figures 6.34 and 6.35, we see that the Triangular fit is considerably worse than the BetaGeneral—its test values (some not shown) are all much larger. By comparison, the test values for the Normal fit in Figure 6.32 are quite comparable to those for the BetaGeneral. The only downside to the Normal distribution, in this example, is that checkout times cannot possibly be negative, as the Normal allows. But the probability of a negative value for this particular Normal distribution is so low that the manager might decide to use it anyway. ∎

At this point, you might wonder why we bother fitting a distribution to a set of data in the first place. The usual reason is given in the following scenario. Suppose a manager needs to make a decision, but there is at least one source of uncertainty. If the manager wants to develop a decision model or perhaps a simulation model to help solve his problem, probability distributions of all uncertain outcomes are typically required. The manager could always choose one of the "well-known" distributions, such as the normal, for all uncertain outcomes, but these might not reflect reality well. Instead, the manager could gather historical data, such as those in the preceding example, find the distribution that fits these data best, and then use this distribution in the decision or simulation model. Of course, as this example has illustrated, it helps to know a few distributions other than the normal—the Weibull and the gamma, for instance. Although we will not pursue these in this book, the more distributions you have in your "tool kit," the more effectively you can model.

PROBLEMS

Level A

47. A production manager is interested in determining the proportion of defective items in a typical shipment of one of the computer components that her company manufactures. The proportion of defective components is recorded for each of 500 randomly selected shipments collected during a 1-month period. The data are in the file **P02_02.xlsx**. Use @RISK to determine which probability distribution best fits these data.

48. The manager of a local fast-food restaurant is interested in improving the service provided to customers who use the restaurant's drive-up window. As a first step in this process, the manager asks his assistant to record the time (in minutes) it takes to serve 200 different customers at the final window in the facility's drive-up system. The given 200 customer service times are all observed during the busiest hour of the day for this fast-food operation. The data are in the file **P02_04.xlsx**. Use @RISK to determine which probability distribution best fits these data.

49. The operations manager of a toll booth, located at a major exit of a state turnpike, is trying to estimate the average number of vehicles that arrive at the toll booth during a 1-minute period during the peak of rush-hour traffic. In an effort to estimate this average throughput value, he records the number of vehicles that arrive at the toll booth over a 1-minute interval commencing at the same time for each of 365 normal weekdays. The data are in the file **P02_09.xlsx**. Use @RISK to determine which probability distribution best fits these data.

50. A finance professor has just given a midterm examination in her corporate finance course and is interested in learning how her class of 100 students performed on this exam. The data are in the file **P02_05.xlsx**. Use @RISK to determine which probability distribution best fits these data.

6.8 CONCLUSION

We have covered a lot of ground in this chapter, and much of the material, especially that on the normal distribution, will be used in later chapters. The normal distribution is the cornerstone for much of statistical theory. As we see when we study statistical inference and regression, an assumption of normality is behind most of the procedures we use. Therefore, it is important to understand the properties of the normal distribution and how to work with it in Excel. The binomial, Poisson, and exponential distributions, although not used as frequently as the normal distribution in this book, are also extremely important. The examples we have discussed indicate how these distributions can be used in a variety of business situations.

Although we have attempted to stress *concepts* in this chapter, we have also described the details necessary to work with these distributions in Excel. Fortunately, these details are not too difficult to master once you understand Excel's built-in functions such as NORMDIST, NORMINV, and BINOMDIST. Figures 6.6 and 6.18 provide typical examples of these functions. We suggest that you keep a copy of these figures handy.

Summary of Key Terms

Term	Explanation	Excel	Page	Equation Number
Probability density function	Specifies the probability distribution of a continuous random variable		258	
Normal distribution	A continuous distribution with possible values ranging over the *entire* number line; its density function is a symmetric bell-shaped curve		259	6.1
Standardizing a normal random variable	Transforms any normal distribution with mean μ and standard deviation σ to the *standard* normal distribution with mean 0 and standard deviation 1	STANDARDIZE	260	6.2
Normal calculations in Excel	Useful for finding probabilities and percentiles for nonstandard and standard normal distributions	NORMDIST, NORMSDIST, NORMINV, NORMSINV	263	
Empirical rules for normal distribution	About 68% of the data fall within 1 standard deviation of the mean, about 95% of the data fall within 2 standard deviations of the mean, and almost all fall within 3 standard deviations of the mean.		265	
Binomial distribution	The distribution of the number of successes in n independent, identical trials, where each trial has probability p of success	BINOMDIST CRITBINOM	278	
Mean and standard deviation of a binomial distribution	The mean and standard deviation of a binomial distribution with parameters n and p are np and $[np(1-p)]^{1/2}$, respectively.		281	6.3, 6.4
Normal approximation to the binomial distribution	If $np > 5$ and $n(1-p) > 5$, the binomial distribution can be approximated well by a normal distribution with mean np and standard deviation $[np(1-p)]^{1/2}$.		282	
Poisson distribution	A discrete probability distribution that often describes the number of events occurring within a specified period of time or space; mean and variance both equal the parameter λ	POISSON	294	
Exponential distribution	A continuous probability distribution useful for measuring *times* between events such as customer arrivals to a service facility; mean and standard deviation both equal $1/\lambda$	EXPONDIST	297	
Relationship between Poisson and exponential distributions	Exponential distribution measures *times* between events; Poisson distribution counts the *number* of events in a certain period of time.		298	
@RISK	An Excel add-in for finding how well a specified distribution fits a set of data, or for finding the distribution that best fits a set of data	Distribution Fitting item on @RISK ribbon	299	

PROBLEMS

Conceptual Exercises

C.1 Explain why the probability that a continuous random variable equals any particular value must be zero.

C.2 What is the relationship between the mean and standard deviation of any normal distribution? Explain.

C.3 A New York Yankees fan would like to determine the probability that his beloved team will sweep the National League Championship team in the first four games of this year's World Series. Explain, in words, how the fan should proceed to assess this probability. Be sure to state all assumptions that the fan needs to make to proceed with the approach you prescribe.

C.4 A production manager would like to determine the probability that a particular production process yields more than 3 defective items per hour. Explain, in words, how the manager should proceed to assess this probability. Be sure to state all assumptions that the manager needs to make to proceed with the approach you prescribe.

C.5 State the major similarities and differences between the *normal* distribution and the *exponential* distribution.

Level A

51. Suppose the annual return on XYZ stock follows a normal distribution with mean 0.12 and standard deviation 0.30.
   a. What is the probability that XYZ's value will decrease during a year?
   b. What is the probability that the return on XYZ during a year will be at least 20%?
   c. What is the probability that the return on XYZ during a year will be between −6% and 9%?
   d. There is a 5% chance that the return on XYZ during a year will be greater than what value?
   e. There is a 1% chance that the return on XYZ during a year will be less than what value?
   f. There is a 95% chance that the return on XYZ during a year will be between what two values (equidistant from the mean)?

52. Assume the annual mean return on Disney stock is around 15% and the annual standard deviation is around 25%. Assume the annual and daily returns on Disney stock are normally distributed.
   a. What is the probability that Disney will lose money during a year?
   b. There is a 5% chance that Disney will earn a return of at least what value during a year?
   c. There is a 10% chance that Disney will earn a return of less than or equal to what value during a year?
   d. What is the probability that Disney will earn at least 35% during a year?

e. Assume there are 252 trading days in a year. What is the probability that Disney will lose money on a given day? [*Hint*: Let Y be the annual return on Disney and Xi be the return on Disney on day i. Then (approximately) $Y = X_1 + X_2 + \cdots + X_{252}$. Use the fact that the sum of independent normal random variables is normally distributed, with mean equal to the sum of the individual means, and variance equal to the sum of the individual variances.]

53. Suppose Comdell Computer receives its disk drives from Diskco. On average, 4% of all floppy disk drives received by Comdell are defective.
   a. Dell has adopted the following policy. It samples 50 disk drives in each shipment and accepts the shipment if all disk drives in the sample are nondefective. What fraction of batches will Comdell accept?
   b. Suppose instead that the batch is accepted if at most 1 disk drive in the sample is defective. What fraction of batches will Comdell accept?
   c. What is the probability that a sample of size 50 will contain at least 10 defectives?

54. A family is considering a move from a midwestern city to a city in California. The distribution of housing costs where the family currently lives is normal with mean $105,000 and standard deviation $18,200. The distribution of housing costs in the California city is normal with mean $235,000 and standard deviation $30,400. The family's current house is valued at $110,000.
   a. What percentage of houses in the family's current city cost less than theirs?
   b. If the family buys a $200,000 house in the new city, what percentage of houses there will cost less than theirs?
   c. What price house will the family need to buy to be in the same percentile (of housing costs) in the new city as they are in the current city?

55. The number of traffic fatalities in a typical month in a given state has a normal distribution with mean 125 and standard deviation 31.
   a. If a person in the highway department claims that there will be at least m fatalities in the next month with probability 0.95, what value of m makes this claim true?
   b. If the claim is that there will be no more than n fatalities in the next month with probability 0.98, what value of n makes this claim true?

56. It can be shown that a sum of independent normally distributed random variables is also normally distributed. Do *all* functions of normal random variables lead to normal random variables? Consider the following.

SuperDrugs is a chain of drugstores with three similar-size stores in a given city. The sales in a given week for any of these stores is normally distributed with mean $15,000 and standard deviation $3000. At the end of each week, the sales figure for the store with the largest sales among the three stores is recorded. Is this maximum value normally distributed? To answer this question, simulate a weekly sales figure at each of the three stores and calculate the maximum. Then replicate this maximum 500 times with a data table and create a histogram of the 500 maximum values. Does it appear to be normally shaped? Whatever this distribution looks like, use your simulated values to estimate its mean and standard deviation.

Level B

57. When we sum 30 or more independent random variables, the sum of the random variables will usually be approximately normally distributed, even if each individual random variable is not normally distributed. Use this fact to estimate the probability that a casino will be behind after 90,000 roulette bets, given that it wins $1 or loses $35 on each bet with probabilities 37/38 and 1/38.

58. The daily demand for six-packs of Coke at Mr. D's supermarket follows a normal distribution with mean 120 and standard deviation 30. Every Monday the Coke delivery driver delivers Coke to Mr. D's. If Mr. D's wants to have only a 1% chance of running out of Coke by the end of the week, how many should Mr. D's order for the week? Assume orders are placed on Sunday at midnight. (Assume also that demands on different days are probabilistically independent. Use the fact that the sum of independent normal random variables is normally distributed, with mean equal to the sum of the individual means, and variance equal to the sum of the individual variances.)

59. Many companies use sampling to determine whether a batch should be accepted. An (n, c) sampling plan consists of inspecting n randomly chosen items from a batch and accepting the batch if c or fewer sampled items are defective. Suppose a company uses a (100, 5) sampling plan to determine whether a batch of 10,000 computer chips is acceptable.
   a. The "producer's risk" of a sampling plan is the probability that an acceptable batch will be rejected by a sampling plan. Suppose the customer considers a batch with 3% defectives acceptable. What is the producer's risk for this sampling plan?
   b. The "consumer's risk" of a sampling plan is the probability that an unacceptable batch will be accepted by a sampling plan. Our customer says

that a batch with 9% defectives is unacceptable. What is the consumer's risk for this sampling plan?

60. Suppose that if a presidential election were held today, 52% of all voters would vote for Kerry over Bush. (You may substitute the names of the current presidential candidates!) This problem shows that even if there are 100 million voters, a sample of several thousand is enough to determine the outcome, even in a fairly close election.
   a. If we were to randomly sample 1500 voters, what is the probability that the sample would indicate (correctly) that Kerry is preferred to Bush?
   b. If we were to randomly sample 6000 voters, what is the probability that the sample would indicate (correctly) that Kerry is preferred to Bush?

61. The Coke factory fills bottles of soda by setting a timer on a filling machine. It has generally been observed that the distribution of the number of ounces the machine puts into a bottle is normal with standard deviation 0.05 ounces. The company wants 99.9% of all its bottles to have at least 16 ounces of soda. To what amount should the mean amount put in each bottle be set? (The company does not want to fill any more than is necessary!)

62. The time it takes me to swim 100 yards in a race is normally distributed with mean 62 seconds and standard deviation 2 seconds. In my next five races, what is the probability that I will swim under a minute exactly twice?

63. We assemble a large part by joining two smaller parts together. In the past, the smaller parts we have produced have a mean length of 1 inch and a standard deviation of 0.01 inch. Assume that the lengths of the smaller parts are normally distributed.
   a. What fraction of the larger parts are longer than 2.05 inches? (Use the fact that the sum of independent normal random variables is normally distributed, with mean equal to the sum of the individual means, and variance equal to the sum of the individual variances.)
   b. What fraction of the larger parts are between 1.96 inches and 2.02 inches long?

64. (Suggested by Sam Kaufmann, Indiana University MBA who runs Harrah's Lake Tahoe Casino.) A high roller has come to the casino to play 300 games of craps. For each game of craps played there is a 0.493 probability that the high roller will win $1 and a 0.507 probability that the high roller will lose $1. After 300 games of craps, what is the probability that the casino will be behind more than $10?

65. (Suggested by Sam Kaufmann, Indiana University MBA who runs Harrah's Lake Tahoe Casino.) A high roller comes to the casino intending to play 500 hands of blackjack for $1 a hand. On each hand,

the high roller will win $1 with probability 0.48 and lose $1 with probability 0.52. After the 500 hands, what is the probability that the casino has lost more than $40?

66. Bottleco produces 100,000 12-ounce bottles of soda per year. By adjusting a timer, Bottleco can adjust the mean number of ounces placed in a bottle. No matter what the mean, the standard deviation of the number of ounces in a bottle is 0.05. Soda costs $0.05 per ounce. Any bottle weighing less than 12 ounces will incur a $10 fine for being underweight. Determine a setting for the mean number of ounces per bottle of soda that will minimize the expected cost per year of producing soda. Your answer should be accurate within 0.001 ounce. Does the number of bottles produced per year influence your answer?

67. The weekly demand for televisions at Lowland Appliance is normally distributed with mean 400 and standard deviation 100. Each time an order for TVs is placed, it arrives exactly 4 weeks later. That is, TV orders have a 4-week lead time. Lowland doesn't want to run out of TVs during any more than 1% of all lead times. How low should Lowland let its TV inventory drop before it places an order for more TVs? (*Hint:* How many standard deviations above the mean lead-time demand must the reorder point be for there to be a 1% chance of a stockout during the lead time? Use the fact that the sum of independent normal random variables is normally distributed, with mean equal to the sum of the individual means, and variance equal to the sum of the individual variances.)

68. An elevator rail is assumed to meet specifications if its diameter is between 0.98 and 1.01 inches. Each year we make 100,000 elevator rails. For a cost of $10/\sigma^2$ per year we can rent a machine that produces elevator rails whose diameters have a standard deviation of σ. (The idea is that we must pay more for smaller variances.) Any machine will produce rails having a mean diameter of 1 inch. Any rail that does not meet specifications must be reworked (at a cost of $12). Assume that the diameter of an elevator rail follows a normal distribution.
   a. What standard deviation (within 0.001 inch) will minimize our annual cost of producing elevator rails? You do not need to try standard deviations in excess of 0.02 inch.
   b. For your answer in part **a**, one elevator rail in 1000 will be at least how many inches in diameter?

69. A 20-question true–false examination is given. Each correct answer is worth 5 points. Consider an unprepared student who randomly guesses on each question.
   a. If no points are deducted for incorrect answers, what is the probability that the student will score at least 60 points?

   b. If 5 points are deducted for each incorrect answer, what is the probability that the student will score at least 60 points?
   c. If 5 points are deducted for each incorrect answer, what is the probability that the student will receive a negative score?

70. The percentage of examinees who took the GMAT (Graduate Management Admission) exam from June 1992 to March 1995 and scored below each total score is given in the file **P06_70.xlsx**. For example, 96% of all examinees scored 690 or below. The mean GMAT score for this time period was 497 and the standard deviation was 105. Does it appear that GMAT scores can accurately be approximated by a normal distribution? (Source: 1995 GMAT Examinee Interpretation Guide)

71. What caused the crash of TWA Flight 800 in 1996? Physics Professors Hailey and Helfand of Columbia University believe there is a reasonable possibility that a meteor hit Flight 800. They reason as follows. On a given day, 3000 meteors of a size large enough to destroy an airplane hit the earth's atmosphere. Around 50,000 flights per day, averaging 2 hours in length, have been flown from 1950 to 1996. This means that at any given point in time, planes in flight cover approximately two-billionths of the world's atmosphere. Determine the probability that at least one plane in the last 47 years has been downed by a meteor. (*Hint:* Use the Poisson approximation to the binomial. This approximation says that if n is large and p is small, a binomial distribution with parameters n and p is approximately Poisson distributed with $\lambda = np$.)

72. In the decade 1982 through 1991, 10 employees working at the Amoco Company chemical research center were stricken with brain tumors. The average employment at the center was 2000 employees. Nationwide, the average incidence of brain tumors in a single year is 20 per 100,000 people. If the incidence of brain tumors at the Amoco chemical research center were the same as the nationwide incidence, what is the probability that at least 10 brain tumors would have been observed among Amoco workers during the decade 1982 through 1991? What do you conclude from your analysis? (Source: AP wire service report, March 12, 1994)

73. Claims arrive at random times to an insurance company. The daily amount of claims is normally distributed with mean $1570 and standard deviation $450. Total claims on different days each have this distribution, and they are probabilistically independent of one another.
   a. Find the probability that the amount of total claims over a period of 100 days is at least $150,000. (Use the fact that the sum of independent normally distributed random variables is normally distributed, with mean equal to the sum of the individual means

and variance equal to the sum of the individual variances.)

b. If the company receives premiums totaling $165,000, find the probability that the company will net at least $10,000 for the 100-day period.

74. A popular model for stock prices is the following. If p_0 is the current stock price, then the price, p_k, k periods from now (where a period could be a day, week, or any other convenient unit of time, and k is any positive integer) is given by

$$p_k = p_0 \exp((\mu - 0.5\sigma^2)k + sZ\sqrt{k})$$

Here, exp is the exponential function (EXP in Excel), μ is the mean percentage growth rate per period of the stock, σ is the standard deviation of the growth rate per period, and Z is a normally distributed random variable with mean 0 and standard deviation 1. Both μ and σ are typically estimated from actual stock price data, and they are typically expressed in decimal form, such as $\mu = 0.01$ for a 1% mean growth rate. Suppose a period is defined as a month, the current price of the stock (as of the end of December 2004) is $75, $\mu = 0.006$, and $\sigma = 0.028$. Use simulation to obtain 500 possible stock price changes from the end of December 2004 to the end of December 2007. (Note that you can simulate a given change in one line and then copy it down.) Create a histogram of these changes to see whether the stock price change is at least approximately normally distributed. Also, use the simulated data to estimate the mean price change and the standard deviation of the change.

75. Continuing the previous problem (with the same parameters), use simulation to generate the ending stock prices for each month in 2005. (Use $k = 1$ to get January's price from December's, use $k = 1$ again to get February's price from January's, and so on.) Then use a data table to replicate the ending December 2005 stock price 500 times. Create a histogram of these 500 values. Do they appear to resemble a normal distribution?

76. Your company is running an audit on the Sleaze Company. Because Sleaze has a bad habit of over-charging its customers, the focus of your audit is on checking whether the billing amounts on its invoices are correct. We'll assume that each invoice is for too high an amount with probability 0.06 and for too low an amount with probability 0.01 (so that the probability of a correct billing is 0.93). Also, we assume that the outcome for any invoice is probabilistically independent of the outcomes for other invoices.

a. If you randomly sample 200 of Sleaze's invoices, what is the probability that you will find at least 15 invoices that overcharge the customer? What is the probability you won't find any that undercharge the customer?

b. Find an integer k such that the probability is at least 0.99 that you will find at least k invoices that over-charge the customer. (*Hint*: Use trial and error with the BINOMDIST function to find k.)

77. Continuing the previous problem, suppose that when Sleaze overcharges a customer, the distribution of the amount overcharged (expressed as a percentage of the correct billing amount) is normally distributed with mean 15% and standard deviation 4%.

a. What percentage of overbilled customers are charged at least 10% more than they should pay?

b. What percentage of *all* customers are charged at least 10% more than they should pay?

c. If your auditing company samples 200 randomly chosen invoices, what is the probability that it will find at least 5 where the customer was overcharged by at least 10%?

78. Let X be normally distributed with a given mean and standard deviation. Sometimes you want to find two values a and b such that $P(a < X < b)$ is equal to some specific probability such as 0.90 or 0.95. There are many answers to this problem, depending on how much probability you put in each of the two tails. For this question, assume the mean and standard deviation are $\mu = 100$ and $\sigma = 10$, and that we want to find a and b such that $P(a < X < b) = 0.90$.

a. Find a and b so that there is probability 0.05 in each tail.

b. Find a and b so that there is probability 0.025 in the left tail and 0.075 in the right tail.

c. The "usual" answer to the general problem is the answer from part **a**, that is, where you put equal probability in the two tails. It turns out that this is the answer that minimizes the length of the interval from a to b. That is, if you solve the problem: min $(b - a)$, subject to $P(a < X < b) = 0.90$, you'll get the same answer as in part **a**. Verify this using Excel's Solver.

79. Your manufacturing process makes parts such that each part meets specifications with probability 0.98. You need a batch of 250 parts that meet specifications. How many parts must you produce to be at least 99% certain of producing at least 250 parts that meet specifications?

80. The Excel functions discussed in this chapter are useful for solving a lot of probability problems, but there are other problems that, even though they are similar to normal or binomial problems, cannot be solved with these functions. In cases like this, computer simulation can often be used. Here are a couple of such problems for you to simulate. For each example, use 500 replications of the experiment.

a. You observe a sequence of parts from a manufacturing line. These parts use a component that is supplied by one of two suppliers. The probability that a given part uses a component supplied by supplier 1 is 0.6; it is supplied by supplier 2 with probability 0.4. Each part made with a component from supplier 1 works properly with probability 0.95, and each part made with a component from supplier 2 works properly with probability 0.98. Assuming that 30 of these parts are made, we want the probability that at least 29 of them work properly.

b. Here we look at a more generic example such as coin flipping. That is, there is a sequence of trials where each trial is a success with probability p and a failure with probability $1 - p$. A "run" is a sequence of consecutive successes or failures. For most of us, intuition says that there should not be "long" runs. Test this by finding the probability that there is at least 1 run of length at least 6 in a sequence of 15 trials. (The run could be of 0's or 1's.) You can use any value of p you like—or try different values of p.

81. As any credit-granting agency knows, there are always some customers who default on credit charges. Typically, customers are grouped into relatively homogeneous categories, so that customers within any category have approximately the same chance of defaulting on their credit charges. Here we'll look at one particular group of customers. We'll assume each of these customers has (1) probability 0.07 of defaulting on his or her current credit charges, and (2) total credit charges that are normally distributed with mean $350 and standard deviation $100. We'll also assume that if a customer defaults, 20% of his or her charges can be recovered. The other 80% are written off as bad debt.

a. What is the probability that a typical customer in this group will default and produce a write-off of more than $250 in bad debt?

b. If there are 500 customers in this group, what are the mean and standard deviation of the number of customers who will meet the description in part **a**?

c. Again assuming there are 500 customers in this group, what is the probability that at least 25 of them will meet the description in part **a**?

d. Suppose now that nothing is recovered from a default—the whole amount is written off as bad debt. Show how to simulate the total amount of bad debt from 500 customers in just two cells, one with a binomial calculation, the other with a normal calculation.

82. You have a device that uses a single battery, and you operate this device continuously, never turning it off. Whenever a battery fails, you replace it with a brand new one immediately. Suppose the lifetime of a typical battery has an exponential distribution with mean 205 minutes. If you operate the device, starting with a new battery, until you have observed 25 battery failures, what is the probability that at least 15 of these 25 batteries lived at least 3.5 hours?

83. In the previous problem, we ran the "experiment" until there are a certain number of failures and then answered a question about the times between failures. In this problem, we take a different point of view. We run the experiment for a certain amount of time and then ask a question about the number of failures during this time. Specifically, suppose you operate the device from the previous problem continuously for 3 days, making battery changes when necessary. Find the probability that you will observe at least 25 failures. (*Hint*: Do a Poisson calculation using an appropriate λ for the number of failures in a 3-day period.)

The EuroWatch Company assembles expensive wristwatches and then sells them to retailers throughout Europe. The watches are assembled at a plant with two assembly lines. These lines are intended to be identical, but line 1 uses somewhat older equipment than line 2 and is typically less reliable. Historical data have shown that each watch coming off line 1, independently of the others, is free of defects with probability 0.98. The similar probability for line 2 is 0.99. Each line produces 500 watches per hour. The production manager has asked you to answer the following questions.

1. She wants to know how many defect-free watches each line is likely to produce in a given hour. Specifically, find the smallest integer k (for each line separately) such that you can be 99% sure that the line will not produce more than k defective watches in a given hour.

2. EuroWatch currently has an order for 500 watches from an important customer. The company plans to fill this order by packing slightly more than 500 watches, all from line 2, and sending this package off to the customer. Obviously, EuroWatch wants to send as few watches as possible, but it wants to be 99% sure that when the customer opens the package, there are at least 500 defect-free watches. How many watches should be packed?

3. EuroWatch has another order for 1000 watches. Now it plans to fill this order by packing slightly more than one hour's production from each line. This package will contain the *same* number of watches from each line. As in the previous question, EuroWatch wants to send as few watches as possible, but it again wants to be 99% sure that when the customer opens the package, there are at least 1000 defect-free watches. The question of how many watches to pack is unfortunately quite difficult because the total number of defect-free watches is *not* binomially distributed. (Why not?) Therefore, the manager asks you to solve the problem with simulation (and some trial and error). (*Hint*: It turns out that it's much faster to simulate small numbers than large numbers, so simulate the number of watches with defects, not the number without defects.)

4. Finally, EuroWatch has a third order for 100 watches. The customer has agreed to pay $50,000 for the order—that is, $500 per watch. If EuroWatch sends more than 100 watches to the customer, its revenue doesn't increase; it can never exceed $50,000. Its unit cost of producing a watch is $450, regardless of which line it is assembled on. The order will be filled entirely from a single line, and EuroWatch plans to send slightly more than 100 watches to the customer.

5. If the customer opens the shipment and finds that there are fewer than 100 defect-free watches (which we'll assume the customer has the ability to do), then he'll pay only for the defect-free watches—EuroWatch's revenue will decrease by $500 per watch short of the 100 required—and on top of this, EuroWatch will be required to make up the difference at an expedited cost of $1000 per watch. The customer won't pay a dime for these expedited watches. (If expediting is required, EuroWatch will make sure that the expedited watches are defect-free. It doesn't want to lose this customer entirely!)

6. You have been asked to develop a spreadsheet model to find EuroWatch's expected profit for any number of watches it sends to the customer. You should develop it so that it responds correctly, regardless of which assembly line is used to fill the order and what the shipment quantity is. (*Hints*: Use the BINOMDIST function, with last argument 0, to fill up a column of probabilities for each possible number of defective watches. Next to each of these, calculate EuroWatch's profit. Then use a SUMPRODUCT to obtain the expected profit. Finally, you can assume that EuroWatch will never send more than 110 watches. It turns out that this large a shipment is not even close to optimal.) ■

Many states supplement their tax revenues with state-sponsored lotteries. Most of them do so with a game called lotto. Although there are various versions of this game, they are all basically as follows. People purchase tickets that contain r distinct numbers from 1 to m, where r is generally 5 or 6 and m is generally around 50. For example, in Virginia, the state discussed in this case, $r = 6$ and $m = 44$. Each ticket costs $1, about 39 cents of which is allocated to the total jackpot.[8] There is eventually a drawing of $r = 6$ distinct numbers from the $m = 44$ possible numbers. Any ticket that matches these 6 numbers wins the jackpot.

There are two interesting aspects of this game. First, the current jackpot includes not only the revenue from this round of ticket purchases but any jackpots carried over from previous drawings because of no winning tickets. Therefore, the jackpot can build from one drawing to the next, and in celebrated cases it has become huge. Second, if there is more than one winning ticket—a distinct possibility—the winners share the jackpot equally. (This is called the "parimutuel" effect.) So, for example, if the current jackpot is $9 million and there are three winning tickets, then each winner receives $3 million.

It can be shown that for Virginia's choice of r and m, there are approximately 7 million possible tickets (7,059,052 to be exact). Therefore, any ticket has about one chance out of 7 million of being a winner. That is, the probability of winning with a single ticket is $p = 1/7,059,052$—not very good odds! If n people purchase tickets, then the number of winners is binomially distributed with parameters n and p. Because n is typically very large and p is small, the number of winners has approximately a Poisson distribution with rate $\lambda = np$. (This makes ensuing calculations somewhat easier.) For example, if 1 million tickets are purchased, then the number of winning tickets is approximately Poisson distributed with $\lambda = 1/7$.

In 1992, an Australian syndicate purchased a huge number of tickets in the Virginia lottery in an attempt to assure itself of purchasing a winner. It

worked! Although the syndicate wasn't able to purchase all 7 million possible tickets (it was about 1.5 million shy of this), it did purchase a winning ticket, and there were no other winners. Therefore, the syndicate won a 20-year income stream worth approximately $27 million, with a net present value of approximately $14 million. This easily covered the cost of the tickets it purchased. Two questions come to mind: (1) Is this "hogging" of tickets unfair to the rest of the public? (2) Is it a wise strategy on the part of the syndicate (or did it just get lucky)?

To answer the first question, consider how the lottery changes for the general public with the addition of the syndicate. To be specific, suppose the syndicate can invest $7 million and obtain *all* of the possible tickets, making itself a sure winner. Also, suppose n people from the general public purchase tickets, each of which has 1 chance out of 7 million of being a winner. Finally, let R be the jackpot carried over from any previous lotteries. Then the total jackpot on this round will be $[R + 0.39(7,000,000 + n)]$ because 39 cents from every ticket goes toward the jackpot. The number of winning tickets for the public will be Poisson distributed with $\lambda = n/7,000,000$. However, any member of the public who wins will *necessarily* have to share the jackpot with the syndicate, which is a sure winner. Use this information to calculate the expected amount the public will win. Then do the same calculation when the syndicate does *not* play. (In this case the jackpot will be smaller, but the public won't have to share any winnings with the syndicate.) For values of n and R that you can select, is the public better off with or without the syndicate? Would you, as a general member of the public, support a move to outlaw syndicates from "hogging" the tickets?

---

[8]Of the remaining 61 cents, the state takes about 50 cents. The other 11 cents is used to pay off lesser prize winners whose tickets match some, but not all, of the winning 6 numbers. To keep this case relatively simple, however, we will ignore these lesser prizes and concentrate only on the jackpot.

The second question is whether the syndicate is wise to buy so many tickets. Again assume that the syndicate can spend $7 million and purchase each possible ticket. (Would this be possible in reality?) Also, assume that n members of the general public purchase tickets, and that the carryover from the previous jackpot is R. The syndicate is thus assured of having a winning ticket, but is it assured of covering its costs? Calculate the expected net benefit (in terms of net present value) to the syndicate, using any reasonable values of n and R, to see whether the syndicate can expect to come out ahead.

Actually, the analysis suggested in the previous paragraph is not complete. There are at least two complications to consider. The first is the effect of taxes. Fortunately for the Australian syndicate, it did not have to pay federal or state taxes on its winnings, but a U.S. syndicate wouldn't be so lucky. Second, the jackpot from a $20 million jackpot, say, is actually paid in 20 annual $1 million payments. The Lottery Commission pays the winner $1 million immediately and then purchases 19 "strips" (bonds with the interest not included) maturing at 1-year intervals with face value of $1 million each. Unfortunately, the lottery prize does not offer the liquidity of the Treasury issues that back up the payments. This lack of liquidity could make the lottery less attractive to the syndicate. ■

Sampling and Sampling Distributions

©Photodisc/Getty Images

CHOOSING SAMPLES OF CUSTOMERS TO RECEIVE MAILINGS

In the first half of this chapter, we discuss methods for selecting random samples. The purpose of these samples is to discover characteristics of a population, such as the proportion who favor the president's economic policy. By selecting a random sample of perhaps 1000 people out of a population of millions, we can make fairly accurate inferences about the population as a whole, at savings of much time and money.

A different type of sample has recently become the focus of many direct response marketers, companies that mail advertisements for their products directly to prospective customers. The experience of one such company, the Franklin Mint (FM) of Philadelphia, is described in Zahavi (1995). The FM markets expensive collectibles, ranging from famous Precision Car models to the Sword of Francis Drake, to a relatively small, but avid, collector population. The FM relies entirely on its mailings to prospective customers for sales. However, it is important for the company to mail ads for any particular products to the right customers; otherwise, mailing costs can seriously erode profits. This is especially the case when, on average, the response rate to products in this type of market is less than one-half percent—that is, no more than 1 person out of every 200 who receive a mailing actually purchases a product.

Until recently, companies such as the FM used relatively subjective rules to choose the sample of customers to receive mailings. However, these companies now have an abundance of data about their customers, and they are

387

beginning to use sophisticated statistical methods to locate the customers who are most likely to purchase any particular type of product. In essence, they build a probability model that relates the probability of purchasing to (1) the customer's purchase history; (2) demographic variables (many of which can be acquired from outside vendors and appended to the customer's record); and (3) the product attributes, such as theme, material, artist, sponsor, and product code. The most challenging part of the model is to identify the best predictor variables from the hundreds available, but techniques (and software) are now available to perform this task efficiently.

Direct marketers such as the FM have found that this is a situation where even a small amount of explanatory power from a statistical model can make a big difference in the bottom line. No model can correctly identify exactly who will respond positively to an ad and who will not, but if the model can identify customer samples where the response rate to mailings is even a little higher than it was, the ratio of mailing costs to eventual sales can decrease significantly. For example, the FM installed its system (called AMOS) in 1992 and realized an increase in profit of approximately 7.5% in 3 years; undoubtedly, it has increased even more since then. As Zahavi states, "Looking beyond the FM, the implications of using AMOS-like systems to support the decision-making process in the database marketing industry are likely to be quite substantial, which, given the size of the industry, could run well in excess of several hundred million dollars a year!" ■

8.1 INTRODUCTION

In a typical statistical inference problem we want to discover one or more characteristics of a given population. For example, we might want to know the proportion of toothpaste customers who have tried, or intend to try, a particular brand. Or we might want to know the average amount owed on credit card accounts for a population of customers at a shopping mall. Generally, the population is large and/or spread out, and it is difficult, maybe even impossible, to contact each member. Therefore, we identify a sample of the population and then obtain information from the members of the sample.

There are two main objectives of this chapter. The first is to discuss the sampling schemes that are generally used in real sampling applications. We focus on several types of *random* samples and see why these are preferable to nonrandom samples. The second objective is to see how the information from a sample of the population—for example, 1% of the population—can be used to infer the properties of the entire population. The key here is the concept of *sampling distributions*. We focus on the sampling distribution of the sample mean, and we see how a famous mathematical result called the *central limit theorem* is the key to the analysis.

8.2 SAMPLING TERMINOLOGY

We begin by introducing some of the terminology that is used in sampling. In any sampling problem there is a relevant *population*. A **population** is the set of all members about which a study intends to make inferences, where an **inference** is a statement about a numerical characteristic of the population, such as an average income or the proportion of incomes below $50,000. It is important to realize that a population is defined in relationship to any particular study. Any analyst planning a survey should first decide which population the conclusions of the study will concern, so that a sample can be chosen from *this* population.

> The relevant **population** contains all members about which a study intends to make inferences.

For example, if a marketing researcher plans to use a questionnaire to infer consumers' reactions to a new product, she must first decide which population of consumers is of interest—all consumers, consumers over 21 years old, consumers who do most of their shopping in shopping malls, or others. Once the relevant consumer population has been designated, a sample from this population can then be surveyed. However, inferences made from the study pertain only to this *particular* population.

Before we can choose a sample from a given population, we typically need a list of all members of the population. This list is called a **frame**, and the potential sample members are called **sampling units**. Depending on the context, sampling units could be individual people, households, companies, cities, or others.

> A **frame** is a list of all members, called **sampling units**, in the population.

In this chapter we assume that the population is finite and consists of N sampling units. We also assume that a frame of these N sampling units is available. Unfortunately, there are situations where a complete frame is practically impossible to obtain. For example, if we want to survey the attitudes of all unemployed teenagers in Chicago, it is practically impossible to obtain a complete frame of them. In this situation all we can hope to obtain is a partial frame, from which the sample can be selected. If the partial frame omits any significant segments of the population—which a complete frame would include—then the resulting sample could be biased. For instance, if we use the Yellow Pages of a Los Angeles telephone book to choose a sample of restaurants, we automatically omit all restaurants that do not advertise in the Yellow Pages. Depending on the purposes of the study, this could be a serious omission.

There are two basic types of samples: *probability samples* and *judgmental samples*. A **probability sample** is a sample in which the sampling units are chosen from the population by means of a random mechanism such as a random number table. In contrast, no formal random mechanism is used to select a **judgmental sample**. In this case the sampling units are chosen according to the sampler's judgment.

> The members of a **probability sample** are chosen according to a random mechanism, whereas the members of a **judgmental sample** are chosen according to the sampler's judgment.

We do not discuss judgmental samples. The reason is very simple—there is no way to measure the accuracy of judgmental samples because the rules of probability do not apply to them. In other words, if we estimate some population characteristic from the observations in a judgmental sample, there is no way to tell how accurate this estimate is. In addition, it is very difficult to choose a representative sample from a population *without* using some random mechanism. Because our judgment is usually not as good as we think, judgmental samples are likely to contain our own built-in biases. Therefore, we focus exclusively on probability samples from here on.

8.3 METHODS FOR SELECTING RANDOM SAMPLES

In this section we discuss the types of random samples that are used in real sampling applications. Different types of sampling schemes have different properties. There is typically a trade-off between cost and accuracy. Some sampling schemes are cheaper and easier to administer, whereas others cost more but provide more accurate information. We discuss some of these issues, but anyone who intends to make a living in survey sampling needs to learn much more about the topic than we can cover here.

8.3.1 Simple Random Sampling

The simplest type of sampling scheme is appropriately called *simple random sampling*. Consider a population of size N and suppose we want to sample n units from this population. Then a **simple random sample** of size n has the property that every possible sample of size n has the same probability of being chosen. Simple random samples are the easiest to understand, and their statistical properties are fairly straightforward. Therefore, we will focus primarily on simple random samples in the rest of this book. However, as we discuss shortly, more complex random samples are often used in real applications.

A **simple random sample** of size n is one where each possible sample of size n has the same chance of being chosen.

We illustrate a simple random sample for a small population. Suppose the population size is $N = 5$, and we label the five members of the population as a, b, c, d, and e. Also, suppose we want to sample $n = 2$ of these members. Then the possible samples are (a, b), (a, c), (a, d), (a, e), (b, c), (b, d), (b, e), (c, d), (c, e), and (d, e). That is, there are 10 possible samples—the number of ways two members can be chosen from five members. Then a *simple* random sample of size $n = 2$ has the property that each of these 10 possible samples has an equal probability, 1/10, of being chosen.

One other property of simple random samples can be seen from this example. If we focus on any member of the population, say, member b, we note that b is a member of 4 of the 10 samples. Therefore, the probability that b is chosen in a simple random sample is 4/10, or 2/5. In general, any member has the same probability n/N of being chosen in a simple random sample. If you are one of 100,000 members of a population, then the probability that you will be selected in a simple random sample of size 100 is 100/100,000, or 1 out of 1000.

There are several ways simple random samples can be chosen, all of which involve random numbers. One approach that works well for our small example with $N = 5$ and $n = 2$ is to generate a single random number with the RAND function in Excel. We divide the interval from 0 to 1 into 10 equal subintervals of length 1/10 each and see into which of these subintervals the random number falls. We then choose the corresponding sample. For example, suppose the random number is 0.465. This is in the fifth subinterval, that is, the interval from 0.4 to 0.5, so we choose the fifth sample, (b, c).

For those who have not yet covered the simulation sections of previous chapters, the RAND function in Excel generates numbers that are distributed randomly and uniformly between 0 and 1.

Clearly, this method is consistent with simple random sampling—each of the samples has the same chance of being chosen—but it is prohibitive when n and N are large. In this case there are too many possible samples to list. Fortunately, there is another method that can be used. The idea is simple. We sort the N members of the population randomly, using Excel's RAND function to generate random numbers for the sort. Then we include the first n members from the sorted sequence in the random sample. We illustrate this procedure in the following example.

EXAMPLE | 8.1 SELECTING A SAMPLE OF FAMILIES TO ANALYZE ANNUAL INCOMES

Consider the frame of 40 families with annual incomes shown in column B of Figure 8.1. (See the file **Random Sampling.xlsm**.) We want to choose a simple random sample of size 10 from this frame. How can this be done? And how do summary statistics of the chosen families compare to the corresponding summary statistics of the population?

Objective   To illustrate how Excel's random number function, RAND, can be used to generate simple random samples.

Figure 8.1

Population
Income Data

	A	B	C	D
1	Simple random sampling			
2				
3	Summary statistics			
4		Mean	Median	Stdev
5	Population	$39,985	$38,500	$7,377
6	Sample			
7				
8	Population			
9	Family	Income		
10	1	$43,300		
11	2	$44,300		
12	3	$34,600		
13	4	$38,000		
14	5	$44,700		
15	6	$45,600		
16	7	$42,700		
17	8	$36,900		
18	9	$38,400		
19	10	$33,700		
20	11	$44,100		
21	12	$51,500		
22	13	$35,900		
23	14	$35,600		
24	15	$43,000		
47	38	$46,900		
48	39	$37,300		
49	40	$41,000		

Solution

The idea is very simple. We first generate a column of random numbers in column C. Then we sort the rows according to the random numbers and choose the first 10 families in the sorted rows. The following procedure produces the results in Figure 8.2. (See the first sheet in the finished version of the file.)

Figure 8.2

Selecting a Simple
Random Sample

	A	B	C	D	E	F
1	Simple random sampling					
2						
3	Summary statistics					
4		Mean	Median	Stdev		
5	Population	$39,985	$38,500	$7,377		
6	Sample	$41,490	$42,850	$5,323		
7						
8	Population			Random sample		
9	Family	Income		Family	Income	Random #
10	1	$43,300		1	$43,300	0.04545
11	2	$44,300		2	$44,300	0.1496768
12	3	$34,600		12	$51,500	0.23527
13	4	$38,000		7	$42,700	0.2746325
14	5	$44,700		13	$35,900	0.3003506
15	6	$45,600		15	$43,000	0.3197393
16	7	$42,700		6	$45,600	0.3610983
17	8	$36,900		3	$34,600	0.3852641
18	9	$38,400		9	$38,400	0.4427564
19	10	$33,700		14	$35,600	0.4447877
20	11	$44,100		5	$44,700	0.4505899
21	12	$51,500		40	$41,000	0.4597361
22	13	$35,900		11	$44,100	0.5621297
23	14	$35,600		4	$38,000	0.5860911
24	15	$43,000		38	$46,900	0.7192539
47	38	$46,900		39	$37,300	0.8644119
48	39	$37,300		8	$36,900	0.9059098
49	40	$41,000		10	$33,700	0.9637509

1 **Random numbers next to a copy.** Copy the original data to columns D and E. Then enter the formula

=RAND( )

in cell F10 and copy it down column F.

2 **Replace with values.** To enable sorting we must first "freeze" the random numbers—that is, replace their formulas with values. To do this, copy the range F10:F49 and select Paste Values from the Paste dropdown on the Home ribbon.

3 **Sort.** Sort on column F in ascending order. Then the 10 families with the 10 smallest random numbers are the ones in the sample. (These are shaded in the figure.)

4 **Means.** Use the AVERAGE, MEDIAN, and STDEV functions in row 6 to calculate summary statistics of the first 10 incomes in column E. Similar summary statistics for the population have already been calculated in row 5. (Cell D5 uses the STDEVP function because this is the *population* standard deviation.)

To obtain more random samples of size 10 (for comparison), we would need to go through this process repeatedly. To save you the trouble of doing so, we wrote a macro to automate the process. (See the Automated sheet in the **Random Samples.xlsm** file.) This sheet looks essentially the same as the sheet in Figure 8.2, except that there is a button to run the macro and only the required data remain on the spreadsheet. Try clicking on this button. (Don't forget to enable the macro first.) Each time you do so, you will get a different random sample—and different summary measures in row 6. By doing this many times and keeping track of the sample summary data, you can see how the summary measures vary from sample to sample. We have much more to say about this variation later in this chapter. ■

The procedure described in Example 8.1 can be used in Excel to select a simple random sample of any size from any population. All we need is a frame, a list of the population values. Then it is just a matter of inserting random numbers, freezing them, and sorting on the random numbers.

Perhaps surprisingly, simple random samples are used infrequently in real applications. There are several reasons for this.

- Because each sampling unit has the same chance of being sampled, simple random sampling can result in samples that are spread over a large geographical region. This can make sampling extremely expensive, especially if personal interviews are used.

- Simple random sampling requires that all sampling units be identified prior to sampling. Sometimes this is infeasible.

- Simple random sampling can result in underrepresentation or overrepresentation of certain segments of the population. For example, if the primary—but not sole— interest is in the graduate student subpopulation of university students, a simple random sample of *all* university students might not provide enough information about the graduate students.

Despite this, most of the statistical analysis in this book assumes simple random samples. The analysis is considerably more complex for other types of random samples and is discussed in more advanced books on sampling.

8.3.2 Using StatTools to Generate Simple Random Samples

The method described in Example 8.1 is simple but somewhat tedious, especially if we want to generate more than one random sample. (Even the macro described at the end of the example works only for that particular file.) Fortunately, a more general method is available in StatTools. This procedure generates any number of simple random samples of any specified sample size from a given data set. It can be found under Data Utilities on the StatTools ribbon.

8.2 Sampling from Accounts Receivable at Spring Mills Company

The file **Accounts Receivable.xlsx** contains 280 accounts receivable for the Spring Mills Company (the same data we discussed in Example 3.9). There are three variables:

- Size: customer size (small, medium, large), depending on its volume of business with Spring Mills
- Days: number of days since the customer was billed
- Amount: amount of the bill

Generate 25 random samples of size 15 each from the small customers only, calculate the average amount owed in each random sample, and construct a histogram of these 25 averages.

Objective   To illustrate StatTools's method of choosing simple random samples, and how sample means are distributed.

Solution

We proceed in several steps. First, because we want random samples of the small customers only and the data are already sorted on Size, we first create a StatTools data set of the small customers only. (It will be the range A1:D151.) Then we use the Random Sample item from StatTools Utilities to generate 25 samples of size 15 each of the Amount variable. (The Random Sample dialog box should be filled out as shown in Figure 8.3.) These will appear on a new Random Sample sheet, as shown in Figure 8.4 (with many columns hidden). Each of these columns is a random sample of 15 Amount values.

Figure 8.3

Random Sample Dialog Box

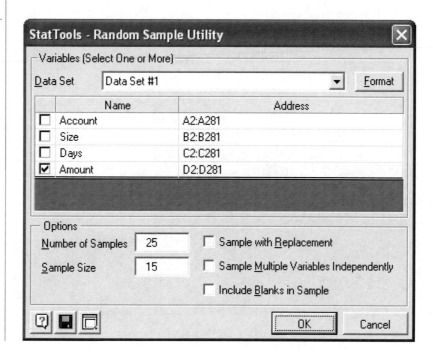

Figure 8.4
Randomly
Generated Samples

	A	B	C	D	X	Y	Z
1		Amount(1)	Amount(2)	Amount(3)	Amount(23)	Amount(24)	Amount(25)
2		260	200	290	250	240	260
3		230	240	260	220	210	290
4		250	310	240	240	230	300
5		280	250	290	260	220	240
6		210	210	330	270	200	250
7		310	270	210	280	220	270
8		280	270	290	220	240	270
9		260	190	260	290	410	250
10		280	240	370	210	300	230
11		240	190	290	260	260	240
12		210	240	260	240	270	250
13		270	240	260	210	210	150
14		240	240	230	240	210	180
15		220	300	240	250	250	310
16		260	320	240	210	280	200
17	Average	253.333	247.333	270.667	243.333	250.000	246.000

Next, we insert a new column A, as shown in Figure 8.4, and we calculate the averages in row 17 for each sample with Excel's AVERAGE function. Finally, because we want a histogram of the averages in row 17, we define a second StatTools data set of the data in row 17 of Figure 8.4 but, for a change, we specify that the only variable for this data set is in a *row,* not a column. (This is an option in the StatTools Data Set Manager.) We can then create a histogram of these 25 averages in the usual way. It appears in Figure 8.5.

The histogram in Figure 8.5 indicates the variability of sample means we might obtain by selecting many *different* random samples of size 15 from this particular population of small customer accounts. This histogram, which is approximately bell shaped, approximates the sampling distribution of the sample mean. We come back to this important idea when we study sampling distributions in Section 8.4.

Figure 8.5   Histogram of 25 Sample Averages

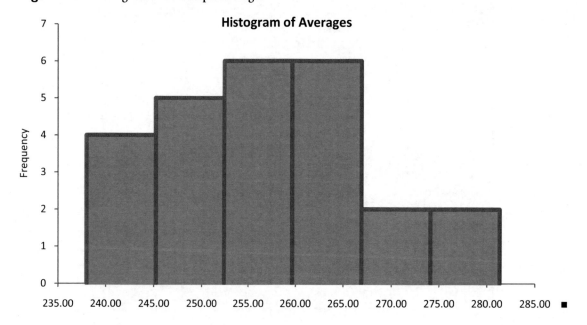

In the next several subsections we describe sampling plans that are often used. These plans differ from simple random sampling both in the way the samples are chosen and in the way the data analysis is performed. However, we will barely touch on this latter issue. The details are quite complicated and are better left to a book devoted entirely to sampling. [See, for example, the excellent book by Levy and Lemeshow (1999).]

8.3.3 Systematic Sampling

Suppose you are asked to select a random sample of 250 names from the white pages of a telephone book. Let's also say that there are 55,000 names listed in the white pages. A *systematic sample* provides a convenient way to choose the sample, as follows. First, we calculate the **sampling interval** as the population size divided by the sample size: 55,000/250 = 220. Conceptually, we can think of dividing the book into 250 "blocks" with 220 names per block. Next, we use a random mechanism to choose a number between 1 and 220. Say this number is 131. Then we choose the 131st name and every 220th name thereafter. So we would choose the 131st name, the 351st name, the 571st name, and so on. The result is a systematic sample of size $n = 250$.

> In **systematic sampling**, one of the first k members is selected randomly, and then every kth member after this one is selected. The value k is called the **sampling interval** and equals the ratio N/n, where N is the population size and n is the desired sample size.

Clearly, systematic sampling is different from simple random sampling because not every sample of size 250 has a chance of being chosen. In fact, there are only 220 different samples possible (depending on the first number chosen), and each of these is equally likely. Nevertheless, systematic sampling is generally similar to simple random sampling in its statistical properties. The key is the relationship between the ordering of the sampling units in the frame (the white pages of the telephone book in this case) and the purpose of the study.

Systematic random samples are typically chosen because of their convenience.

If the purpose of the study is to analyze personal incomes, say, then there is probably no relationship between the alphabetical ordering of names in the telephone book and personal income. However, there are situations where the ordering of the sampling units is not random, which could make systematic sampling more or less appealing. For example, suppose that a company wants to sample randomly from its customers, and its customer list is in decreasing order of order volumes. That is, the largest customers are at the top of the list and the smallest are at the bottom. Then systematic sampling might be more representative than simple random sampling because it guarantees a wide range of customers in terms of order volumes.

However, some type of cyclical ordering in the list of sampling units can lead to very *unrepresentative* samples. As an extreme, suppose a company has a list of daily transactions and it decides to draw a systematic sample with the sampling interval equal to 7. Then if the first sampled day is Monday, all other days in the sample will be Mondays! This could clearly bias the sample. Except for obvious examples like this one, however, systematic sampling can be an attractive alternative to simple random sampling and is often used because of its convenience.

8.3.4 Stratified Sampling

Suppose we can identify various subpopulations within the total population. We call these subpopulations **strata**. Then instead of taking a simple random sample from the entire population, it might make more sense to select a simple random sample from each stratum separately. This sampling method is called **stratified sampling**. It is a particularly useful approach when there is considerable variation *between* the various strata but relatively little variation *within* a given stratum.

> In **stratified sampling**, the population is divided into relatively homogeneous subsets called **strata**, and then random samples are taken from each of the strata.

Stratified samples are typically chosen because they provide more accurate estimates of population parameters for a given sampling cost.

There are several advantages to stratified sampling. One obvious advantage is that we obtain separate estimates within each stratum—which we would not obtain if we took a simple random sample from the entire population. Even if we eventually plan to pool the samples from the individual strata, it cannot hurt to have the total sample broken down into separate samples initially.

A more important advantage of stratified sampling is that the accuracy of the resulting population estimates can be increased by using appropriately defined strata. The trick is to define the strata so that there is less variability within the individual strata than in the population as a whole. We want strata such that there is relative homogeneity within the strata, but relative heterogeneity among the strata, with respect to the variable(s) being analyzed. By choosing the strata in this way, we can generally obtain more accuracy for a given sampling cost than we could obtain from a simple random sample at the same cost. Alternatively, we can achieve the same level of accuracy at a lower sampling cost.

The key to using stratified sampling effectively is selecting the appropriate strata. Suppose a company that advertises its product on television wants to estimate the reaction of viewers to the advertising. Here the population consists of all viewers who have seen the advertising. But what are the appropriate strata? The answer depends on the company's objectives and its product. The company could stratify the population by gender, by income, by amount of television watched, by the amount of the product class consumed, and probably others. Without knowing more specific information about the company's objectives, it is impossible to say which of these stratification schemes is most appropriate.

Suppose that we have identified I nonoverlapping strata in a given population. Let N be the total population size, and let N_i be the population size of stratum i, so that

$$N = N_1 + N_2 + \cdots + N_I$$

To obtain a stratified random sample, we must choose a total sample size n, and we must choose a sample size n_i from each stratum i, such that

$$n = n_1 + n_2 + \cdots + n_I$$

We can then select a simple random sample of the specified size from *each* stratum exactly as in Example 8.1.

However, how do we choose the individual sample sizes n_1 through n_I, given that the total sample size n has been chosen? For example, if we decide to sample 500 customers in total, how many should come from each stratum? There are many ways that we could choose numbers n_1 through n_I that sum to n, but probably the most popular method is to use *proportional sample sizes*. The idea is very simple. If one stratum has, say, 15% of the total population, then we select 15% of the total sample from this stratum. For example, if the total sample size is $n = 500$, we select $0.15(500) = 75$ members from this stratum.

With **proportional sample sizes**, the proportion of a stratum in the sample is the same as the proportion of that stratum in the population.

The advantage of proportional sample sizes is that they are very easy to determine. The disadvantage is that they ignore differences in variability among the strata. To illustrate, suppose that we are attempting to estimate the population mean amount paid annually per student for textbooks at a large university. We identify three strata: undergraduates, master's students, and doctoral students. Their population sizes are 20,000, 4000, and 1000, respectively. Therefore, the proportions of students in these strata are 20,000/25,000 = 0.80, 4000/25,000 = 0.16, and 1000/25,000 = 0.04. If the total sample size is $n = 150$, then the sample should include 120 undergraduates, 24 master's students, and 6 doctoral students if proportional sample sizes are used.

However, let σ_i be the standard deviation of annual textbook payments in stratum i, and suppose that $\sigma_1 = \$50$, $\sigma_2 = \$120$, and $\sigma_3 = \$180$. Thus, there is considerably more variation in the amounts paid by doctoral students than by undergraduates, with the master's students in the middle. If we are interested in estimating the mean amount spent per student, then despite its small sample size, the doctoral sample is likely to have a large effect on the accuracy of our estimate of the mean. This is because of its relatively large standard deviation. In contrast, we might not need to sample as heavily from the undergraduate population because of its relatively small standard deviation. In general, strata with less variability can afford to be sampled less heavily than proportional sampling calls for, and the opposite is true for strata with larger variability. In fact, there are *optimal* sample size formulas that take the σ_i's into account, but we do not present them here.

In the following example we illustrate how stratified sampling can be accomplished with Excel by using random numbers.

EXAMPLE

8.3 STRATIFIED SAMPLING FROM THE SMALLTOWN POPULATION OF SEARS CREDIT CARD HOLDERS

The file **Stratified Sampling.xlsx** contains a frame of all 1000 people in the city of Smalltown who have Sears credit cards. Sears is interested in estimating the average number of *other* credit cards these people own, as well as other information about their use of credit. The company decides to stratify these customers by age, select a stratified sample of size 100 with proportional sample sizes, and then contact these 100 people by phone. How might Sears proceed?

Objective   To illustrate how stratified sampling, with proportional sample sizes, can be implemented in Excel.

Solution

First, Sears has to decide exactly how to stratify by age. Their reasoning is that different age groups probably have different attitudes and behavior regarding credit. After some preliminary investigation, they decide to use three age categories: 18–30, 31–62, and 63–80. (We assume that no one in the population is younger than 18 or older than 80.)

Figure 8.6 shows how the calculations might then proceed. We begin with the following inputs: (1) the total sample size in cell C3, (2) the definitions of the strata in rows 6 through 8, and (3) the customer data in the range A11:B1010. To see which age category each customer is in, we enter the formula

=IF(B11<=$D$6,1,IF(B11<=$D$7,2,3))

in cell C11 and then copy it down column C.

Figure 8.6 Selecting a Stratified Sample

	A	B	C	D	E	F	G	H	I	J	K	L	M	N
1	Stratified sampling by Sears													
2														
3	Total sample size		100											
4														
5	Strata based on age					Counts	Sample size							
6	Stratum 1	18	to	30		132	13							
7	Stratum 2	31	to	62		766	77							
8	Stratum 3	63	to	80		102	10							
9														
10	Customer	Age	Category		Customer(1)	Age(1)	Customer(2)	Age(2)	Customer(3)	Age(3)		Customer(1)	Age(1)	Random #
11	1	49	2		11	23	1	49	4	66		124	22	0.0017915
12	2	39	2		13	24	2	39	12	63		371	22	0.009226
13	3	55	2		15	30	3	55	38	75		563	27	0.009469
14	4	66	3		20	29	5	52	40	64		521	25	0.0159193
15	5	52	2		26	30	6	37	42	71		790	29	0.0170073
16	6	37	2		34	26	7	34	53	63		122	27	0.0181953
17	7	34	2		43	25	8	34	64	71		475	25	0.0209581
18	8	34	2		55	25	9	33	68	66		520	27	0.0285292
19	9	33	2		56	28	10	36	95	64		544	28	0.030113
20	10	36	2		60	21	14	47	102	76		919	29	0.047836
21	11	23	1		62	28	16	59	117	63		281	20	0.0500385
22	12	63	3		67	27	17	31	127	67		404	28	0.0611028
23	13	24	1		79	30	18	34	128	71		802	20	0.0670667
24	14	47	2		80	29	19	35	130	74		322	29	0.0895438
25	15	30	1		87	23	21	47	138	63		412	26	0.0941503
26	16	59	2		99	26	22	31	149	67		797	29	0.0974123
27	17	31	2		101	22	23	54	168	72		409	27	0.0996534
28	18	34	2		116	25	24	41	178	69		116	25	0.1083134
29	19	35	2		119	25	25	38	181	70		652	24	0.1123277
30	20	29	1		122	27	27	44	187	63		390	24	0.1131511

Next, it is useful to "unstack" the data into three groups, one for each age category, as shown in columns E through J. For example, columns E and F list the customer numbers and ages for all customers in the first age category. It is easy to unstack the data in columns A through C with StatTools. After identifying the A10:C1010 range as a StatTools data set, use the Unstack option in StatTools Utilities, select Category as the "Cat" variable, and select Customer and Age as the "Val" variables to unstack. You can then move the unstacked data to a different location, as in Figure 8.6.

Once the variables are unstacked, we can calculate the information in the range F6:G8 by entering the formulas

=COUNTIF(ST_Category, 1)

and

=ROUND($B$3*F6/1000,0)

in cells F6 and G6, with similar formulas for the other two categories. (ST_Category is the range name StatTools gives to the Category data in column C.) In words, if Sears wants to use proportional sample sizes, then it should sample 13, 77, and 10 customers from the three age categories. The formula for proportional sample sizes might lead to fractional values, so we use Excel's ROUND function to round to integers.

Finally, we can proceed as in Example 8.1 for each of the three categories separately. Figure 8.6 illustrates the selection of 13 customers from age category 1. We copy the data in columns E and F to columns L and M, append a column of random numbers with the RAND function in column N, freeze these random numbers (with Copy and Paste Values), sort on the random number column, and choose the first 13 customers. (The finished version of the file shows similar calculations for the other two age categories to the right of column N.) Note that if we wanted a *different* sample of 13 from age category 1, all we would need to do is generate new random numbers in column N with the RAND function, freeze them, and sort again. ∎

8.3.5 Cluster Sampling

Suppose that a company is interested in various characteristics of households in a particular city. The sampling units are households. We could select a random sample of households by one of the sampling methods already discussed. However, it might be more convenient to proceed somewhat differently. We could first divide the city into city blocks and consider the city blocks as sampling units. We could then select a simple random sample of city blocks and then sample all of the households in the chosen blocks. In this case the city blocks are called **clusters** and the sampling scheme is called **cluster sampling**.

> In **cluster sampling**, the population is separated into clusters, such as cities or city blocks, and then a random sample of the clusters is selected.

Cluster analysis is typically more convenient and less costly than other random sampling methods.

The primary advantage of cluster sampling is sampling convenience (and possibly less cost). If an agency is sending interviewers to interview heads of household, it is much easier for them to concentrate on particular city blocks than to contact households throughout the city. The downside, however, is that the inferences drawn from a cluster sample can be less accurate, for a given sample size, than for other sampling plans.

Consider the following scenario. A nationwide company wants to survey its salespeople with regard to management practices. It decides to randomly select several sales districts (the clusters) and then interview all salespeople in the selected districts. It is likely that in any particular sales district the attitudes toward management are somewhat similar. This overlapping information means that the company is probably not getting the maximum amount of information per sampling dollar spent. Instead of sampling 20 salespeople from a given district who all have similar attitudes, it might be better to sample 20 salespeople from different districts who have a wider variety of attitudes. Nevertheless, the relative convenience of cluster sampling sometimes outweighs these statistical considerations.

Selecting a cluster sample is straightforward. The key is to define the sampling units as the *clusters*—the city blocks, for example. Then we can select a simple random sample of clusters exactly as in Example 8.1. Once the clusters are selected, we typically sample all of the population members in each selected cluster.

8.3.6 Multistage Sampling Schemes

The cluster sampling scheme just described, where a sample of clusters is chosen and then all of the sampling units within each chosen cluster are taken, is called a **single-stage** sampling scheme. Real applications are often more complex than this, resulting in **multistage** sampling schemes. For example, the Gallup organization uses multistage sampling in its nationwide surveys. A random sample of approximately 300 locations is chosen in the first stage of the sampling process. City blocks or other geographical areas are then randomly sampled from the first-stage locations in the second stage of the process. This is followed by a systematic sampling of households from each second-stage area. A total of about 1500 households comprise a typical Gallup poll.

We do not pursue the topic of multistage sampling schemes in this book. However, you should realize that real-world sampling procedures can be very complex.

PROBLEMS

Level A

1. Consider the frame of 52 full-time employees of Beta Technologies, Inc. Beta's human resources manager has collected current annual salary figures and related data for these employees. The data are in the file **P02_01.xlsx**. In particular, these data include each selected employee's gender, age, number of years of relevant work experience prior to employment at Beta, the number of years of employment at Beta, the number of years of postsecondary education, and annual salary.
   a. Compute the mean, median, and standard deviation of the annual salaries for the 52 employees in the given frame.
   b. Use Excel to choose a simple random sample of size 15 from this frame.
   c. Compute the mean, median, and standard deviation of the annual salaries for the 15 employees included in your simple random sample. Compare these statistics with your computed descriptive measures for the frame obtained in part **a**. Is your simple random sample representative of the frame with respect to the annual salary variable?

2. A manufacturing company's quality control personnel have recorded the proportion of defective items for each of 500 monthly shipments of one of the computer components that the company produces. The data are in the file **P02_02.xlsx**. The quality control department manager does not have sufficient time to review all of these data. Rather, she would like to examine the proportions of defective items for a simple random sample of 50 shipments.
   a. Use Excel to generate such a random sample from the given frame.
   b. What are the advantages and disadvantages of the sampling method requested by this quality control manager?

3. The manager of a local fast-food restaurant is interested in improving the service provided to customers who use the restaurant's drive-up window. As a first step in this process, the manager asks his assistant to record the time (in minutes) it takes to serve a large number of customers at the final window in the facility's drive-up system. The given frame of 200 customer service times are all observed during the busiest hour of the day for this fast-food operation. The data are in the file **P02_04.xlsx**.

   a. Compute the mean, median, and standard deviation of the customer service times in the given frame.
   b. Use Excel to choose a simple random sample of size 20 from this frame.
   c. Compute the mean, median, and standard deviation of the service times for the 20 customers included in your simple random sample. Compare these statistics with your computed descriptive measures for the frame obtained in part **a**.

4. A finance professor has just given a midterm examination in her corporate finance course, and she is interested in learning how her large class of 100 students peformed on this exam. The data are in the file **P02_05.xlsx**.
   a. Using these 100 students as the frame, generate a simple random sample of size 10 with Excel.
   b. Compare the mean of the scores in the frame with that of the scores contained in the simple random sample.

5. Consider a frame consisting of 500 households in a middle-class neighborhood that was the recent focus of an economic development study conducted by the local government. Specifically, for each of the 500 households, information was gathered on each of the following variables: family size, location of the household within the neighborhood, an indication of whether those surveyed owned or rented their home, gross annual income of the first household wage earner, gross annual income of the second household wage earner (if applicable), monthly home mortgage or rent payment, average monthly expenditure on utilities, and the total indebtedness (excluding the value of a home mortgage) of the household. The data are in the file **P02_06.xlsx**.
   a. Compute the mean, median, and standard deviation of the monthly home mortgage or rent payments of all households in the given frame.
   b. Use Excel to choose a simple random sample of size 25 from this frame.
   c. Compute the mean, median, and standard deviation of the monthly home mortgage or rent payments for the 25 households included in your simple random sample. Compare these statistics with your computed descriptive measures for the frame obtained in part **a**.

6. A real estate agent has received data on 150 houses that were recently sold in a suburban community. Included

in this data set are observations for each of the following variables: the appraised value of each house (in thousands of dollars), the selling price of each house (in thousands of dollars), the size of each house (in hundreds of square feet), and the number of bedrooms in each house. The data are in the file **P02_07.xlsx**. Suppose that this real estate agent wishes to examine a representative subset of these 150 houses. Use Excel to assist her by finding a simple random sample of size 10 from this frame.

7. Consider the given set of average annual household income levels of citizens of selected U.S. metropolitan areas in the file **P03_06.xlsx**. Use Excel to obtain a simple random sample of size 15 from this frame.

8. The operations manager of a toll booth located at a major exit of a state turnpike is trying to estimate the average number of vehicles that arrive at the toll booth during a 1-minute period during the peak of rush-hour traffic. In an effort to estimate this average throughput value, he records the number of vehicles that arrive at the toll booth over a 1-minute interval commencing at the same time for each of 365 normal weekdays. The data are provided in the file **P02_09.xlsx**. Choose a simple random sample of size 20 from the given frame of 365 values to help the operations manager estimate the average throughput value.

9. In ranking metropolitan areas in the United States, the *Places Rated Almanac* considers the average time (in minutes) it takes a citizen of each metropolitan area to travel to work and back home each day. The data are in the file **P02_11.xlsx**. Use Excel to obtain a simple random sample of 20 average commute times from the given set of such values.

10. Given data in the file **P02_13.xlsx** from a recent survey of chief executive officers from the largest U.S. public companies, choose a simple random sample of 25 executives and find the mean, median, and standard deviation of the bonuses awarded to them in fiscal year 2003. How do these sample statistics compare to the mean, median, and standard deviation of the bonuses given to all executives included in the frame?

11. A lightbulb manufacturer wants to know the number of defective bulbs contained in a typical box shipped by the company. Production personnel at this company have recorded the number of defective bulbs found in each of the 1000 boxes shipped during the past week. These data are provided in **P08_11.xlsx**. Using this shipment of boxes as a frame, select a simple random sample of 50 boxes and compute the mean number of defective bulbs found in a box.

12. Consider the frame of 52 full-time employees of Beta Technologies, Inc. Beta's human resources manager has collected current annual salary figures and related data for these employees. The data are in the file **P02_01.xlsx**.

a. Compute the mean, median, and standard deviation of the annual salaries for the 52 employees in the given frame.

b. Use Excel to choose a systematic sample of size 13 from this frame.

c. Compute the mean, median, and standard deviation of the annual salaries for the 13 employees included in your systematic sample. Compare these statistics with your computed descriptive measures for the frame obtained in part **a**. Is your systematic sample representative of the frame with respect to the annual salary variable?

13. A manufacturing company's quality control personnel have recorded the proportion of defective items for each of 500 monthly shipments of one of the computer components that the company produces. The data are in the file **P02_02.xlsx**. The quality control department manager does not have sufficient time to review all of these data. Rather, she would like to examine the proportions of defective items for a systematic sample of 50 shipments.

a. Use Excel to generate such a systematic sample from the given frame.

b. What are the advantages and disadvantages of the sampling method requested by this quality control manager?

14. The manager of a local fast-food restaurant is interested in improving the service provided to customers who use the restaurant's drive-up window. As a first step in this process, the manager asks his assistant to record the time (in minutes) it takes to serve a large number of customers at the final window in the facility's drive-up system. The given frame of 200 customer service times are all observed during the busiest hour of the day for this fast-food operation. The data are in the file **P02_04.xlsx**.

a. Compute the mean, median, and standard deviation of the customer service times in the given frame.

b. Use Excel to choose a systematic sample of size 20 from this frame.

c. Compute the mean, median, and standard deviation of the service times for the 20 customers included in your systematic sample. Compare these statistics with your computed descriptive measures for the frame obtained in part **a**.

15. A finance professor has just given a midterm examination in her corporate finance course. In particular, she is interested in learning how her large class of 100 students performed on this exam. The data are in the file **P02_05.xlsx**.

a. Using these 100 students as the frame, generate a systematic sample of size 10 with Excel.

b. Compare the mean of the scores in the frame with that of the scores included in the systematic sample.

16. Consider a frame consisting of 500 households in a middle-class neighborhood that was the recent focus

of an economic development study conducted by the local government. The data are in the file **P02_06.xlsx**.

a. Compute the mean, median, and standard deviation of the monthly home mortgage or rent payments of all households in the given frame.

b. Use Excel to choose a systematic sample of size 25 from this frame.

c. Compute the mean, median, and standard deviation of the monthly home mortgage or rent payments for the 25 households included in your systematic sample. Compare these statistics with your computed descriptive measures for the frame obtained in part **a**.

17. A real estate agent has received data on 150 houses that were recently sold in a suburban community. Included in this data set are observations for each of the following variables: the appraised value of each house (in thousands of dollars), the selling price of each house (in thousands of dollars), the size of each house (in hundreds of square feet), and the number of bedrooms in each house. The data are in the file **P02_07.xlsx**. Suppose that this real estate agent wishes to examine a representative subset of these 150 houses. Use Excel to assist her by finding a systematic sample of size 10 from this frame.

18. Consider the given set of average annual household income levels of citizens of selected U.S. metropolitan areas in the file **P03_06.xlsx**. Use Excel to obtain a systematic sample of size 25 from this frame.

19. The operations manager of a toll booth located at a major exit of a state turnpike is trying to estimate the average number of vehicles that arrive at the toll booth during a 1-minute period during the peak of rush-hour traffic. In an effort to estimate this average throughput value, he records the number of vehicles that arrive at the toll booth over a 1-minute interval commencing at the same time for each of 365 normal weekdays. The data are provided in the file **P02_09.xlsx**. Choose a systematic sample of size 20 from the given frame of 365 values to help the operations manager estimate the average throughput value.

20. Consider the average time (in minutes) it takes citizens of each of the metropolitan areas across the United States to travel to work and back home each day. The data are in the file **P02_11.xlsx**. Use Excel to obtain a systematic sample of 25 average commute times from the given set of such values.

21. Consider the data on Beta Technologies employees in the file **P02_01.xlsx**.

a. Compute the mean, median, and standard deviation of the annual salaries for the 52 employees in the given frame.

b. Assuming that the human resources manager wishes to stratify these employees by the number

of years of postsecondary education, select such a stratified sample of size 15 with approximately proportional sample sizes.

c. Compute the mean, median, and standard deviation of the annual salaries for the 15 employees included in your stratified sample. Compare these statistics with your computed descriptive measures for the frame obtained in part **a**. Is your stratified sample representative of the frame with respect to the annual salary variable?

22. Consider the economic development data in the file **P02_06.xlsx**.

a. Compute the mean, median, and standard deviation of the gross annual income of the first wage earner of all households in the given frame.

b. Given that researchers have decided to stratify the given households by location within the neighborhood, choose a stratified sample of size 25 with proportional sample sizes.

c. Compute the mean, median, and standard deviation of the gross annual income of the first wage earner of the 25 households included in your stratified sample. Compare these statistics with your computed descriptive measures for the frame obtained in part **a**.

d. Explain how economic researchers could apply cluster sampling in selecting a sample of size 25 from this frame. What are the advantages and disadvantages of employing cluster sampling in this case?

23. Consider the data on real estate sales in the file **P02_07.xlsx**.

a. Suppose that this real estate agent wishes to examine a representative subset of these 150 houses that has been stratified by the number of bedrooms. Use Excel to assist her by finding such a stratified sample of size 15 with proportional sample sizes.

b. Explain how the real estate agent could apply cluster sampling in selecting a sample of size 15 from this frame. What are the advantages and disadvantages of employing cluster sampling in this case?

24. Given the data in the file **P02_13.xlsx** from a recent survey of chief executive officers from the largest U.S. public companies, choose a sample of 25 executives stratified by company type with proportional sample sizes. Next, find the mean, median, and standard deviation of the salaries earned by the selected CEOs in fiscal year 2003. How do these sample statistics compare to the mean, median, and standard deviation of the salaries earned by all executives included in the frame?

Level B

25. The employee benefits manager of a small private university would like to know the proportion of its full-time employees who prefer adopting each of three available health care plans in the forthcoming annual enrollment period. A reliable frame of the university's employees and their tentative health care preferences are given in **P08_25.xlsx**.

a. Compute the proportion of the employees in the given frame who favor *each* of the three plans (i.e., plans A, B, and C).

b. Use Excel to choose a sample of 45 employees stratified by employee classification with proportional sample sizes.

c. Compute the proportion of the 45 employees in the stratified sample who favor each health plan. Compare these sample proportions to the corresponding values obtained in part **a**. Explain any differences between the corresponding values.

d. What are the advantages and disadvantages of employing stratified sampling in this particular case?

e. Explain how the benefits manager could apply cluster sampling in selecting a sample of size 30 from this frame. What are the advantages and disadvantages of employing cluster sampling in this case?

26. The file **P02_17.xlsx** reports the number of short-term general hospitals in each of a large number of U.S. metropolitan areas. Suppose that you are a sales manager for a major pharmaceutical producer and are interested in estimating the average number of such hospitals in *all* metropolitan areas across the entire country. Assuming that you do not have access to the data for each metropolitan location, you decide to select a sample that will be representative of all such areas.

a. Choose a simple random sample of 30 metropolitan areas from the given frame. Compute the mean number of short-term general hospitals for the metropolitan areas included in your sample.

b. Do you believe that simple random sampling is the best approach to obtaining a representative subset of the metropolitan areas in the given frame? Explain. If not, how might you proceed to select a better sample of size 30 using the data provided in the file? Compute the mean number of short-term general hospitals for the metropolitan areas included in your revised sample. How does this

sample mean compare to that computed from your simple random sample in part **a**?

27. As human resources manager of a manufacturing plant, you are quite concerned about recent reports of sexual and racial harassment from the production workers within the organization. In an effort to gain a better understanding of the apparent problems, you decide that it would be wise to interview a cross section of your employees about this and other issues in the workplace.

a. Using the frame of employees provided in the file **P08_27.xlsx**, select a subset of 30 production workers stratified by sex with proportional sample sizes.

b. Next, select another subset of 30 workers stratified by race with proportional sample sizes.

c. Finally, select one more subset of 30 workers stratified by *both* sex and race (e.g., black women, white men, Asian women, Hispanic men, etc.) with proportional sample sizes.

d. Explain how the human resources manager could apply cluster sampling in selecting a sample of size 30 from this frame. What are the advantages and disadvantages of employing cluster sampling in this case?

28. Is the overall cost of living higher or lower for urban areas in particular geographical regions of the United States?

a. Begin by first selecting 40 urban areas from the given frame provided in the file **P08_28.xlsx**. The urban areas you select should be stratified by geographical location within the United States (e.g., northeast, southeast, midwest, northwest, or southwest) and should reflect proportional sample sizes. Note that you will first need to assign the given urban areas to one of any number of such geographical regions before you can generate a stratified sample.

b. Explain how you could apply cluster sampling in selecting a sample of size 40 from this frame. What are the advantages and disadvantages of employing cluster sampling in this case?

8.4 AN INTRODUCTION TO ESTIMATION

The purpose of any random sample is to estimate properties of a population from the data observed in the sample. The following is a good example to keep in mind. Suppose a government agency wants to know the average household income, where this average is taken over the population of all households in Atlanta. Then this unknown average is the population parameter of interest, and the government is likely to estimate it by sampling several "representative" households in Atlanta and reporting the average of their incomes.

The mathematical procedures appropriate for performing this estimation depend on which properties of the population are of interest and which type of random sampling scheme is used. Because the details are considerably more complex when a more complex sampling scheme such as multistage sampling is used, we will focus on *simple* random samples, where the mathematical details are relatively straightforward. Details for other sampling schemes such as stratified sampling can be found in Levy and Lemeshow (1999). However, even for more complex sampling schemes, the *concepts* are the same as those we discuss here; only the details change.

Throughout most of this section, we focus on the population mean of some variable such as household income. Our goal is to estimate this population mean by using the data in a randomly selected sample. We first discuss the types of errors that can occur in this estimation problem.

8.4.1 Sources of Estimation Error

There are two basic sources of errors that can occur when we sample randomly from a population: *sampling error* and all other sources, usually lumped together as *nonsampling error.* Sampling error results from "unlucky" samples. As such, the term *error* is somewhat misleading. Suppose, for example, that the mean grade-point average (GPA) in a large class of 400 students is 2.85. The instructor wants to know this mean but doesn't want to ask *each* student for his or her GPA. Therefore, the instructor asks a random sample of 20 students for their GPAs, and it turns out that the sample mean for these 20 students is 2.97. If the instructor then infers that the mean of *all* GPAs is 2.97, the resulting sampling error is the difference between the reported value and the true value, 0.12. Note that the instructor hasn't done anything "wrong." This sampling error is essentially due to bad luck.

> **Sampling error** is the inevitable result of basing an inference on a random sample rather than on the entire population.

We see shortly how to measure the potential sampling error involved. The point here is that the resulting estimation error is not caused by anything we're doing wrong—we might just get unlucky.

Nonsampling error is quite different and can occur for a variety of reasons. We discuss a few of them.

- Perhaps the most serious type of nonsampling error is **nonresponse bias**. This occurs when a portion of the sample fails to respond to the survey. Anyone who has ever conducted a questionnaire, whether by mail, by phone, or any other method, knows that the percentage of nonrespondents can be quite large. The question is whether this introduces estimation error. If the nonrespondents *would* have responded similarly to the respondents, had they responded, we don't lose much by not hearing from them. However, because the nonrespondents don't respond, we typically have no way of knowing whether they differ in some important respect from the respondents. Therefore, unless we are able to persuade the nonrespondents to respond—through a follow-up phone call, for example—we must guess at the amount of nonresponse bias.

- Another source of nonsampling error is **nontruthful responses**. This is particularly a problem when we ask sensitive questions in a questionnaire. For example, if the questions "Have you ever had an abortion?" or "Do you regularly use cocaine?" are asked, most people will answer "no," regardless of whether the true answer is "yes" or "no."

There is a way of getting at such sensitive information, called the **randomized response** technique. Here the investigator presents each respondent with two questions, one of which is the sensitive question. The other is innocuous, such as, "Were you born in the summer?" The respondent is asked to decide randomly which of the two questions to answer—by flipping a coin, say—and then answer the chosen question truthfully. The investigator sees only the answer (yes or no), not the result of the coin flip. That is, the investigator doesn't know which question is being answered. However, by using probability theory, it is possible for the investigator to infer from many such responses the percentage of the population whose truthful answer to the sensitive question is "yes."

■ Another type of nonsampling error is **measurement error**. This occurs when the responses to the questions do not reflect what the investigator had in mind. It might result from poorly worded questions, questions the respondents don't fully understand, questions that require the respondents to supply information they don't have, and so on. Undoubtedly, there have been times when you were filling out a questionnaire and said to yourself, "OK, I'll answer this as well as I can, but I know it's not what they want to know."

■ One final type of nonsampling error is **voluntary response bias**. This occurs when the subset of people who respond to a survey differ in some important respect from all potential respondents. For example, suppose a population of students are surveyed to see how many hours they study per night. If the students who respond are predominantly those who get the best grades, the resulting sample mean number of hours will be biased on the high side.

From this discussion and your own experience with questionnaires, you should realize that the potential for nonsampling error is enormous. However, unlike sampling error, it cannot be measured with probability theory. It can be controlled only by using appropriate sampling procedures and designing good survey instruments. We do not pursue this topic any further here. If you are interested, however, you can learn about methods for controlling nonsampling error, such as proper questionnaire design, from books on marketing research.

8.4.2 Key Terms in Sampling

We now set the stage for the rest of this chapter, as well as for several later chapters. Suppose there is some numerical population parameter we would like to know. This parameter could be a population mean, a population proportion, the difference between two population means, the difference between two population proportions, or many others. Unless we measure each member of the population—that is, we take a complete census—we cannot learn the exact value of this population parameter. Therefore, we instead take a random sample of some type and try to *estimate* the population parameter from the data in the sample.

We typically begin by calculating a **point estimate** (or, simply, an **estimate**) from the sample data, a "best guess" of the population parameter. The difference between the point estimate and the true value of the population parameter is called the **estimation error** (or **sampling error**). We then try to use probability theory to gauge the magnitude of the estimation error. The key to this is the **sampling distribution** of the point estimate, which is defined as the distribution of the point estimates we would see from *all* possible samples (of a given sample size) from the population. Often we report the accuracy of the point estimate with an accompanying *confidence interval*. A **confidence interval** is an interval around the point estimate, calculated from the sample data, where we strongly believe the true value of the population parameter lies.

A **point estimate** is a single numeric value, a "best guess" of a population parameter, based on the data in a sample.

The **estimation error** (or **sampling error**) is the difference between the point estimate and the true value of the population parameter being estimated.

> The **sampling distribution** of any point estimate is the distribution of the point estimates we would see from *all* possible samples (of a given sample size) from the population.

> A **confidence interval** is an interval around the point estimate, calculated from the sample data, where we strongly believe the true value of the population parameter lies.

Additionally, there are two other key terms you should know. First, consider the *mean* of the sampling distribution of a point estimate. It is the average value of the point estimates we would see from all possible samples. When this mean is equal to the true value of the population parameter, we say that that point estimate is **unbiased**. Otherwise, we say that it is **biased**. Naturally, we prefer unbiased estimates. They sometimes miss on the low side and sometimes on the high side, but on average they tend to be right on target.

> An **unbiased estimate** is a point estimate such that the mean of its sampling distribution is equal to the true value of the population parameter being estimated.

Unbiased estimates are desirable because they average out to the correct value. However, this isn't enough. We do not want point estimates from different samples to vary wildly from sample to sample. If they did, we couldn't rely much on an estimate from any particular sample. Therefore, we measure the standard deviation of the sampling distribution of the estimate, which indicates how much point estimates from different samples vary. In the context of sampling, this standard deviation is called the **standard error** of the estimate. Ideally, we want estimates that have *small* standard errors.

> The **standard error** of an estimate is the standard deviation of the sampling distribution of the estimate. It measures how much estimates vary from sample to sample.

The terms in this subsection are relevant for practically any population parameter we might want to estimate. In the following subsection we discuss them in the context of estimating a population mean.

8.4.3 Sampling Distribution of the Sample Mean

In this section we discuss the estimation of the population mean from some population. For example, we might be interested in the mean household income for all families in a particular city, the mean diameter of all parts from a manufacturing process, the mean pollution count over all cities in the world with a population of at least 100,000, and so on. We label the unknown population mean by μ.

The point estimate of μ we use, based on a sample from the population, is the sample mean $\overline{X}$, the average of the observations in the sample. There are *other* possible point estimates for a population mean besides the sample mean. We could use the sample median, the *trimmed mean* (where we average all but the few most extreme observations), and others. However, it turns out that the "natural" estimate, the sample mean, has very good theoretical properties, so it is the point estimate used most often.

How accurate is $\overline{X}$ in estimating μ? That is, how large does the estimation error $\overline{X} - \mu$ tend to be? As we discussed in the previous subsection, the sampling distribution of the sample mean $\overline{X}$ provides the key. Before describing this sampling distribution in some generality, we provide some insight into it by revisiting the population of 40 incomes in Example 8.1. There we showed how to generate a single random sample of size 10. For the particular sample we generated (see Figure 8.2), the sample mean was $38,750. Because we know that the population mean of all 40 incomes is $39,985, the estimation error based on this particular sample is the difference $38,750 − $39,985, or $1235 on the low side.

However, this is only one of many possible samples. To see other possibilities, we used StatTools's procedure for generating random samples to generate 100 random samples of size 10 from the population of 40 incomes. We then calculated the sample mean for each random sample and created a histogram of these sample means, shown in Figure 8.7. Although this is not *exactly* the sampling distribution of the sample mean (because there are many more than 100 possible samples of size 10 from a population of size 40), it indicates how the possible sample means are distributed. They are most likely to be near the population mean ($39,985), they are very unlikely to be more than about $3000 from this population mean, and the distribution is approximately bell shaped.

The insights in the previous paragraph can be generalized. It turns out that the sampling distribution of the sample mean has the following properties, regardless of the underlying population. First, it is an unbiased estimate of the population mean, as indicated in equation (8.1). The sample means from some samples will be too low, and those from other samples will be too high, but on the average, they will be just right.

Unbiased Property of Sample Mean

$$E(\overline{X}) = \mu \tag{8.1}$$

The second property involves the variability of the $\overline{X}$ estimate. Recall that the standard deviation of an estimate, called the standard error, indicates how much the estimates vary from sample to sample. The standard error of $\overline{X}$ is given in equation (8.2). Here, $\mathrm{SE}(\overline{X})$ is our abbreviation for the standard error of $\overline{X}$, σ is the standard deviation of the population, and n is the sample size. We see that the standard error is large when the observations in the population are spread out (large σ), but that the standard error can be reduced by taking a larger sample.[1]

Figure 8.7
Approximate Sampling Distribution of Sample Mean

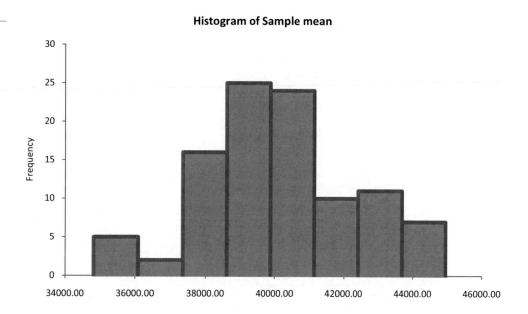

Histogram of Sample mean

[1]This formula for $\mathrm{SE}(\overline{X})$ assumes that the sample size n is small relative to the population size N. As a rule of thumb, we assume that n is no more than 5% of N. Later we provide a "correction" to this formula when n is a larger percentage of N.

Standard Error of Sample Mean

$$\text{SE}(\overline{X}) = \sigma/\sqrt{n} \tag{8.2}$$

There is one problem with the standard error in equation (8.2). Its value depends on another unknown population parameter, σ. Therefore, it is customary to approximate the standard error by substituting the *sample* standard deviation, s, for σ. This leads to equation (8.3).

Approximate Standard Error of Sample Mean

$$\text{SE}(\overline{X}) = s/\sqrt{n} \tag{8.3}$$

As we discuss in the next subsection, the shape of the sampling distribution of $\overline{X}$ is approximately normal. Therefore, we can use the standard error exactly as we have used standard deviations in previous chapters to obtain confidence intervals of the population mean.[2] Specifically, if we go out 2 standard errors on either side of the sample mean, as shown in expression (8.4), we are 95% confident of capturing the population mean. Alternatively, we are 95% confident that the estimation error will be no greater than 2 standard errors in magnitude.

Confidence Interval for Population Mean

$$\overline{X} \pm 2s/\sqrt{n} \tag{8.4}$$

The following example illustrates a typical use of sample information.

EXAMPLE | **8.4 ESTIMATING THE MEAN OF ACCOUNTS RECEIVABLE FOR A FURNITURE RETAILER**

An internal auditor for a furniture retailer wants to estimate the average of all accounts receivable, where this average is taken over the population of all customer accounts. Because the company has approximately 10,000 accounts, an exhaustive enumeration of all accounts receivable is impractical. Therefore, the auditor randomly samples 100 of the accounts. The observed data appear in Figure 8.8. (See the file **Auditing Receivables.xlsx**.) What can the auditor conclude from this sample?

Figure 8.8

Sampling in Auditing Example

	A	B	C	D	E
1	Random sample of accounts receivable				
2					
3	Population size	10000			
4	Sample size	100			
5					
6	Sample of receivables			Summary measures from sample	
7	Account	Amount		Sample mean	$278.92
8	1	$85		Sample stdev	$419.21
9	2	$1,061		Std Error of mean	$41.92
10	3	$0			
11	4	$1,260		With fpc	$41.71
12	5	$924			
13	6	$129			
105	98	$657			
106	99	$86			
107	100	$0			

[2]Strictly speaking, as we discuss in the next chapter, this is an approximate 95% confidence interval for the mean.

Objective To illustrate the meaning of standard error of the mean in a sample of accounts receivable.

Solution

The receivables for the 100 sampled accounts appear in column B. This is the only information available to the auditor, so he must base all conclusions on these sample data. We calculate the sample mean and sample standard deviation in cells E7 and E8 with the formulas

=AVERAGE(B8:B107)

and

=STDEV(B8:B107)

Then we use equation (8.3) to calculate the (approximate) standard error of the mean in cell E9 with the formula

=E8/SQRT(B4)

The auditor should interpret these values as follows. First, the sample mean $279 can be used to estimate the unknown population mean. It provides a best guess for the average of the receivables from all 10,000 accounts. In fact, because the sample mean is an unbiased estimate of the population mean, there is no reason to suspect that $279 either underestimates or overestimates the population mean. Second, the standard error $42 provides a measure of accuracy of the $279 estimate. Specifically, there is about a 95% chance that the estimate differs by no more than 2 standard errors (about $84) from the true (but unknown) population mean. Therefore, the auditor can be 95% certain that the mean from all 10,000 accounts is within the interval $279 ± $84, that is, between $195 and $363. ∎

It is important to distinguish between the sample standard deviation s and the standard error of the mean, approximated by $s/\sqrt{n}$. The sample standard deviation in the auditing example, $419, measures the variability in *individual* receivables in the sample (or in the population). By scrolling down column B, we see that there are some very low amounts (many zeros) and some fairly large amounts. This variability is indicated by the rather large sample standard deviation s. However, this value does not measure the accuracy of the sample mean as an estimate of the population mean. To judge *its* accuracy, we need to divide s by the square root of the sample size n. The resulting standard error, about $42, is much smaller than the sample standard deviation. It indicates that we can be about 95% certain that the sampling error is no greater than $84.

The Finite Population Correction We mentioned that equation (8.2) [or equation (8.3)] for the standard error of $\overline{X}$ is appropriate when the sample size n is small relative to the population size N. Generally, "small" means that n is no more than 5% of N. In most realistic samples this is certainly true. For example, political polls are typically based on samples of approximately 1000 people from the entire U.S. population.

There are situations, however, when we sample more than 5% of the population. In this case the formula for the standard error of the mean should be modified with a *finite population correction,* or *fpc,* factor. Then the modified standard error of the mean appears in equation (8.5), where the *fpc* is given by equation (8.6). Note that this factor is always less than 1 (when $n > 1$) and it decreases as n increases. Therefore, the standard error of the mean decreases—and the accuracy increases—as n increases.

> **Standard Error of Mean with Finite Population Correction Factor**
> $$\text{SE}(\overline{X}) = fpc \times (s/\sqrt{n}) \tag{8.5}$$

> **Finite Population Correction Factor**
> $$fpc = \sqrt{\dfrac{N-n}{N-1}} \tag{8.6}$$

To see how the *fpc* varies with n and N, consider the values in Table 8.1. Rather than listing n, we have listed the percentage of the population sampled, that is, $n/N \times 100\%$. It is clear that when 5% or less of the population is sampled, the *fpc* is very close to 1 and can safely be ignored. In this case we can use $s/\sqrt{n}$ as the standard error of the mean. Otherwise, we should use the modified formula in equation (8.5).

Table 8.1   Finite Population Correction Factors

N	% Sampled	*fpc*
100	5%	0.980
100	10%	0.953
10,000	1%	0.995
10,000	5%	0.975
10,000	10%	0.949
1,000,000	1%	0.995
1,000,000	5%	0.975
1,000,000	10%	0.949

If less than 5% of the population is sampled, as is often the case, the fpc can safely be ignored.

In the auditing example, $n/N = 100/100{,}000 = 0.1\%$. This suggests that the *fpc* can safely be omitted. We illustrate this in cell E11 of Figure 8.8, which uses the formula from equation (8.5):

=SQRT((B3-B4)/(B3-1))*E9

Clearly, it makes no practical difference in this example whether we use the *fpc* or not. The standard error, rounded to the nearest dollar, is $42 in either case.

Virtually all standard error formulas used in sampling include an *fpc* factor. However, because it is rarely necessary—the sample size is usually very small relative to the population size—we omit it from here on.

8.4.4 The Central Limit Theorem

Our discussion to this point has concentrated primarily on the mean and standard deviation of the sampling distribution of the sample mean. In this section we discuss this sampling distribution in more detail. Because of an important theoretical result called the *central limit theorem*, we know that this distribution is approximately *normal* with mean μ and standard deviation $\sigma/\sqrt{n}$. This theorem is the reason why the normal distribution appears in so many statistical results. We can state the theorem as follows.

> For any population distribution with mean μ and standard deviation σ, the sampling distribution of the sample mean $\overline{X}$ is approximately normal with mean μ and standard deviation $\sigma/\sqrt{n}$, and the approximation improves as n increases.

The important part of this result is the *normality* of the sampling distribution. We know, without any conditions placed upon the sample size n, that the mean and standard deviation are μ and $\sigma/\sqrt{n}$. However, the central limit theorem also implies normality, provided that n is reasonably large.

How large must n be for the approximation to be valid? Most analysts suggest $n \geq 30$ as a rule of thumb. However, this depends on the population distribution. If the population distribution is very *nonnormal*—extremely skewed or bimodal, for example—then the normal approximation might not be accurate unless n is considerably greater than 30. On the other hand, if the population distribution is already approximately symmetric, then the normal approximation is quite good for n considerably less than 30. In fact, in the special case where the population distribution itself is normal, the sampling distribution of $\overline{X}$ is *exactly* normal for *any* value of n.

The central limit theorem is not a simple concept to grasp. To help explain it, we employ simulation in the following example.

EXAMPLE | **8.5 AVERAGE WINNINGS FROM SPINNING A WHEEL OF FORTUNE**

Suppose you have the opportunity to play a game with a "wheel of fortune" (similar to a popular television game show). When you spin a large wheel, it is equally likely to stop in any position. Depending on where it stops, you win anywhere from $0 to $1000. Let's suppose your winnings are actually based on not one, but n spins of the wheel. For example, if $n = 2$, your winnings are based on the average of two spins. If the first spin results in $580 and the second spin results in $320, then you win the average, $450. How does the distribution of your winnings depend on n?

Objective   To illustrate the central limit theorem in the context of winnings in a game of chance.

Solution

First, we need to discuss what this experiment has to do with random sampling. Here, the population is the set of all outcomes we could obtain from a *single* spin of the wheel—that is, all dollar values from $0 to $1000. Each spin results in one randomly sampled dollar value from this population. Furthermore, because we have assumed that the wheel is equally likely to land in any position, all possible values in the continuum from $0 to $1000 have the same chance of occurring. The resulting population distribution is called the **uniform distribution** on the interval from $0 to $1000. (See Figure 8.9, where the 1 on the horizontal axis corresponds to $1000.) It can be shown (with calculus) that the mean and standard deviation of this uniform distribution are $\mu = \$500$ and $\sigma = \$289$.[3]

Figure 8.9
Uniform
Distribution

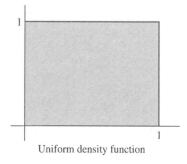

Uniform density function

---

[3]In general, if a distribution is uniform on the interval from a to b, then its mean is the midpoint $(a + b)/2$ and its standard deviation is $(b - a)/\sqrt{12}$.

Before we go any further, take a moment to test your own intuition. If you play this game once and your winnings are based on the average of n spins, how likely is that you will win at least $600 if $n = 1$? if $n = 3$? if $n = 10$? (The answers are 0.4, 0.27, and 0.14, respectively, where the last two answers are approximate and are based on the central limit theorem or on our simulations. So you are much less likely to "win big" if your winnings are based on the average of many spins.)

Now we analyze the distribution of winnings based on the average of n spins. We do so by means of a sequence of simulations in Excel, for $n = 1$, $n = 2$, $n = 3$, $n = 6$, and $n = 10$. (See the file **Wheel of Fortune Simulation.xlsx**, which is set up to work for any number of spins up to 10.) For each simulation we consider 1000 replications of an experiment. Each replication of the experiment simulates n spins of the wheel and calculates the average—that is, the winnings—from these n spins. Based on these 1000 replications, we can then calculate the average winnings, the standard deviation of winnings, and a histogram of winnings for each n. These will show clearly how the distribution of winnings depends on n.

The values in Figure 8.10 and the histogram in Figure 8.11 show the results for $n = 1$. Here there is no averaging—we spin the wheel once and win the amount shown. To replicate this experiment 1000 times and collect statistics, we proceed as follows.

1 **Random outcomes.** To generate outcomes uniformly distributed between $0 and $1000, enter the formula

=IF(B$9<=$B$6,$B$3+($B$4-$B$3)*RAND(),"")

in cell B11 and copy it to the entire range B11:K1010. The effect of this formula, given the values in cells B3 and B4, is to generate a random number between 0 and 1 and multiply it by $1000. The effect of the IF part is to fill up as many Outcome columns as there are spins in cell B6 and to leave the rest blank.

2 **Winnings.** Calculate the winnings in each row in column L as the average of the outcomes of the spins in that row. (Note that the AVERAGE function ignores blanks.)

3 **Summary measures.** Calculate the average and standard deviation of the 1000 winnings in column L with the AVERAGE and STDEV functions. These values appear in cells L4 and L5.

4 **Frequency table and histogram.** Use the StatTools Histogram procedure to create a histogram of the values in column L.

Figure 8.10
Simulation of Winnings from a Single Spin

	A	B	C	D	E	F	G	H	I	J	K	L
1	Wheel of fortune simulation											
2												
3	Minimum winnings	$0								Summary measures of winnings		
4	Maximum winnings	$1,000									Mean	$506
5											Stdev	$294
6	Number of spins	1										
7												
8	Simulation of spins											
9	Spin	1	2	3	4	5	6	7	8	9	10	
10	Replication	Outcome	Outcome	Outcome	Outcome	Outcome	Outcome	Outcome	Outcome	Outcome	Outcome	Winnings
11	1	$678										$678
12	2	$127										$127
13	3	$287										$287
14	4	$623										$623
15	5	$883										$883
16	6	$884										$884
17	7	$700										$700
18	8	$973										$973
19	9	$860										$860
20	10	$32										$32

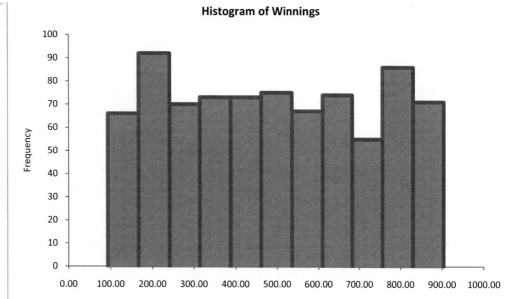

Figure 8.11

Histogram of Simulated Winnings from a Single Spin

Note the following from Figures 8.10 and 8.11.

- The sample mean of the winnings (cell L4) is very close to the population mean, $500.
- The standard deviation of the winnings (cell L5) is very close to the population standard deviation, $289.
- The histogram is nearly flat.

These properties should come as no surprise. When $n = 1$, the "sample mean" is a single observation—that is, no averaging takes place. Therefore, the sampling distribution of the sample mean is *equivalent* to the flat population distribution in Figure 8.9.

But what happens when $n > 1$? Figure 8.12 shows the results for $n = 2$. All you need to do is change the number of spins in cell B6, and everything updates automatically. The average winnings is again very close to $500, but the standard deviation of winnings is much lower. In fact, it is close to $\sigma/\sqrt{2} = 289/\sqrt{2} = \$204$, exactly as theory predicts. In addition, the histogram of winnings is no longer flat. It is triangularly shaped—symmetric, but not yet bell shaped.

To develop similar simulations for $n = 3$, $n = 6$, $n = 10$, or any other n, just change the number of spins in cell B6. The resulting histograms appear in Figures 8.13 through 8.15. They clearly show two effects of increasing n: (1) the histogram becomes more bell shaped, and (2) there is less variability. However, the mean stays right at $500. This behavior is exactly what the central limit theorem predicts. In fact, because the population distribution is symmetric in this example—it is flat—we see the effect of the central limit theorem for n much less than 30; it is already evident for n as low as 6.

Figure 8.12

Histogram of
Simulated Winnings
from Two Spins

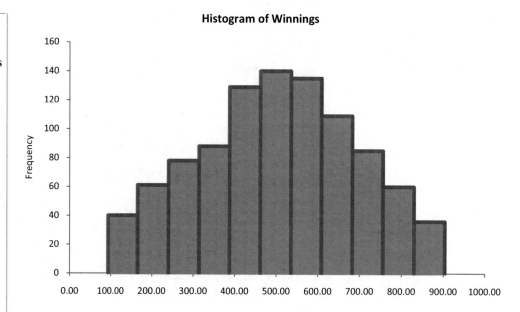

Figure 8.13

Histogram of
Simulated Winnings
from Three Spins

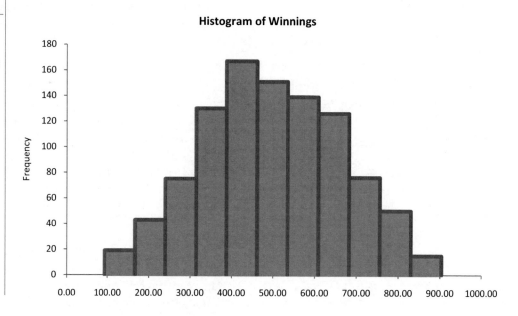

Figure 8.14
Histogram of
Simulated Winnings
from Six Spins

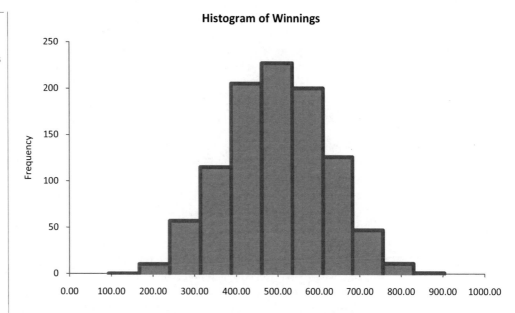

Figure 8.15
Histogram of
Simulated Winnings
from Ten Spins

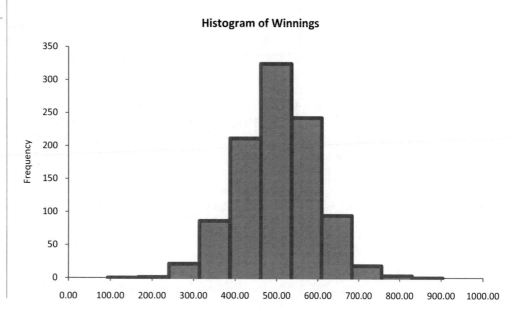

Finally, although the numerical results are not shown here, we could find the answers to the question we posed previously: How does the probability of winning at least $600 depend on n? For any specific value of n, we would simply find the fraction of the 1000 replications where the average of n spins is greater than $600. (This information is given by StatTools as part of its histogram output if you set one of the bin limits to $600.) You can check that the answers we gave previously are supported by the simulation results. ■

What are the main lessons from this example? For one, we see that the sampling distribution of the sample mean (winnings) is bell shaped when n is reasonably large. This is in spite of the fact that the population distribution is flat—far from bell shaped. Actually, the population distribution could have *any* shape, not just uniform, and the bell-shaped property would still hold (although n might have to be larger than in the example). This bell-shaped normality property allows us to perform probability calculations, as we will see in subsequent examples.

Equally important, this example demonstrates the *decreased variability* in the sample means as n increases. Why should an increased sample size lead to decreased variability? The reason is the averaging process. Think about obtaining a winnings of $750 based on the average of two spins. All we need is two lucky spins. In fact, one really lucky spin and an average spin will do. But think about obtaining a winnings of $750 based on the average of *10* spins. Now we need a *lot* of really lucky spins—and virtually no unlucky ones. The point is that we are much less likely to obtain a really large (or really small) sample mean when n is large than when n is small. This is exactly what we mean when we say that the variability of the sample means decreases with increasing sample size.

This decreasing variability is predicted by the formula for the standard error of the mean, $\sigma/\sqrt{n}$. As n increases, the standard error obviously decreases. This is what drives the behavior in Figures 8.12 through 8.15. In fact, using $\sigma = \$289$, the standard errors for $n = 2$, $n = 3$, $n = 6$, and $n = 10$ are $204, $167, $118, and $91, respectively.

Finally, what does this decreasing variability have to do with estimating a population mean with a sample mean? Very simply, it means that the sample mean tends to be a more *accurate* estimate when the sample size is large. Because of the approximate normality from the central limit theorem, we know from Chapter 6 that there is about a 95% chance that the sample mean will be within 2 standard errors of the population mean. In other words, there is about a 95% chance that the sampling error will be no greater than two standard errors in magnitude. Therefore, because the standard error decreases as the sample size increases, the sampling error is likely to decrease as well.

To illustrate this, reconsider the auditor in Example 8.4. The standard error based on a sample of size $n = 100$ yielded a sample standard deviation of $419 and a standard error of about $42. Therefore, the sampling error has a 95% chance of being less than 2 standard errors, or $84, in magnitude. If the auditor believes that this sampling error is too large and therefore randomly samples 300 more accounts, then the new standard error will be $419/\sqrt{400} \approx \$21$. Now there is about a 95% chance that the sampling error will be no more than $42. Note that because of the square root, small standard errors come at a high price. To halve the standard error, we must quadruple the sample size!

8.4.5 Sample Size Determination

The problem of determining the appropriate sample size in any sampling context is not an easy one, but it must be faced in the planning stages, *before* any sampling is done. We focus here on the relationship between sampling error and sample size. As we discussed previously, the sampling error tends to decrease as the sample size increases, so the desire to minimize sampling error encourages us to select larger sample sizes. We should note, however, that several other factors encourage us to select *smaller* sample sizes. The ultimate sample size selection must achieve a trade-off between these opposing forces.

What are these other factors? First, there is the obvious cost of sampling. Larger sample sizes require larger costs. Sometimes, a company or agency might have a budget for a given sampling project. If the sample size required to achieve an "acceptable" sampling error is 500, say, but the budget allows for a sample size of only 300, budget considerations will probably prevail.

Another problem caused by large sample sizes is timely collection of the data. Suppose a retailer wants to collect sample data from its customers to decide whether to run an advertising blitz in the coming week. Obviously, the retailer needs to collect these data quickly if they are to be of any use, and a large sample could require too much time to collect.

Finally, a more subtle problem caused by large sample sizes is the increased chance of *nonsampling* error, such as nonresponse bias. As we discussed previously in this chapter, there are many potential sources of nonsampling error, and they are usually very difficult to quantify. However, they are likely to increase as the sample size increases. Arguably, the potential increase in *sampling* error from a smaller sample could be more than offset by a decrease in nonsampling error, especially if the cost saved by the smaller sample size is used to reduce the sources of nonsampling error—more follow-up of nonrespondents, for example.

Nevertheless, the determination of sample size is usually driven by sampling error considerations. If we want to estimate a population mean with a sample mean, then the key is the standard error of the mean, given by

$$\text{SE}(\overline{X}) = \sigma/\sqrt{n}$$

We know from the central limit theorem that if n is reasonably large, there is about a 95% chance that the magnitude of the sampling error will be no more than 2 standard errors. Because σ is fixed in the formula for $\text{SE}(\overline{X})$, we can choose n to make $2\text{SE}(\overline{X})$ acceptably small.

We postpone further discussion of sample size selection until the next chapter, where we discuss in detail how it can be used to control confidence interval length.

8.4.6 Summary of Key Ideas for Simple Random Sampling

To this point, we have covered some very important concepts. Because we build on these concepts in later chapters, we summarize them here.

Key Concepts of Simple Random Sampling

- To estimate a population mean with a simple random sample, we use the sample mean as a "best guess." This estimate is called a *point estimate*. That is, $\overline{X}$ is a point estimate of μ.

- The accuracy of the point estimate is measured by its standard error. It is the standard deviation of the sampling distribution of the point estimate. The standard error of $\overline{X}$ is approximately $s/\sqrt{n}$, where s is the sample standard deviation.

- A *confidence interval* (with 95% confidence) for the population mean extends to approximately 2 standard errors on either side of the sample mean.

- From the *central limit theorem*, the sampling distribution of $\overline{X}$ is approximately normal when n is reasonably large.

- There is approximately a 95% chance that any particular $\overline{X}$ will be within 2 standard errors of the population mean μ.

- The sampling error can be reduced by increasing the sample size n. Appropriate sample size formulas for controlling confidence interval length are given in the next chapter.

PROBLEMS

Level A

29. A manufacturing company's quality control personnel have recorded the proportion of defective items for each of 500 monthly shipments of one of the computer components that the company produces. The data are in the file **P02_02.xlsx**. The quality control department manager does not have sufficient time to review all of these data. Rather, she would like to examine the proportions of defective items for a sample of these shipments.
    a. Use Excel to generate a simple random sample of size 25 from the given frame.
    b. Compute a point estimate of the population mean from the sample selected in part **a**. What is the sampling error in this case? Assume that the population consists of the proportion of defective items for each of the given 500 monthly shipments.
    c. Determine a good approximation to the standard error of the mean in this case.
    d. Repeat parts **b** and **c** after generating a simple random sample of size 50 from the given frame.

30. The manager of a local fast-food restaurant is interested in improving the service provided to customers who use the restaurant's drive-up window. As a first step in this process, the manager asks his assistant to record the time (in minutes) it takes to serve a large number of customers at the final window in the facility's drive-up system. The given frame of 200 customer service times are all observed during the busiest hour of the day for this fast-food operation. The data are in the file **P02_04.xlsx**.
    a. Use Excel to generate a simple random sample of size 10 from this frame.
    b. Compute a point estimate of the population mean from the sample selected in part **a**. What is the sampling error in this case? Assume that the population consists of the given 200 customer service times.
    c. Determine a good approximation to the standard error of the mean in this case.
    d. Repeat parts **b** and **c** after generating a simple random sample of size 20 from the given frame.

31. Consider the given set of average annual household income levels of citizens of selected U.S. metropolitan areas in the file **P03_06.xlsx**.
    a. Use Excel to obtain a simple random sample of size 15 from this frame.
    b. Compute a point estimate of the population mean from the sample selected in part **a**. What is the sampling error in this case? Assume that the population consists of all average annual household income levels in the given frame.
    c. Determine a good approximation to the standard error of the mean in this case.

    d. Repeat parts **b** and **c** after generating a simple random sample of size 30 from the given frame.

32. The operations manager of a toll booth located at a major exit of a state turnpike is trying to estimate the average number of vehicles that arrive at the toll booth during a 1-minute period during the peak of rush-hour traffic. In an effort to estimate this average throughput value, he records the number of vehicles that arrive at the toll booth over a 1-minute interval commencing at the same time for each of 365 normal weekdays. The data are provided in the file **P02_09.xlsx**.
    a. Choose a simple random sample of size 18 from the given frame to help the operations manager estimate the average throughput value.
    b. Compute a point estimate of the population mean from the sample selected in part **a**. What is the sampling error in this case? Assume that the population consists of the numbers of vehicle arrivals over the 365 weekdays in the given frame.
    c. Determine a good approximation to the standard error of the mean in this case.
    d. Repeat parts **b** and **c** after generating a simple random sample of size 36 from the given frame.

33. Continuing the previous problem with the same data file, answer the following questions.
    a. What sample size would be required for the operations manager to be approximately 95% sure that his estimate of the average throughput value is within 1 unit of the true mean? Assume that his best estimate of the population standard deviation σ is 1.7 arrivals per minute.
    b. How does the answer to part **a** change if the operations manager wants his estimate to be within 0.75 unit of the actual population mean? Explain the difference in your answers to parts **a** and **b**.

34. A lightbulb manufacturer wants to estimate the average number of defective bulbs contained in a box shipped by the company. Production personnel at this company have recorded the number of defective bulbs found in each of the 1000 boxes shipped during the past week. These data are provided in **P08_11.xlsx**.
    a. What sample size would be required for the production personnel to be approximately 95% sure that their estimate of the average number of defective bulbs per box is within 0.25 unit of the true mean? Assume that their best estimate of the population standard deviation σ is 0.9 defective bulb per box.
    b. How does the answer to part **a** change if the production personnel want their estimate to be within 0.40 unit of the actual population mean? Explain the difference in your answers to parts **a** and **b**.

35. Senior management of a certain consulting services firm is concerned about a growing decline in the organization's productivity. In an effort to understand the depth and extent of this problem, management would like to estimate the average number of hours its employees spend on work-related activities in a typical week. The frame of virtually all of the firm's full-time employees, including the employees' self-reported amounts of time typically devoted to work activities each week, is provided in **P08_35.xlsx**.

    a. What sample size would be required for management to be approximately 95% sure that its estimate of the average number of hours the employees spend on work-related activities in a typical week is within 6 hours of the true mean? Assume that management's best estimate of the population standard deviation σ is 10 hours per week.

    b. How does the answer to part **a** change if management want its estimate to be within 3 hours of the actual population mean? Explain the difference in your answers to parts **a** and **b**.

36. Elected officials in a small Florida town are preparing the annual budget for their community. Specifically, they would like to estimate how much their constituents living in this town are typically paying each year in real estate taxes. Given that there are more than 3000 homeowners in this small community, officials have decided to sample a representative subset of taxpayers and thoroughly study their tax payments. The latest frame of homeowners is given in **P08_36.xlsx**.

    a. What sample size would be required for elected officials to be approximately 95% sure that their estimate of the average annual real estate tax payment made by homeowners in their community is within $100 of the true mean? Assume that their best estimate of the population standard deviation σ is $535.

    b. Choose a simple random sample of the size found in part **a**.

    c. Compute the observed sampling error based on the sample you have drawn from the population given in the file. How does the actual sampling error compare to the maximum probable absolute error established in part **a**? Explain.

Level B

37. Continuing Problem 29, what proportion of the given 500 monthly shipments contain fractions of defective components within 1 standard deviation of the mean (based on the original simple random sample of size 25)? What proportion of the 500 monthly shipments contain fractions of defective components within 2 standard deviations of the mean (again, based on the original simple random sample of size 25)?

38. Continuing Problem 30, what proportion of the given 200 customer service times are within 2 standard deviations of the mean (based on the original simple random sample of size 10)? What proportion of the 200 customer service times are within 3 standard deviations of the mean (again, based on the original simple random sample of size 10)?

39. Continuing Problem 31, what proportion of the given average annual household income levels are within 2 standard deviations of the mean (based on the original simple random sample of size 15)? What proportion of the given average annual household income levels are within 2 standard deviations of the mean (now, based on the second simple random sample of size 30)?

40. Continuing Problem 32, what proportion of the numbers of vehicle arrivals over the given 365 weekdays are within 2 standard deviations of the mean (based on the original simple random sample of size 18)? What proportion of the given numbers of vehicle arrivals are within 2 standard deviations of the mean (now, based on the second simple random sample of size 36)?

41. Wal-Mart buyers seek to purchase adequate supplies of various brands of toothpaste to meet the ongoing demands of its customers. In particular, Wal-Mart is interested in estimating the proportion of its customers who favor the country's leading brand of toothpaste, Crest. The file **P08_41.xlsx** contains the toothpaste brand preferences of 2000 Wal-Mart customers, obtained recently through the administration of a customer survey.

    a. Use Excel to choose a simple random sample of size 100 from the given frame.

    b. Using the sample found in part **a**, compute a point estimate (called the sample proportion, $\hat{p}$) of the true proportion of Wal-Mart customers who prefer Crest toothpaste. What is the sampling error in this case? Assume that the population consists of the preferences of all customers in the given frame.

    c. Given that the standard error of the sampling distribution of the sample proportion $\hat{p}$ is approximately $\sqrt{\hat{p}(1-\hat{p})/n}$, compute a good approximation to the standard error of the sample proportion in this case.

    d. Repeat parts **b** and **c** after generating a simple random sample of size 50 from the given frame. How do you explain the differences in your results?

42. A finance professor has just given a midterm examination in her corporate finance course. The 100 scores are provided in **P02_05.xlsx**.

    a. Generate an appropriate histogram for the given distribution of 100 examination scores. Characterize this distribution. Also, compute the mean and standard deviation of the given scores.

b. Repeatedly choose simple random samples of size 2 from the original distribution given in the file. Record the sample mean for each of 100 sampling repetitions and generate an appropriate histogram of the resulting sampling distribution. Characterize this sampling distribution and compute its mean and standard deviation.

c. Repeatedly choose simple random samples of size 5 from the original distribution given in the file. Record the sample mean for each of 100 sampling repetitions and generate an appropriate histogram of the resulting sampling distribution. Characterize this sampling distribution and compute its mean and standard deviation.

d. Repeatedly choose simple random samples of size 10 from the original distribution given in the file. Record the sample mean for each of 100 sampling repetitions and generate an appropriate histogram of the resulting sampling distribution. Characterize this sampling distribution and compute its mean and standard deviation.

e. Explain the changes in your constructed sampling distributions as the sample size was increased from $n = 2$ to $n = 10$. In particular, how does the sampling distribution you constructed in part d compare to the original distribution (where $n = 1$) you described in part a?

43. The annual base salaries for 200 students graduating from a reputable MBA program this year are of interest to those in the admissions office who are responsible for marketing the program to prospective students. These salaries are given in the file **P02_74.xlsx**.

a. Generate an appropriate histogram for the given distribution of 200 annual salaries. Characterize this distribution. Also, compute the mean and standard deviation of the given salaries.

b. Repeatedly choose simple random samples of size 3 from the original distribution given in the file. Record the sample mean for each of 100 sampling repetitions and generate an appropriate histogram of the resulting sampling distribution. Characterize

this sampling distribution and compute its mean and standard deviation.

c. Repeatedly choose simple random samples of size 6 from the original distribution given in the file. Record the sample mean for each of 100 sampling repetitions and generate an appropriate histogram of the resulting sampling distribution. Characterize this sampling distribution and compute its mean and standard deviation.

d. Repeatedly choose simple random samples of size 12 from the original distribution given in the file. Record the sample mean for each of 100 sampling repetitions and generate an appropriate histogram of the resulting sampling distribution. Characterize this sampling distribution and compute its mean and standard deviation.

e. Explain the changes in your constructed sampling distributions as the sample size was increased from $n = 3$ to $n = 12$. In particular, how does the sampling distribution you constructed in part d compare to the original distribution (where $n = 1$) you described in part a?

44. A market research consultant hired by the Pepsi-Cola Co. is interested in determining the proportion of consumers who favor Pepsi-Cola over Coke Classic in a particular urban location. A frame of customers from the market under investigation is provided in **P08_44.xlsx**.

a. What sample size would be required for the market research consultant to be approximately 95% sure that her estimate of the proportion of consumers who favor Pepsi-Cola in the given urban location is within 0.20 of the true proportion? Assume that her best estimate of the population proportion parameter p is 0.45. [*Hint:* The required sample size formula in this case is given by $n = 4p(1 - p)/B^2$, where p is the population proportion parameter and B is the specified error, in this case 0.20.]

b. How does the answer to part a change if the market research consultant wants her estimate to be within 0.15 of the actual population proportion? Explain the difference in your answers to parts a and b.

8.5 CONCLUSION

This chapter has provided the fundamental concepts behind statistical inference. We discussed ways to obtain random samples from a population; how to calculate a point estimate of a particular population parameter, the population mean; and how to measure the accuracy of this point estimate. The key idea is the sampling distribution of the estimate and specifically its standard deviation, called the standard error of the estimate. From the central limit theorem, we saw that the sampling distribution of the sample mean is approximately normal, which implies that the sample mean will be within 2 standard errors of the population mean in approximately 95% of all random samples. In the next two chapters we build on these important concepts.

Summary of Key Terms

Term	Symbol	Explanation	Excel	Page	Equation Number
Population		Contains all members about which a study intends to make inferences		388	
Frame		A list of all members of the population		389	
Sampling units		Potential members of a sample from a population		389	
Probability sample		Any sample that is chosen by using a random mechanism		389	
Judgmental sample		Any sample that is chosen according to a sampler's judgment rather a random mechanism		389	
Simple random sample		A sample where each member of the population has the same chance of being chosen	StatTools/ Data Utilities/ Random Sample	390	
Systematic sample		A sample where one of the first k members is selected randomly, and then every kth member after this one is selected		395	
Stratified sample		A sample where the population is divided into relatively homogeneous subsets called strata, and then random samples are taken from each of the strata		396	
Proportional sample sizes (in stratified sampling)		Occurs when the proportion of each stratum selected is the same from stratum to stratum		397	
Cluster sampling		A sample where the population is separated into clusters, such as cities or city blocks, and then a random sample of the clusters is selected		399	
Sampling error		The inevitable result of basing an inference on a sample rather than on the entire population		404	
Nonsampling error		Any type of estimation error that is not sampling error, including nonresponse bias, nontruthful responses, measurement error, and voluntary response bias		404	
Point estimate		A single numeric value, a "best guess" of a population parameter, based on the data in a sample		405	
Estimation error		Difference between the estimate of a population parameter and the true value of the parameter		405	

(continued)

Term	Symbol	Explanation	Excel	Page	Equation Number
Sampling distribution		The distribution of the point estimates we would see from *all* possible samples (of a given sample size) from the population		406	
Confidence interval		An interval around the point estimate, calculated from the sample data, where we strongly believe the true value of the population parameter lies		406	
Unbiased estimate		An estimate where the mean of its sampling distribution equals the value of the parameter being estimated		406	
Standard error of an estimate		The standard deviation of the sampling distribution of the estimate		406	
Mean of sample mean	$E(\overline{X})$	Indicates property of unbiasedness of sample mean		407	8.1
Standard error of sample mean	$SE(\overline{X})$	Indicates how sample means from different samples vary		408	8.2, 8.3
Confidence interval for population mean		We are very confident that the population mean is within this interval		408	8.4
Finite population correction	*fpc*	A correction for the standard error when the sample size is fairly large relative to the population size		410	8.5, 8.6
Central limit theorem		States that the distribution of the sample mean is approximately normal for sufficiently large sample sizes		410	

PROBLEMS

Conceptual Exercises

C.1. Suppose that you want to know the opinions of American secondary school teachers about establishing a national test for high school graduation. You obtain a list of the members of the National Education Association (the largest teachers' union) and mail a questionnaire to 3000 teachers chosen at random from this list. In all, 1529 teachers return the questionnaire. Identify the relevant *population* and *frame* in this case.

C.2. A sportswriter wants to know how strongly the residents of Indianapolis, Indiana, support the local minor league baseball team, the Indianapolis Indians. She stands outside the stadium before a game and interviews the first 30 people who enter the stadium. Suppose that the newspaper asks you to comment on the approach taken by this sportswriter in performing the survey of local opinion. How do you respond?

C.3. A large corporation has 4520 male and 1167 female employees. The organization's equal employment opportunity officer wants to poll the opinions of a random sample of employees. To give adequate attention to the opinions of female employees, exactly how should the EEO officer sample from the given population? Explain in detail.

C.4. Suppose that you want to estimate the mean monthly gross income of all households in your local community. You decide to estimate this population parameter by calling 150 randomly selected residents and asking each individual to report the household's monthly income. Assume that you use the local phone directory as the frame in selecting the households to be included in your sample. What are some possible sources of error that might arise in your effort to estimate this population mean?

C.5. What is the difference between a *standard deviation* and a *standard error*?

Level A

45. The annual base salaries for 200 students graduating from a reputable MBA program this year are of interest to those in the admissions office who are responsible for marketing the program to prospective students. The data are in the file **P02_74.xlsx**. Use Excel to choose 10 simple random samples of size 15 from the given frame. For each simple random sample you obtain, compute the mean annual salary. Are these sample means equivalent? Explain why or why not.

46. A market research consultant hired by the Pepsi-Cola Co. is interested in determining who favors the Pepsi-Cola brand over Coke Classic in a particular urban location. A frame of customers from the market under investigation is provided in **P08_44.xlsx**.
   a. Compute the proportion of the customers in the given frame who favor Pepsi.
   b. Use Excel to choose a simple random sample of size 30 from the given frame.
   c. Compute the proportion of the 30 customers in the random sample who favor Pepsi. Compare this sample proportion to the value obtained in part **a**. Explain any difference between the two values.
   d. What are the advantages and disadvantages of employing simple random sampling in this particular case?

47. The employee benefits manager of a small private university would like to know the proportion of its full-time employees who prefer adopting each of three available health care plans in the forthcoming annual enrollment period. A reliable frame of the university's employees and their tentative health care preferences are given in **P08_25.xlsx**.
   a. Compute the proportion of the employees in the given frame who favor *each* of the three plans (i.e., plans A, B, and C).
   b. Use Excel to choose a simple random sample of size 45 from the given frame.
   c. Compute the proportion of the 45 employees in the random sample who favor each health plan. Compare these sample proportions to the corresponding values obtained in part **a**. Explain any differences between the corresponding values.
   d. What are the advantages and disadvantages of employing simple random sampling in this particular case?

48. Senior management of a certain consulting services firm is concerned about a growing decline in the organization's productivity. In an effort to understand the depth and extent of this problem, management would like to determine the average number of hours its employees spend on work-related activities in a typical week. The frame of virtually all of the firm's full-time employees, including the employees' self-reported amounts of time typically devoted to work activities each week, is provided in **P08_35.xlsx**.
   a. Select a simple random sample of size 100 from the given frame.
   b. Compute the mean and standard deviation of the weekly number of hours worked by all employees in the frame. Also, compute the mean and standard deviation of the weekly number of hours worked by employees in the simple random sample. How do these two sets of descriptive measures compare?

49. Elected officials in a small Florida town are preparing the annual budget for their community. Specifically, they would like to know how much their constituents living in this town are typically paying each year in real estate taxes. Given that there are more than 3000 homeowners in this small community, officials have decided to sample a representative subset of taxpayers and thoroughly study their tax payments. The latest frame of homeowners is given in **P08_36.xlsx**. Note that this file contains the real estate tax payment made by each homeowner last year.
   a. Compute the average real estate tax payment made by the homeowners included in the frame. Is the overall mean a valid measure of central tendency in this case?
   b. Use Excel to choose a simple random sample of 150 homeowners from the given frame.
   c. Compute the average real estate tax payment for the 150 homeowners in the random sample. Compare this sample mean to the corresponding summary measure obtained in part **a**.
   d. Is the sample mean computed in part **c** a good estimate of the average real estate tax payment made by homeowners living in this small town? Explain why or why not.

50. Auditors of a particular bank are interested in comparing the reported value of customer savings account balances with their own findings regarding the actual value of such assets. Rather than reviewing the records of each savings account at the bank, the auditors decide to examine a representative sample of savings account balances. The frame from which they will sample is given in the file **P08_50.xlsx**.
   a. Assist the bank's auditors by selecting a simple random sample of 100 savings accounts.
   b. Explain how the auditors might use the simple random sample identified in part **a** to estimate the value of *all* savings accounts balances within this bank.

51. The manager of a local supermarket wants to know the average amount (in dollars) customers spend at his store on Fridays. He would like to study the buying behavior of each customer who makes a purchase at the store on a typical Friday. However, the manager's assistant, who is currently enrolled in a managerial statistics course at a local college, urges the manager to save his scarce time and money by studying a sample of customer purchases. The available frame of relevant customer purchases is provided in file **P08_51.xlsx**.

    a. Compute the average purchase amount made by the customers included in the given frame.

    b. Use Excel to choose a simple random sample of 25 customers from the given frame.

    c. Compute the average purchase amount made by the 25 customers in the random sample. Compare this sample mean to the corresponding summary measure obtained in part **a**.

    d. Is the sample mean a good estimate of the overall population mean in this case? Explain why or why not.

52. The annual base salaries for 200 students graduating from a reputable MBA program this year are of interest to those in the admissions office who are responsible for marketing the program to prospective students. The data are in the file **P02_74.xlsx**. Use Excel to choose 15 systematic samples of size 10 from the given frame. For each systematic sample you obtain, compute the mean annual salary. Are these sample means equivalent? Explain why or why not.

53. Given the data in the file **P02_13.xlsx** from a recent survey of chief executive officers from the largest U.S. public companies, choose a systematic sample of 25 executives and find the mean, median, and standard deviation of the bonuses awarded to them in fiscal year 2003. How do these sample statistics compare to the mean, median, and standard deviation of the bonuses given to all executives included in the frame?

54. A market research consultant hired by the Pepsi-Cola Co. is interested in determining who favors the Pepsi-Cola brand over Coke Classic in a particular urban location. A frame of customers from the market under investigation is provided in **P08_44.xlsx**.

    a. Compute the proportion of the customers in the given frame who favor Pepsi.

    b. Use Excel to choose a systematic sample of size 30 from the given frame.

    c. Compute the proportion of the 30 customers in the systematic sample who favor Pepsi. Compare this sample proportion to the value obtained in part **a**. Explain any difference between the two values.

    d. What are the advantages and disadvantages of employing systematic sampling in this particular case?

55. A lightbulb manufacturer wants to know the number of defective bulbs contained in a typical box shipped by the company. Production personnel at this company have recorded the number of defective bulbs found in each of the 1000 boxes shipped during the past week. These data are provided in **P08_11.xlsx**. Using this shipment of boxes as a frame, select a systematic sample of 50 boxes and compute the mean number of defective bulbs found in a box.

56. The employee benefits manager of a small private university would like to know the proportion of its full-time employees who prefer adopting each of three available health care plans in the forthcoming annual enrollment period. A reliable frame of the university's employees and their tentative health care preferences are given in **P08_25.xlsx**.

    a. Compute the proportion of the employees in the given frame who favor *each* of the three plans (i.e., plans A, B, and C).

    b. Use Excel to choose a systematic sample of size 47 from the given frame.

    c. Compute the proportion of the 47 employees in the systematic sample who favor each health plan. Compare these sample proportions to the corresponding values obtained in part **a**. Explain any differences between the corresponding values.

    d. What are the advantages and disadvantages of employing systematic sampling in this particular case?

57. Senior management of a certain consulting services firm is concerned about a growing decline in the organization's productivity. In an effort to understand the depth and extent of this problem, management would like to determine the average number of hours their employees spend on work-related activities in a typical week. The frame of virtually all of the firm's full-time employees, including the employees' self-reported amounts of time typically devoted to work activities each week, is provided in **P08_35.xlsx**.

    a. Select a systematic sample of size 100 from the given frame.

    b. Compute the mean and standard deviation of the weekly number of hours worked by all employees in the frame. Also, compute the mean and standard deviation of the weekly number of hours worked by employees in the systematic sample. How do these two sets of descriptive measures compare?

58. Elected officials in a small Florida town are preparing the annual budget for their community. Specifically, they would like to know how much their constituents living in this town are typically paying each year in real estate taxes. Given that there are more than 3000 homeowners in this small community, officials have decided to sample a representative subset of taxpayers and thoroughly study their tax payments. The latest frame of homeowners is given in **P08_36.xlsx**. Note that this file contains the real estate tax payment made by each homeowner last year.

a. Use Excel to choose a systematic sample of 150 homeowners from the given frame.

b. Compute the average real estate tax payment for the 150 homeowners in the systematic sample.

c. Is the sample mean computed in part **b** a good estimate of the average real estate tax payment made by homeowners living in this small town? Explain why or why not.

59. Auditors of a particular bank are interested in comparing the reported value of customer savings account balances with their own findings regarding the actual value of such assets. Rather than reviewing the records of each savings account at the bank, the auditors decide to examine a representative sample of savings account balances. The frame from which they will sample is given in the file **P08_50.xlsx**.

a. Assist the bank's auditors by selecting a systematic sample of 151 savings accounts.

b. Explain how the auditors might use the systematic sample identified in part **a** to estimate the value of *all* savings accounts balances within this bank.

60. The manager of a local supermarket wants to know the average amount (in dollars) customers spend at his store on Fridays. He would like to study the buying behavior of each customer who makes a purchase at the store on a typical Friday. However, the manager's assistant, who is currently enrolled in a managerial statistics course at a local college, urges the manager to save his scarce time and money by studying a sample of customer purchases. The available frame of relevant customer purchases is provided in file **P08_51.xlsx**.

a. Compute the average purchase amount made by the customers included in the given frame.

b. Use Excel to choose a systematic sample of 43 customers from the given frame.

c. Compute the average purchase amount made by the 43 customers in the systematic sample. Compare this sample mean to the corresponding summary measure obtained in part **a**.

d. Is the sample mean a good estimate of the overall population mean in this case? Explain why or why not.

61. Elected officials in a small Florida town are preparing the annual budget for their community. Specifically, they would like to know how much their constituents living in this town are typically paying each year in real estate taxes. Given that there are more than 3000 homeowners in this small community, officials have decided to sample a representative subset of taxpayers and thoroughly study their tax payments. The latest frame of homeowners is given in **P08_36.xlsx**. Note that this file contains the real estate tax payment made by each homeowner last year.

a. Compute the average real estate tax payment made by the homeowners included in the frame. Is the overall mean a valid measure of central tendency in this case?

b. Use Excel to choose a sample of 150 homeowners stratified by neighborhood with proportional sample sizes.

c. Compute the average real estate tax payment for the 150 homeowners in the stratified sample. Compare this sample mean to the corresponding summary measure obtained in part **a**.

d. Is the sample mean computed in part **c** a good estimate of the average real estate tax payment made by homeowners living in this small town? Explain why or why not.

e. Explain how the elected officials could apply cluster sampling in selecting a sample of size 150 from this frame. What are the advantages and disadvantages of employing cluster sampling in this case?

62. Auditors of a particular bank are interested in comparing the reported value of customer savings account balances with their own findings regarding the actual value of such assets. Rather than reviewing the records of each savings account at the bank, the auditors decide to examine a representative sample of savings account balances. The frame from which they will sample is given in the file **P08_50.xlsx**.

a. What sample size would be required for the auditors to be approximately 95% sure that their estimate of the average savings account balance at this bank is within $100 of the true mean? Assume that their best estimate of the population standard deviation σ is $500.

b. Choose a simple random sample of the size found in part **a**.

c. Compute the observed sampling error based on the sample you have drawn from the population given in the file. How does the actual sampling error compare to the error ($100) specified in part **a**? Explain.

63. The manager of a local supermarket wants to estimate the average amount customers spend at his store on Fridays. He would like to study the buying behavior of each customer who makes a purchase at the store on a typical Friday. However, the manager's assistant, who is currently enrolled in a managerial statistics course at a local college, urges the manager to save his scarce time and money by studying a sample of customer purchases. The available frame of relevant customer purchases is provided in file **P08_51.xlsx**.

a. What sample size would be required for the supermarket manager to be approximately 95% sure that his estimate of the average customer expenditure on Fridays is within $25 of the true mean? Assume that his best estimate of the population standard deviation σ is $72.

b. Choose a simple random sample of the size found in part **a**.

c. Compute the observed sampling error based on the sample you have drawn from the population given in the file. How does the actual sampling error compare to the error ($25) specified in part **a**? Explain.

64. *The Hite Report* was Sheri Hite's survey of the attitudes of American women toward sexuality. She sent out more than 100,000 surveys; each contained multiple-choice and open-ended questions. These surveys were given to women's groups and announced in church newsletters. Ads were also placed in women's magazines. A total of 3019 surveys were returned. Sheri Hite's findings challenged much conventional wisdom about sexuality. She found that most women were unhappy in their romantic relationships (some for reasons that are too graphic for this book!). How would you criticize Hite's methodology? A later poll, by the way, contradicted many of her findings.

a. Give two criticisms of Hite's sampling methodology.

b. Despite these criticisms, what value might you see in Hite's results?

65. A market research consultant hired by the Pepsi-Cola Co. is interested in determining who favors the Pepsi-Cola brand over Coke Classic in a particular urban location. A frame of customers from the market under investigation is provided in **P08_44.xlsx**.

a. Compute the proportion of the consumers in the given frame who favor Pepsi.

b. Use Excel to choose a sample of size 30 stratified by gender with proportional sample sizes.

c. Compute the proportion of the 30 consumers in the stratified sample who favor Pepsi. Compare this sample proportion to the value obtained in part **a**. Explain any difference between the two values.

d. What are the advantages and disadvantages of employing stratified sampling in this particular case?

Level B

66. Repeat the previous problem, but now stratify the consumers in the given frame by *age* rather than by gender. How does this modification affect your answers to the questions posed in parts **b** and **c**? Finally, stratify the consumers by both gender *and* age (e.g., all females over 60) with proportional sample sizes. How does this change affect your answers to the questions posed in parts **b** and **c**? Which approach to stratification appears to give the best results in estimating the actual proportion of the customers in the given frame who favor Pepsi?

67. Wal-Mart buyers seek to purchase adequate supplies of various brands of toothpaste to meet the ongoing demands of their customers. In particular, Wal-Mart is interested in knowing the proportion of its customers who favor such leading brands of toothpaste as Aquafresh, Colgate, Crest, and Mentadent. The file **P08_41.xlsx** contains the toothpaste brand preferences of 2000 Wal-Mart customers, obtained recently through the administration of a customer survey.

a. Determine the proportion of Wal-Mart customers who favor each major brand of toothpaste.

b. Assuming that the given data constitute an appropriate frame, choose a simple random sample of 100 of these customers.

c. Calculate the proportion of Wal-Mart customers in the random sample who favor each major brand of toothpaste. Compare these sample proportions to the corresponding values found in part **a**. How do you explain any disparities between corresponding proportions for customers included in the sample and those in the frame?

68. Suppose that you are an entrepreneur interested in establishing a new Internet-based sports information service. Furthermore, suppose that you have gathered basic demographic information on a large number of Internet users. Assume that these 1000 individuals were carefully selected through stratified sampling. These data are stored in the file **P02_43.xlsx**.

a. To assess potential interest in your proposed enterprise, you would like to conduct telephone interviews with a representative subset of the 1000 Internet users you surveyed previously. How would you proceed to stratify the given frame of 1000 individuals to choose 50 for telephone interviews? Explain your approach and implement it to select a useful sample of size 50.

b. Explain how the entrepreneur could apply cluster sampling to obtain a sample of size 50 from this frame. What are the advantages and disadvantages of employing cluster sampling in this case?

69. A market research consultant hired by the Pepsi-Cola Co. is interested in determining the proportion of consumers who favor Pepsi-Cola over Coke Classic in a particular urban location. A frame of customers from the market under investigation is provided in **P08_44.xlsx**.

a. Use Excel to choose a simple random sample of size 30 from the given frame.

b. Using the sample found in part **a**, compute a point estimate (called the sample proportion, $\hat{p}$) of the true proportion of consumers who favor Pepsi-Cola in this market. What is the sampling error in this case? Assume that the population consists of the preferences of all consumers in the given frame.

c. Given that the standard error of the sampling distribution of the sample proportion $\hat{p}$ is approximately $\sqrt{\hat{p}(1-\hat{p})/n}$, compute a good approximation to the standard error of the sample proportion in this case.

d. Repeat parts **b** and **c** after generating a simple random sample of size 15 from the given frame. How do you explain the differences in your computed results?

70. The employee benefits manager of a small private university would like to estimate the proportion of full-time employees who prefer adopting the first (i.e., plan A) of three available health care plans in the forthcoming annual enrollment period. A reliable frame of the university's employees and their tentative health care preferences are given in **P08_25.xlsx**.
   a. Use Excel to choose a simple random sample of size 45 from the given frame.
   b. Using the sample found in part **a**, compute a point estimate (called the sample proportion, $\hat{p}$) of the true proportion of university employees who prefer plan A. What is the sampling error in this case? Assume that the population consists of the preferences of all employees in the given frame.
   c. Given that the standard error of the sampling distribution of the sample proportion p is approximately $\sqrt{\hat{p}(1 - \hat{p})/n}$, compute a good approximation to the standard error of the sample proportion in this case.
   d. Repeat parts **b** and **c** after generating a simple random sample of size 25 from the given frame. How do you explain the differences in your computed results?

71. Auditors of a particular bank are interested in comparing the reported value of customer savings account balances with their own findings regarding the actual value of such assets. Rather than reviewing the records of each savings account at the bank, the auditors decide to examine a representative sample of savings account balances. The frame from which they will sample is given in the file **P08_50.xlsx**.
   a. Generate an appropriate histogram for the given distribution of savings account balances. Characterize this distribution. Also, compute the mean and standard deviation of the given scores.
   b. Repeatedly choose simple random samples of size 2 from the original distribution given in the file. Record the sample mean for each of 500 sampling repetitions and generate an appropriate histogram of the resulting sampling distribution. Characterize this sampling distribution and compute its mean and standard deviation.
   c. Repeatedly choose simple random samples of size 5 from the original distribution given in the file. Record the sample mean for each of 500 sampling repetitions and generate an appropriate histogram of the resulting sampling distribution. Characterize this sampling distribution and compute its mean and standard deviation.
   d. Repeatedly choose simple random samples of size 10 from the original distribution given in the file. Record the sample mean for each of 500 sampling repetitions and generate an appropriate histogram of the resulting sampling distribution. Characterize this sampling distribution and compute its mean and standard deviation.

   e. Explain the changes in your constructed sampling distributions as the sample size was increased from $n = 2$ to $n = 10$. In particular, how does the sampling distribution you constructed in part **d** compare to the original distribution (where $n = 1$) you described in part **a**?

72. A lightbulb manufacturer wants to estimate the number of defective bulbs contained in a typical box shipped by the company. Production personnel at this company have recorded the number of defective bulbs found in each of the 1000 boxes shipped during the past week. These data are provided in **P08_11.xlsx**.
   a. Generate an appropriate histogram for the given distribution of 1000 numbers of defective bulbs. Characterize this distribution. Also, compute the mean and standard deviation of the given numbers.
   b. Repeatedly choose simple random samples of size 3 from the original distribution given in the file. Record the sample mean for each of 100 sampling repetitions and generate an appropriate histogram of the resulting sampling distribution. Characterize this sampling distribution and compute its mean and standard deviation.
   c. Repeatedly choose simple random samples of size 6 from the original distribution given in the file. Record the sample mean for each of 100 sampling repetitions and generate an appropriate histogram of the resulting sampling distribution. Characterize this sampling distribution and compute its mean and standard deviation.
   d. Repeatedly choose simple random samples of size 12 from the original distribution given in the file. Record the sample mean for each of 100 sampling repetitions and generate an appropriate histogram of the resulting sampling distribution. Characterize this sampling distribution and compute its mean and standard deviation.
   e. Explain the changes in your constructed sampling distributions as the sample size was increased from $n = 3$ to $n = 12$. In particular, how does the sampling distribution you constructed in part **d** compare to the original distribution (where $n = 1$) you described in part **a**?

73. The employee benefits manager of a small private university would like to estimate the proportion of full-time employees who prefer adopting the first (i.e., plan A) of three available health care plans in the forthcoming annual enrollment period. A reliable frame of the university's employees and their tentative health care preferences are given in **P08_25.xlsx**.
   a. What sample size would be required for the benefits manager to be approximately 95% sure that her estimate of the proportion of full-time university employees who prefer adopting plan A is within 0.15 of the true proportion? Assume that her best estimate of the population proportion parameter p is 1/3.

[*Hint*: The required sample size formula in this case is given by $n = 4p(1 - p)/B^2$, where p is the population proportion parameter and B is the specified error, in this case, 0.15.]

    b. How does the answer to part **a** change if the benefits manager wants her estimate to be within 0.25 of the actual population proportion? Explain the difference in your answers to parts **a** and **b**.

74. Suppose the monthly unpaid balance on a Citicorp MasterCard is normally distributed with a mean of \$1200 and standard deviation of \$240. We want to show that the sample mean $\overline{X}$ is an unbiased estimate of the population mean μ, and the sample variance s^2 is an unbiased estimate of the population variance σ^2. Note that you can generate observations from CITICORP accounts by using the formula **=NORMINV(RAND(),1200,240)**. Develop a simulation as follows:

- Generate 50 samples of five credit card balances each. Do *not* freeze the random numbers.
- Calculate $\overline{X}$ and s^2 for each sample.
- Show that the $\overline{X}$'s average to a value near the actual mean of \$1200.
- Show that the s^2's average to a value near the true value $\sigma^2 = 240^2$.

75. (Based on an actual case) Indiana audits nursing homes to see whether and how much the nursing home has overbilled Medicaid. Here is how they do it. Nurseco has 70 homes in Indiana. The state randomly samples one invoice per nursing home and determines Nurseco's liability as follows. Suppose nursing home 1 has billed Medicaid \$100,000. If the one surveyed invoice at nursing home 1 indicates Nurseco has overbilled by 40%, then Nurseco would have to return 40%

(or \$40,000) that it has collected from the state. What is wrong with this approach? Assuming all nursing homes have overbilled at a similar rate, can you suggest a better plan to determine how much money should be returned to the state?

76. The central limit theorem states that when many independent random variables are summed, the result follows a normal distribution even if the individual random variables in the sum do not. To illustrate this idea, simulate 500 samples of size 15 from the uniform (0, 1) distribution (generated with the RAND function). Are the 500 sums (where each is a sum of 15 values) normally distributed? Show by constructing a histogram and also by checking the empirical rules.

77. Assume a very large normally distributed population of scores on a test with mean 70 and standard deviation 7.

    a. Find an interval that includes 95% of the population.

    b. Suppose you randomly sample a single member from this population. Find an interval so that you are 95% confident that this member's score will be in the interval.

    c. Now suppose you sample 30 members randomly from this population. Find an interval so that you are 95% confident that the average of these members' scores will be in the interval.

    d. Finally, suppose you sample 300 members randomly from this population. Find an interval so that you are 95% confident that the average of these members' scores will be in the interval.

    e. Explain intuitively why the answers to parts **a** through **d** are not all the same.

The file **Videos.xlsx** contains a large database on 10,000 customer transactions for a fictional chain of video stores in the United States. Each row corresponds to a different customer and lists (1) a customer ID number (1–10,000); (2) the state where the customer lives; (3) the city where the customer lives; (4) the customer's gender; (5) the customer's favorite type of movie (drama, comedy, science fiction, or action); (6) the customer's next favorite type of movie; (7) the number of times the customer has rented movies in the past year; and (8) the total dollar amount the customer has spent on movie rentals during the past year. The data are sorted by state, then city, then gender. We assume that this database represents the entire population of customers for this video chain. (Of course, national chains would have significantly larger customer populations, but this database is large enough to illustrate the ideas.)

Imagine that only the data in columns A through D are readily available for this population. The company is interested in summary statistics of the data in columns E through H, such as the percentage of customers whose favorite movie type is drama or the average amount spent annually per customer, but it will have to do some work to obtain the data in columns E through H for any particular customer.

Therefore, the company wants to perform sampling. The question is: What form of sampling—simple random sampling, systematic sampling, stratified sampling, cluster sampling, or even some type of multistage sampling—is most appropriate?

Your job is to investigate the possibilities and to write a report on your findings. For any sampling method, any sample size, and any quantity of interest (such as average dollar amount spent annually), you should be concerned with sampling cost and accuracy. One way to judge the latter is to generate several random samples from a particular method and calculate the mean and standard deviation of your point estimates from these samples. For example, you might generate 10 systematic samples, calculate the average amount spent (an $\overline{X}$) for each sample, and then calculate the mean and standard deviation of these 10 $\overline{X}$'s. If your sampling method is accurate, the mean of the $\overline{X}$'s should be close to the population average, and the standard deviation should be small. By doing this for several sampling methods and possibly several sample sizes, you can experiment to see what is most cost efficient for the company. You can make any reasonable assumptions about the cost of sampling with any particular method. ∎

Regression Analysis: Estimating Relationships

© Digital Vision/Photodisc/Getty Images

SITE LOCATION OF LA QUINTA MOTOR INNS

Regression analysis is an extremely flexible tool that can aid decision making in many areas. Kimes and Fitzsimmons (1990) describe how it has been used by La Quinta Motor Inns, a moderately priced hotel chain oriented toward serving the business traveler, to help make site location decisions. Location is one of the most important decisions for a lodging firm. All hotel chains search for ideal locations and often compete against each other for the same sites. A hotel chain that can select good sites more accurately and quickly than its competition has a distinct competitive advantage.

Kimes and Fitzsimmons, academics hired by La Quinta to model its site location decision process, used regression analysis. They collected data on 57 mature inns belonging to La Quinta during a 3-year business cycle. The data included profitability for each inn (defined as operating margin percentage—profit plus depreciation and interest expenses, divided by the total revenue), as well as a number of potential explanatory variables that could be used to predict profitability. These explanatory variables fell into five categories: competitive characteristics (such as number of hotel rooms in the vicinity and average room rates); demand generators (such as hospitals and office buildings within a 4-mile radius that might attract customers to the area); demographic characteristics (such as local population, unemployment rate, and median family income); market awareness (such as years the inn has been open and state population per inn); and physical considerations (such as accessibility, distance to downtown, and sign visibility).

The analysts then determined which of these potential explanatory variables were most highly correlated (positively or negatively) with profitability and entered these variables into a regression equation for profitability. The estimated regression equation was

$$\text{Predicted Profitability} = 39.05 - 5.41\text{StatePop} + 5.81\text{Price}$$
$$- 3.09\sqrt{\text{MedIncome}} + 1.75\text{ColStudents}$$

where *StatePop* is the state population (1000s) per inn, *Price* is the room rate for the inn, *MedIncome* is the median income ($1000s) of the area, *ColStudents* is the number of college students (1000s) within 4 miles, and all variables in this equation are standardized to have mean 0 and standard deviation 1. This equation predicts that profitability will increase when room rate and the number of college students *increase* and when state population and median income *decrease*. The R^2 value (to be discussed in this chapter) was a respectable 0.51, indicating a reasonable predictive ability. Using good statistical practice, the analysts validated this equation by feeding it explanatory variable data on a set of *different* inns, attempting to predict profitability for these new inns. The validation was a success—the regression equation predicted profitability fairly accurately for this new set of inns.

La Quinta management, however, was not as interested in predicting the exact profitability of inns as in predicting which would be profitable and which would be unprofitable. A cutoff value of 35% for operating margin was used to divide the profitable inns from the unprofitable inns. (Approximately 60% of the inns in the original sample were profitable by this definition.) The analysts were still able to use the regression equation they had developed. For any prospective site, they used the regression equation to predict profitability, and if the predicted value was sufficiently high, they predicted that this site would be profitable. They selected a decision rule—that is, how high was "sufficiently high"—from considerations of the two potential types of errors. One type of error, a false positive, was predicting that a site would be profitable when in fact it was headed for unprofitability. The opposite type of error, a false negative, was predicting that a site would be unprofitable (and rejecting the site) when in fact it would have been profitable. La Quinta management was more concerned about false positives, so it was willing to be conservative in its decision rule and miss a few potential opportunities for profitable sites.

Since the time of the study, La Quinta has implemented the regression model in spreadsheet form. For each potential site, it collects data on the relevant explanatory variables, uses the regression equation to predict the site's profitability, and applies the decision rule on whether to build. Of course, the model's recommendation is only that—a recommendation. Top management has the ultimate say on whether any site is used. As Sam Barshop, then chairman of the board and president of La Quinta Motor Inns stated, "We currently use the model to help us in our site-screening process and have found that it has raised the 'red flag' on several sites we had under consideration. We plan to continue using and updating the model in the future in our attempt to make La Quinta a leader in the business hotel market." ∎

11.1 INTRODUCTION

Regression analysis is the study of relationships between variables. It is one of the most useful tools for a business analyst because it applies to so many situations. Some potential uses of regression analysis in business include the following:

- How do wages of employees depend on years of experience, years of education, and gender?

- How does the current price of a stock depend on its own past values, as well as the current and past values of a market index?

- How does a company's current sales level depend on its current and past advertising levels, the advertising levels of its competitors, the company's own past sales levels, and the general level of the market?

- How does the unit cost of producing an item depend on the total quantity of items that have been produced?

- How does the selling price of a house depend on such factors as the appraised value of the house, the square footage of the house, the number of bedrooms in the house, and perhaps others?

Each of these questions asks how a single variable, such as selling price or employee wages, depends on other relevant variables. If we can estimate this relationship, then we can not only better understand how the world operates, but we can also do a better job of predicting the variable in question. For example, we can not only understand how a company's sales are affected by its advertising, but we can also use the company's records of current and past advertising levels to predict future sales.

The branch of statistics that studies such relationships is called *regression analysis*, and it is the subject of this chapter and the next. Regression analysis is one of the most pervasive of all statistical methods in the business world. This is because of its generality and applicability.

There are several ways to categorize regression analysis. One categorization is based on the overall purpose of the analysis. As suggested previously, there are two potential objectives of regression analysis: to understand how the world operates and to make predictions. Either of these objectives could be paramount in any particular application. If the variable in question is employee wages and we are using variables such as years of experience, years of education, and gender to explain wage levels, then the purpose of the analysis is probably to understand how the world operates—that is, to explain how the variables combine in any given company to determine wages. More specifically, the purpose of the analysis might be to discover whether there is any gender discrimination in wages, after allowing for differences in work experience and education level.

Regression can be used to understand how the world operates, and it can be used for prediction.

On the other hand, the primary objective of the analysis might be prediction. A good example of this is when the variable in question is company sales, and variables such as advertising and past sales levels are used as explanatory variables. In this case it is certainly important for the company to know how the relevant variables impact its sales. But the company's primary objective is probably to predict *future* sales levels, given current and past values of the explanatory variables. A company might also use a regression model for a what-if analysis, where it predicts future sales for many conceivable patterns of advertising and then selects its advertising level on the basis of these predictions.

Fortunately, the same regression analysis enables us to solve both problems simultaneously. That is, it indicates how the world operates and it enables us to make predictions. So although the objectives of regression studies might differ, the same basic analysis always applies.

A second categorization of regression analysis is based on the type of data being analyzed. There are two basic types: *cross-sectional data* and *time series data*. **Cross-sectional data** are usually data gathered from approximately the same period of time from a cross section of a population. The housing and wage examples mentioned previously are typical cross-sectional studies. The first concerns a sample of houses, presumably sold during a short period of time, such as houses sold in Florida during the first couple of months of 2004. The second concerns a sample of employees observed at a particular point in time, such as a sample of automobile workers observed at the beginning of 2005.

In contrast, **time series data** involve one or more variables that are observed at several, usually equally spaced, points in time. The stock price example mentioned previously fits this description. We observe the price of a particular stock and possibly the price of a market index at the beginning of every week, say, and then try to explain the movement of the stock's price through time.

Regression can be used to analyze cross-sectional data or time series data.

Regression analysis can be applied equally well to cross-sectional and time series data. However, there are technical reasons for treating time series analysis somewhat differently. The primary reason is that time series variables are usually related to their own past values. This property of many time series variables is called **autocorrelation**, and it adds complications to the analysis that we will discuss briefly.

A third categorization of regression analysis involves the number of explanatory variables in the analysis. First, we need to introduce some terms. In every regression study there is a single variable that we are trying to explain or predict, called the **dependent** variable or the **response** variable. To help explain or predict the dependent variable, we use one or more **explanatory** variables. These explanatory variables are also called **independent** variables or **predictor** variables. If there is a single explanatory variable, the analysis is called **simple regression**. If there are several explanatory variables, it is called **multiple regression**.[1]

> The **dependent** (or **response**) variable is the single variable being explained by the regression. The **explanatory** (or **independent**) variables are used to explain the dependent variable.

There are important differences between simple and multiple regression. The primary difference, as the name implies, is that simple regression is simpler. The calculations are simpler, the interpretation of output is somewhat simpler, and fewer complications can occur. We begin with simple regression examples to introduce the ideas of regression. But we soon see that simple regression is no more than a special case of multiple regression, and there is little need to single it out for separate discussion—especially when computer software is available to perform the calculations in either case.

> A **simple** regression includes a single explanatory variable, whereas a **multiple** regression can include any number of explanatory variables.

"Linear" regression allows us to estimate linear relationships as well as some nonlinear relationships.

A final categorization of regression analysis concerns linear versus nonlinear models. The only type of regression analysis we study here is *linear* regression. Generally, this means that the relationships between variables are *straight-line* relationships, whereas the term *nonlinear* implies curved relationships. By focusing on linear regression, it might appear that we are ignoring the many nonlinear relationships that exist in the business world. Fortunately, linear regression can often be used to estimate nonlinear relationships. As we will see, the term *linear regression* is more general than it appears. Admittedly, many of the relationships we study can be explained adequately by straight lines. But it is also true that many nonlinear relationships can be "linearized" by suitable mathematical transformations. Therefore, the only relationships we are ignoring in this book are those—and there are some—that cannot be transformed to linear. Such relationships can be studied, but only by advanced methods beyond the level of this book.

In this chapter we focus on line-fitting and curve-fitting, that is, on estimating equations that describe relationships between variables. We also discuss the interpretation of these equations, and we provide numerical measures that indicate the goodness of fit of the equations we estimate. In the next chapter we extend the analysis to statistical inference of regression output.

---

[1]The traditional terms used in regression are *dependent* and *independent* variables. However, because these terms can cause confusion with probabilistic independence, a totally different concept, there has been an increasing use of the terms *response* and *explanatory* (or *predictor*) variables. We tend to prefer the terms *dependent* and *explanatory*, but this is largely a matter of taste.

11.2 SCATTERPLOTS: GRAPHING RELATIONSHIPS

A good way to begin any regression analysis is to draw one or more scatterplots. As discussed in Chapter 2, a scatterplot is a graphical plot of two variables, an X and a Y. If there is any relationship between the two variables, it is usually apparent from the scatterplot.

The following example, which we will continue through this chapter, illustrates the usefulness of scatterplots. It is a typical example of cross-sectional data.

EXAMPLE	11.1 SALES VERSUS PROMOTIONS AT PHARMEX

Pharmex is a chain of drugstores that operate around the country. To see how effective its advertising and other promotional activities are, the company has collected data from 50 randomly selected metropolitan regions. In each region it has compared its own promotional expenditures and sales to those of the leading competitor in the region over the past year. There are two variables:

- Promote: Pharmex's promotional expenditures as a percentage of those of the leading competitor
- Sales: Pharmex's sales as a percentage of those of the leading competitor

Note that each of these variables is an "index," not a dollar amount. For example, if Promote equals 95 for some region, this tells us only that Pharmex's promotional expenditures in that region are 95% as large as those for the leading competitor in that region. The company expects that there is a positive relationship between these two variables, so that regions with relatively larger expenditures have relatively larger sales. However, it is not clear what the nature of this relationship is. The data are listed in the file **Drugstore Sales.xlsx**. (See Figure 11.1 for a partial listing of the data.) What type of relationship, if any, is apparent from a scatterplot?

Figure 11.1

Data for Drugstore Example

	A	B	C	D	E	F	G	H
1	Region	Promote	Sales					
2	1	77	85					
3	2	110	103					
4	3	110	102		Each value is a percentage of what			
5	4	93	109		the leading competitor did.			
6	5	90	85					
7	6	95	103					
8	7	100	110					
9	8	85	86					
10	9	96	92					
11	10	83	87					

Objective To use a scatterplot to examine the relationship between promotional expenses and sales at Pharmex.

Solution

First, recall from Chapter 2 that there are two ways to create a scatterplot in Excel. We can use Excel's Chart Wizard to create an X–Y chart, or we can use StatTools's Scatterplot procedure. The advantages of the latter are that it is slightly easier to implement and it provides automatic formatting of the chart.

Which variable should be on the horizontal axis? In regression we always put the explanatory variable on the horizontal axis and the dependent variable on the vertical axis. In this example the store believes large promotional expenditures tend to "cause" larger values of sales, so we put Sales on the vertical axis and Promote on the horizontal axis. The resulting scatterplot appears in Figure 11.2.

Figure 11.2

Scatterplot of Sales versus Promote

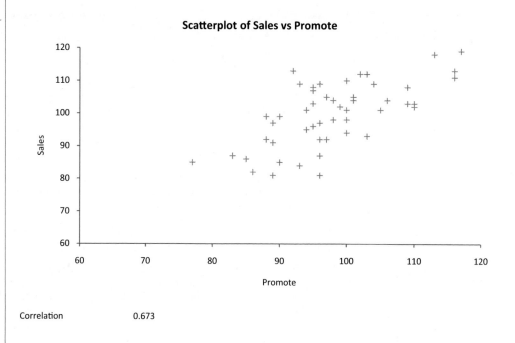

Scatterplot of Sales vs Promote

Correlation   0.673

Remember that a StatTools chart is really just an Excel chart. So you can manipulate it using Excel tools. For this scatterplot, we changed the scales of the axes so that the scatter filled up more of the chart area.

This scatterplot indicates that there is indeed a positive relationship between Promote and Sales—the points tend to rise from bottom left to top right—but the relationship is not perfect. If it were perfect, a given value of Promote would prescribe the value of Sales exactly. Clearly, this is not the case. For example, there are five regions with promotional values of 96 but all of them have different sales values. So the scatterplot indicates that while the variable Promote is helpful for predicting Sales, it will not yield perfect predictions.

Note the correlation of 0.673 shown at the bottom of Figure 11.2. StatTools inserts this value automatically (if you request it) to indicate the strength of the linear relationship between the two variables. For now, just note that it is positive and its magnitude is moderately large. We say more about correlations in the next section.

Finally, we briefly discuss causation. There is a tendency for an analyst (such as a drugstore manager) to say that larger promotional expenses *cause* larger sales values. However, unless the data are obtained in a carefully controlled experiment—which is certainly not the case here—we can never make definitive statements about causation in regression analysis. The reason is that we can almost never rule out the possibility that some other variable is causing the variation in *both* of the observed variables. While this might be unlikely in this drugstore example, it is still a possibility. ∎

The following example uses time series data to illustrate several other features of scatterplots. We will also follow this example throughout the chapter.

EXAMPLE | 11.2 EXPLAINING OVERHEAD COSTS AT BENDRIX

The Bendrix Company manufactures various types of parts for automobiles. The manager of the factory wants to get a better understanding of overhead costs. These overhead costs include supervision, indirect labor, supplies, payroll taxes, overtime premiums, depreciation, and a number of miscellaneous items such as insurance, utilities, and janitorial and maintenance expenses. Some of these overhead costs are "fixed" in the sense that they do not vary appreciably with the volume of work being done, whereas others are "variable" and do vary directly with the volume of work. The fixed overhead costs tend to come from the supervision, depreciation, and miscellaneous categories, whereas the variable overhead costs tend to come from the indirect labor, supplies, payroll taxes, and overtime categories. However, it is not easy to draw a clear line between the fixed and variable overhead components.

The Bendrix manager has tracked total overhead costs for the past 36 months. To help "explain" these, he has also collected data on two variables that are related to the amount of work done at the factory. These variables are:

- MachHrs: number of machine hours used during the month
- ProdRuns: the number of separate production runs during the month

The first of these is a direct measure of the amount of work being done. To understand the second, we note that Bendrix manufactures parts in large batches. Each batch corresponds to a production run. Once a production run is completed, the factory must "set up" for the next production run. During this setup there is typically some downtime while the machinery is reconfigured for the part type scheduled for production in the next batch. Therefore, the manager believes that both of these variables could be responsible (in different ways) for variations in overhead costs. Do scatterplots support this belief?

Objective   To use scatterplots to examine the relationships among overhead, machine hours, and production runs at Bendrix.

Solution

The data appear in Figure 11.3. (See the **Overhead Costs.xlsx** file.) Each observation (row) corresponds to a single month. We want to investigate any possible relationship between the Overhead variable and the MachHrs and ProdRuns variables, but because these are time series variables, we should also be on the lookout for any relationships between these variables and the Month variable. That is, we should also investigate any time series behavior in these variables.

Figure 11.3

Data for Bendrix Overhead Example

	A	B	C	D
1	Month	MachHrs	ProdRuns	Overhead
2	1	1539	31	99798
3	2	1284	29	87804
4	3	1490	27	93681
5	4	1355	22	82262
6	5	1500	35	106968
7	6	1777	30	107925
8	7	1716	41	117287
9	8	1045	29	76868
10	9	1364	47	106001
11	10	1516	21	88738
35	34	1723	35	107828
36	35	1413	30	88032
37	36	1390	54	117943

This data set illustrates, even with a modest number of variables, how the number of potentially useful scatterplots can grow quickly. At the very least, we should examine the scatterplot between each potential explanatory variable (MachHrs and ProdRuns) and the dependent variable (Overhead). These appear in Figures 11.4 and 11.5. We see that Overhead tends to increase as either MachHrs increases or ProdRuns increases. However, both relationships are far from perfect.

Figure 11.4

Scatterplot of Overhead versus Machine Hours

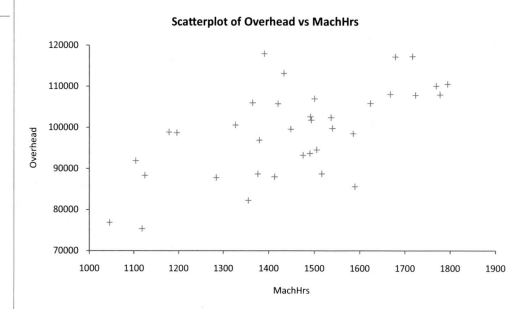

Figure 11.5

Scatterplot of Overhead versus Production Runs

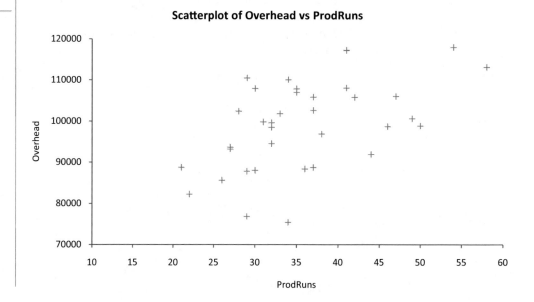

To check for possible time series patterns, we can also create a time series graph for any of the variables. One of these, the time series graph for Overhead, is shown in Figure 11.6. It indicates a fairly random pattern through time, with no apparent upward trend or other obvious time series pattern. You can check that time series graphs of the MachHrs and ProdRuns variables also indicate no obvious time series patterns.

Figure 11.6

Time Series Graph of Overhead versus Month

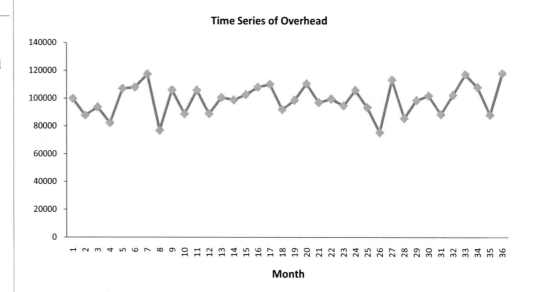

This is precisely the role of scatterplots: to give us a visual representation of relationships or the lack of relationships between variables.

Finally, when there are multiple explanatory variables, we can check for relationships among them. The scatterplot of MachHrs versus ProdRuns appears in Figure 11.7. (Either variable could be chosen for the vertical axis.) This "cloud" of points indicates no relationship worth pursuing.

Figure 11.7

Scatterplot of Machine Hours versus Production Runs

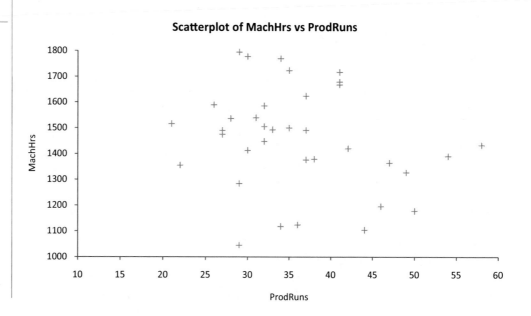

In summary, the Bendrix manager should continue to explore the positive relationship between Overhead and each of the MachHrs and ProdRuns variables. However, none of the variables appears to have any time series behavior, and the two potential explanatory variables do not appear to be related to each other. ∎

11.2.1 Linear Versus Nonlinear Relationships

Scatterplots are extremely useful for detecting behavior that might not be obvious otherwise. We illustrate some of these in the next few subsections. First, the typical relationship we hope to see is a straight-line, or *linear*, relationship. This doesn't mean that all points lie on a straight line—this is too much to expect in business data—but that the points tend to cluster around a straight line. The scatterplots in Figures 11.2, 11.4, and 11.5 all exhibit linear relationships, at least in the sense that no curvature is obvious.

The scatterplot in Figure 11.8, on the other hand, illustrates a relationship that is clearly nonlinear. The data in this scatterplot are 1990 data on more than 100 countries. The variables listed are life expectancy (of newborns, based on current mortality conditions) and GNP per capita. The obvious curvature in the scatterplot can be explained as follows. For poor countries, a slight increase in GNP per capita has a large effect on life expectancy. However, this effect decreases for wealthier countries. A straight-line relationship is definitely not appropriate for these data. However, as we discussed previously, *linear* regression—after an appropriate transformation of the data—still might be applicable.

Figure 11.8

Scatterplot of Life Expectancy versus GNP per Capita

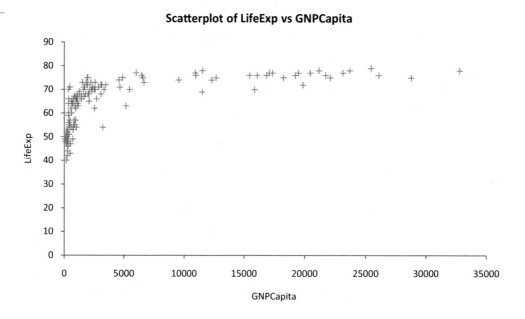

11.2.2 Outliers

Scatterplots are especially useful for identifying **outliers**, observations that lie outside the typical pattern of points. The scatterplot in Figure 11.9 shows annual salaries versus years of experience for a sample of employees at a particular company. There is a clear linear relationship between these two variables—for all employees except the point at the top right. Closer scrutiny of the data reveals that this one employee is the company president, whose salary is well above that of all the other employees!

> An **outlier** is an observation that falls outside of the general pattern of the rest of the observations.

Figure 11.9   Scatterplot of Salary versus Years of Experience

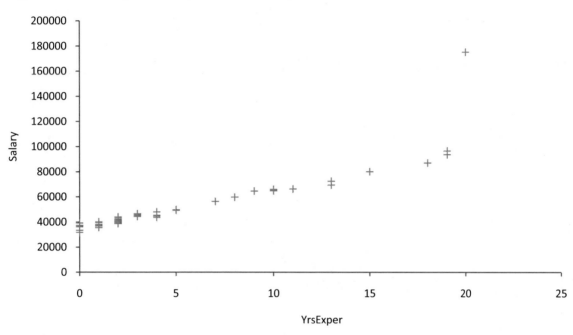

Although scatterplots are good for detecting outliers, they do not necessarily indicate what we ought to do about any outliers we find. This depends entirely on the particular situation. If we are attempting to investigate the salary structure for "typical" employees at a company, then we probably should not include the company president. First, the president's salary is not determined in the same way as the salaries for typical employees. Second, if we do include the president in the analysis, it can greatly distort the results for the mass of typical employees. In other situations, however, it might *not* be appropriate to eliminate outliers just to make the analysis come out more nicely.

It is difficult to generalize about the treatment of outliers, but the following points are worth noting.

- If an outlier is clearly not a member of the population of interest, then it is probably best to delete it from the analysis. This is the case for the company president in Figure 11.9.

- If it isn't clear whether outliers are members of the relevant population, we should run the regression analysis with them and without them. If the results are practically the same in both cases, then it is probably best to report the results with the outliers included. Otherwise, we should report both sets of results with a verbal explanation of the outliers.

11.2.3 Unequal Variance

Occasionally, there is a clear relationship between two variables, but the variance of the dependent variable depends on the value of the explanatory variable. We saw a good example of this in the catalog data in Example 3.11 of Chapter 3. Figure 11.10 reproduces one of the scatterplots from the data in that example. It shows AmountSpent versus Salary for the customers in the data set. There is a clear linear relationship, but the variability of AmountSpent increases as Salary increases. This is evident from the "fan" shape. As we see in the next chapter, this unequal variance violates one of the assumptions of linear regression analysis, and there are special techniques to deal with it.

Figure 11.10

Unequal Variance of Dependent Variable in a Scatterplot

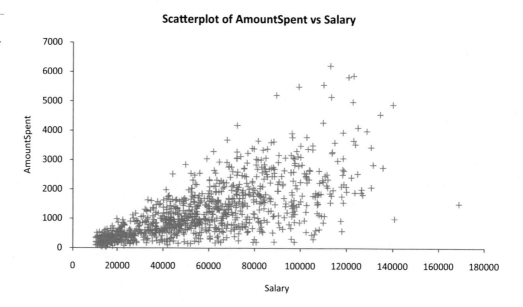

11.2.4 No Relationship

A scatterplot can provide one other useful piece of information—it can indicate that there is *no* relationship between a pair of variables, at least none worth pursuing. This is usually the case when the scatterplot appears as a shapeless swarm of points, as illustrated in Figure 11.11. Here the variables are an employee performance score and the number of overtime hours worked in the previous month for a sample of employees. There is virtually no hint of a relationship between these two variables in this plot, and if these are the only two variables in the data set, the analysis could stop right here. Many people who use statistics evidently believe that a computer can perform magic on a set of numbers and find relationships that were completely hidden. Occasionally this is true, but when a scatterplot appears as in Figure 11.11, the variables are not related in any useful way, and that's all there is to it.

Figure 11.11 An Example of No Relationship

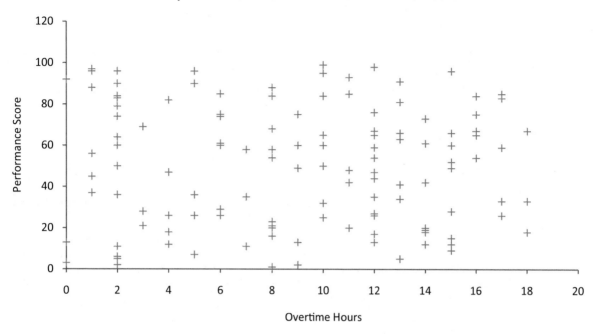

11.3 CORRELATIONS: INDICATORS OF LINEAR RELATIONSHIPS

Scatterplots provide graphical indications of relationships, whether they be linear, nonlinear, or essentially nonexistent. **Correlations** are numerical summary measures that indicate the strength of linear relationships between pairs of variables.[2] A correlation between a pair of variables is a single number that summarizes the information in a scatterplot. A correlation can be very useful, but it has an important limitation: It can only measure the strength of a *linear* relationship. If there is a nonlinear relationship, as suggested by a scatterplot, the correlation can be completely misleading. With this important limitation in mind, let's look a bit more closely at correlations.

The usual notation for a correlation between two variables X and Y is r_{XY}. (The subscripts can be omitted if the variables are clear from the context of the problem.) The formula for r_{XY} is given by equation (11.1). Note that it is a sum of products in the numerator, divided by the product $s_X s_Y$ of the sample standard deviations of X and Y. This requires a considerable amount of computation, so that correlations are almost always computed by software packages.

Formula for Correlation

$$r_{XY} = \frac{\Sigma(X_i - \overline{X})(Y_i - \overline{Y})/(n - 1)}{s_X s_Y}$$

(11.1)

---

[2]This section includes some material from Section 3.7, which we repeat here for convenience.

The numerator of equation (11.1) is also a measure of association between two variables X and Y, called the **covariance** between X and Y. Like a correlation, a covariance is a single number that measures the strength of the linear relationship between two variables. By looking at the sign of the covariance or correlation—plus or minus—we can tell whether the two variables are positively or negatively related. The drawback to a covariance, however, is that its magnitude depends on the units in which the variables are measured.

The magnitude of a covariance is difficult to interpret because it depends on the units of measurement.

To illustrate, the covariance between Overhead and MachHrs in the Bendrix manufacturing data set is 1,333,138. (It can be found with Excel's COVAR function or with StatTools.) However, if we divide each overhead value by 1000, so that overhead costs are expressed in thousands of dollars, and we divide each value of MachHrs by 100, so that machine hours are expressed in hundreds of hours, the covariance decreases by a factor of 100,000 to 13.33138. This is in spite of the fact that the basic relationship between these variables has not changed and the revised scatterplot has exactly the same shape. For this reason it is often difficult to interpret the magnitude of a covariance, and we concentrate instead on correlations.

Unlike covariances, correlations have the attractive property that they are completely unaffected by the units of measurement. The rescaling described in the previous paragraph has absolutely no effect on the correlation between Overhead and MachHrs. In either case the correlation is 0.632. Moreover, all correlations are between -1 and $+1$, inclusive. The sign of a correlation, plus or minus, determines whether the linear relationship between two variables is positive or negative. In this respect, a correlation is just like a covariance. However, the strength of the linear relationship between the variables is measured by the absolute value, or magnitude, of the correlation. The closer this magnitude is to 1, the stronger the linear relationship is.

A correlation close to -1 or $+1$ indicates a strong linear relationship. A correlation close to 0 indicates virtually no linear relationship.

A correlation equal to zero or near zero indicates practically no linear relationship. A correlation with magnitude close to 1, on the other hand, indicates a strong linear relationship. At the extreme, a correlation equal to -1 or $+1$ occurs only when the linear relationship is perfect—that is, when all points in the scatterplot lie on a single straight line. Although such extremes practically never occur in business applications, "large" correlations, say, greater than 0.9 in magnitude, are not at all uncommon.

Looking back at the scatterplots for the Pharmex drugstore data in Figure 11.2, we see that the correlation between Sales and Promote is positive—as we would guess from the upward-sloping scatter of points—and that it is equal to 0.673. This is a moderately large correlation. It indicates what we see in the scatterplot, namely, that the points vary considerably around any particular straight line.

Similarly, the scatterplots for the Bendrix manufacturing data in Figures 11.4 and 11.5 indicate moderately large positive correlations, 0.632 and 0.521, between Overhead and MachHrs and between Overhead and ProdRuns. However, the correlation indicated in Figure 11.7 between MachHrs and ProdRuns, -0.229, is quite small and indicates almost no relationship between these two variables.

Correlations can be misleading when variables are related nonlinearly.

We must be a bit more careful when interpreting the correlations in Figures 11.8 and 11.9. The scatterplot between life expectancy and GNP per capita in Figure 11.8 is obviously nonlinear, and correlations are relevant descriptors only for *linear* relationships. If anything, the correlation of 0.616 in this example tends to underestimate the true strength of the relationship—the nonlinear one—between life expectancy and GNP per capita. In contrast, the correlation between salary and years of experience in Figure 11.9 is large, 0.894, but it is not nearly as large as it would be if the outlier were omitted. (It is then 0.992.) This example illustrates the considerable effect a single outlier can have on a correlation.

An obvious question is whether a given correlation is "large." This is a difficult question to answer directly. Clearly, a correlation such as 0.992 is quite large—the points tend to cluster very closely around a straight line. Similarly, a correlation of 0.034 is quite small—the points tend to be a shapeless swarm. But there is a continuum of in-between values, as exhibited in Figures 11.2, 11.4, and 11.5. We give a more definite answer to this question when we examine the *square* of the correlation later in this chapter.

As for calculating correlations, there are two possibilities in Excel. To calculate a *single* correlation r_{XY} between variables X and Y, we can use Excel's CORREL function in the form

=CORREL(*X*-range,*Y*-range)

Alternatively, we can use StatTools to obtain a whole table of correlations between a set of variables.

Finally, we reiterate the important limitation of correlations (and covariances), namely, that they apply only to *linear* relationships. If a correlation is close to zero, we cannot automatically conclude that there is no relationship between the two variables. We should look at a scatterplot first. The chances are that the points are a shapeless swarm and that no relationship exists. But it is also possible that the points cluster around some curve. In this case the correlation is a misleading measure of the relationship.

11.4 SIMPLE LINEAR REGRESSION

Scatterplots and correlations are very useful for indicating linear relationships and the strengths of these relationships. But they do not actually *quantify* the relationships. For example, we know from the Pharmex drugstore data that sales are related to promotional expenditures. But from the knowledge presented so far, we do not know exactly what this relationship is. If the expenditure index for a given region is 95, what would we predict this region's sales index to be? Or if one region's expenditure index is 5 points higher than another region's, we would expect the former to have a larger sales index, but how much larger? To answer these questions, we need to quantify the relationship between the dependent variable Sales and the explanatory variable Promote.

Remember that "simple" linear regression does not mean "easy"; it means only that there is a single *explanatory variable.*

In this section we answer these types of questions for simple linear regression, where there is a *single* explanatory variable. We do so by fitting a straight line through the scatterplot of the dependent variable Y versus the explanatory variable X and then basing the answers to the questions on the fitted straight line. But which straight line? We address this issue next.

11.4.1 Least Squares Estimation

The scatterplot between Sales and Promote, repeated in Figure 11.12, hints at a linear relationship between these two variables. It would not be difficult to draw a straight line through these points to produce a reasonably good fit. In fact, a possible linear fit is indicated in the graph. But we proceed more systematically than simply drawing lines freehand. Specifically, we choose the line that makes the vertical distances from the points to the line as small as possible, as explained next.

Consider the magnified graph in Figure 11.13. Here we show several points in the scatterplot, along with a line drawn through them. Note that the vertical distance from the horizontal axis to any point, which is just the value of Sales for that point, can be decomposed into two parts: the vertical distance from the horizontal axis to the line, and the vertical distance from the line to the point. The first of these is called the **fitted value**, and the second is called the **residual**. The idea is very simple. By using a straight line to reflect the relationship between Sales and Promote, we expect a given Sales to be at the height of the line above any particular value of Promote. That is, we expect Sales to equal the fitted value. These terms are summarized in the box.

Figure 11.12

Scatterplot with Possible Linear Fit Superimposed

Scatterplot of Sales vs Promote

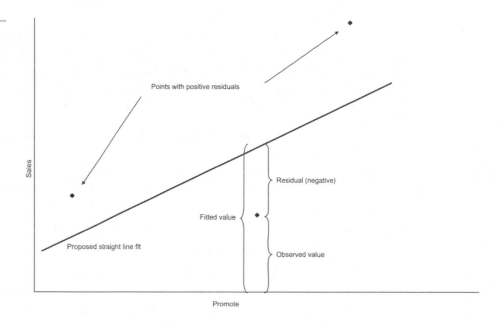

Figure 11.13

Fitted Values and Residuals

> A **fitted value** is the predicted value of the dependent variable. Graphically, it is the height of the line above a given explanatory value. The corresponding **residual** is the difference between the actual and fitted values of the dependent variable.

But the relationship is not perfect. Not all (perhaps not any) of the points lie exactly on the line. The differences are the residuals. They show how much the observed values differ from the fitted values. If a particular residual is positive, the corresponding point is above the line; if it is negative, the point is below the line. The only time a residual is zero is when the point lies directly on the line. The relationship between observed values, fitted values, and residuals is very general and is stated in equation (11.2).

Fundamental Equation for Regression

$$\text{Observed Value} = \text{Fitted Value} + \text{Residual} \qquad \textbf{(11.2)}$$

We can now explain how to choose the "best-fitting" line through the points in the scatterplot. We choose the one with the *smallest sum of squared residuals*. The resulting line is called the **least squares line**. Why do we use the sum of *squared* residuals? Why not minimize some other measure of the residuals? First, we do not simply minimize the sum of the residuals. This is because the positive residuals would cancel the negative residuals. In fact, the least squares line has the property that the sum of the residuals is always exactly zero. To adjust for this, we could minimize the sum of the *absolute values* of the residuals, and this is a perfectly reasonable procedure. However, for technical reasons it is not the procedure usually chosen. We settle on the sum of squared residuals because this method is deeply rooted in statistical tradition, and it works well.

The **least squares line** is the line that minimizes the sum of the squared residuals. It is the line quoted in regression outputs.

The minimization problem itself is a calculus problem that we do not discuss here. Virtually all statistical software packages perform this minimization automatically, so we need not be concerned with the technical details. However, we do provide the formulas for the least squares line.

Recall from basic algebra that the equation for any straight line can be written as

$$Y = a + bX$$

Here, a is the Y-intercept of the line, the value of Y when $X = 0$, and b is the slope of the line, the change in Y when X increases by 1 unit. Therefore, to specify the least squares line, all we need to specify is the slope and intercept. These are given by equations (11.3) and (11.4).

Equation for Slope in Simple Linear Regression

$$b = \frac{\Sigma(X_i - \overline{X})(Y_i - \overline{Y})}{\Sigma(X_i - \overline{X})^2} = r_{XY}\frac{s_Y}{s_X} \qquad \textbf{(11.3)}$$

Equation for Intercept in Simple Linear Regression

$$a = \overline{Y} - b\overline{X} \qquad \textbf{(11.4)}$$

We have presented these formulas primarily for conceptual purposes, not for hand calculations—the computer takes care of the calculations. From the right-hand formula for b, we see that it is closely related to the correlation between X and Y. Specifically, if we keep the standard deviations, s_X and s_Y, of X and Y constant, then the slope b of the least squares line varies directly with the correlation between the two variables. A relationship with a large correlation (negative or positive) has a steep slope, and a relationship with a small correlation has a shallow slope. At the extreme, a nonrelationship with a correlation of 0 has a slope of 0; that is, it results in a horizontal line. The effect of the formula for a is not quite as interesting. It simply forces the least squares line to go through the point of sample means, $(\overline{X}, \overline{Y})$.

It is easy to obtain the least squares line in Excel with StatTools's Regression procedure. We illustrate this in the following continuations of Examples 11.1 and 11.2.

EXAMPLE | 11.1 SALES VERSUS PROMOTIONS AT PHARMEX (CONTINUED)

Find the least squares line for the Pharmex drugstore data, using Sales as the dependent variable and Promote as the explanatory variable.

Objective To use StatTools's Regression procedure to find the least squares line for sales as a function of promotional expenses at Pharmex.

Solution

We select Regression from the StatTools Regression and Classification dropdown. The resulting dialog box should be filled in as shown in Figure 11.14. Specifically, select Multiple as the Regression Type (this type is used for both single and multiple regression in StatTools), and select Promote as the single I variable and Sales as the single D variable, where I and D stand for independent and dependent. (There is always a *single D* variable, but in multiple regression there can be several I variables.) Note that there is an option to create several scatterplots involving the fitted values and residuals. We suggest checking the third option, as shown. Finally, there is an Include Prediction option. We explain it in a later section. You can leave it unchecked for now.

Figure 11.14

Regression
Dialog Box

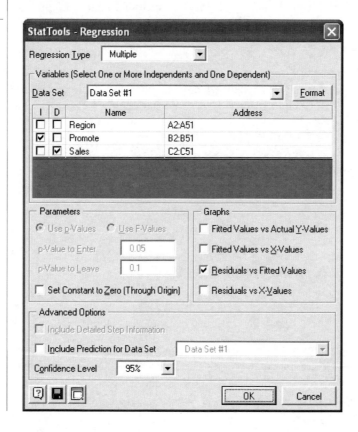

The regression output includes three parts. The first is the main regression output shown in Figure 11.15. The last two are a scatterplot of residuals and fitted values requested in the regression dialog box and a list of fitted values and residuals, a few of which are shown in Figure 11.16. (The list of fitted values and residuals is part of the output only if at least one of the optional scatterplots in the regression dialog box is selected.)

Figure 11.15

Regression Output for Drugstore Example

	A	B	C	D	E	F	G
7		Multiple R	R-Square	Adjusted R-Square	StErr of Estimate		
8	Summary						
9		0.6730	0.4529	0.4415	7.3947		
10							
11		Degrees of Freedom	Sum of Squares	Mean of Squares	F-Ratio	p-Value	
12	ANOVA Table						
13	Explained	1	2172.8804	2172.8804	39.7366	< 0.0001	
14	Unexplained	48	2624.7396	54.6821			
15							
16		Coefficient	Standard Error	t-Value	p-Value	Confidence Interval 95%	
17	Regression Table					Lower	Upper
18	Constant	25.1264	11.8826	2.1146	0.0397	1.2349	49.0180
19	Promote	0.7623	0.1209	6.3037	< 0.0001	0.5192	1.0054

Figure 11.16

Scatterplot and Partial List of Residuals versus Fitted Values

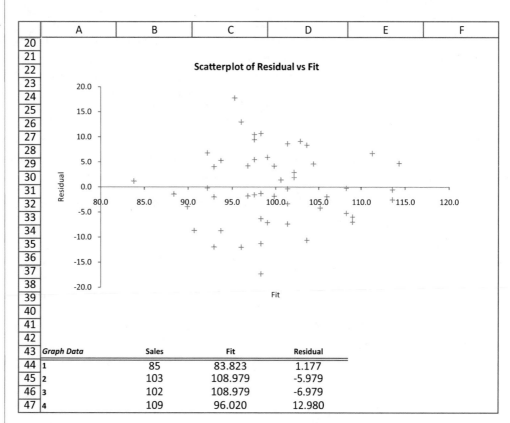

	A	B	C	D
43	Graph Data	Sales	Fit	Residual
44	1	85	83.823	1.177
45	2	103	108.979	-5.979
46	3	102	108.979	-6.979
47	4	109	96.020	12.980

We eventually learn what all of the output in Figure 11.15 means, but for now, we concentrate on only a small part of it. Specifically, we find the intercept and slope of the least squares line under the Coefficient label in cells B18 and B19. They imply that the equation for the least squares line is[3]

$$\text{Predicted Sales} = 25.1264 + 0.7623\text{Promote}$$

[3]We always report the left side of the estimated regression equation as the *predicted* value of the dependent variable. It is not the *actual* value of the dependent variable because the observations do not all lie on the estimated regression line.

Excel Tip *The Regression procedure for simple regression uses special StatTools functions to calculate all of the regression output. However, it can also be generated by taking advantage of several built-in statistical functions available in Excel. These include the CORREL, RSQ, STEYX, INTERCEPT, and SLOPE functions. For example, the slope and intercept of the least squares line can be calculated directly with the formulas*

=SLOPE(Y-range,X-range)

and

=INTERCEPT(Y-range,X-range)

*These formulas (with the appropriate X and Y ranges) can be entered anywhere in a spreadsheet to obtain the slope and intercept for a **simple** regression equation—no add-ins are necessary. You can look up the other functions in Excel's online help.*

In many applications it makes no sense to have the explanatory variable(s) equal to 0. Then the intercept term has no practical or economic meaning.

We can interpret the regression equation for this example as follows. The slope, 0.7623, indicates that the sales index tends to increase by about 0.76 for each 1-unit increase in the promotional expenses index. Alternatively, if we compare two regions, where region 2 spends 1 unit higher than region 1, we predict the sales index for region 2 to be 0.76 larger than the sales index for region 1. The interpretation of the intercept is less important. It is literally the predicted sales index for a region that does no promotions. However, no region in the sample has anywhere near a zero promotional value. Therefore, in a situation like this, where the range of observed explanatory variable values does not include 0, it is best to think of the intercept term as an "anchor" for the least squares line that allows us to predict *Y* values for the range of *observed X* values.

We typically like a shapeless "swarm" of points in a scatterplot of residuals versus fitted values.

A useful graph in almost any regression analysis is a scatterplot of residuals (on the vertical axis) versus fitted values. This scatterplot for the Pharmex data appears in Figure 11.16 (along with a few of the residuals and fitted values used to create the chart). We typically examine such a scatterplot for any striking patterns. A "good" fit not only has small residuals, but it has residuals scattered *randomly* around 0 with no apparent pattern. This appears to be the case for the Pharmex data. ■

EXAMPLE | 11.2 EXPLAINING OVERHEAD COSTS AT BENDRIX (CONTINUED)

The Bendrix manufacturing data set has two potential explanatory variables, MachHrs and ProdRuns. Eventually, we will estimate a regression equation with *both* of these variables included. However, if we include only one at a time, what do they tell us about overhead costs?

Objective To use StatTools's Regression procedure to regress overhead expenses at Bendrix against machine hours and then against production runs.

Solution

The regression output for Overhead with MachHrs as the single explanatory variable appears in Figure 11.17. The output when ProdRuns is the only explanatory variable appears in Figure 11.18. The two least squares lines are therefore

$$\text{Predicted Overhead} = 48{,}621 + 34.7\text{MachHrs} \qquad (11.5)$$

and

$$\text{Predicted Overhead} = 75{,}606 + 655.1\text{ProdRuns} \qquad (11.6)$$

Figure 11.17

Regression Output for Overhead versus MachHrs

	A	B	C	D	E	F	G
7		Multiple	R-Square	Adjusted	StErr of		
8	Summary	R		R-Square	Estimate		
9		0.6319	0.3993	0.3816	8584.739		
10							
11		Degrees of	Sum of	Mean of	F-Ratio	p-Value	
12	ANOVA Table	Freedom	Squares	Squares			
13	Explained	1	1665463368	1665463368	22.5986	< 0.0001	
14	Unexplained	34	2505723492	73697749.75			
15							
16		Coefficient	Standard	t-Value	p-Value	Confidence Interval 95%	
17	Regression Table		Error			Lower	Upper
18	Constant	48621.355	10725.333	4.5333	< 0.0001	26824.856	70417.853
19	MachHrs	34.702	7.300	4.7538	< 0.0001	19.867	49.537

Figure 11.18

Regression Output for Overhead versus ProdRuns

	A	B	C	D	E	F	G
7		Multiple	R-Square	Adjusted	StErr of		
8	Summary	R		R-Square	Estimate		
9		0.5205	0.2710	0.2495	9457.239		
10							
11		Degrees of	Sum of	Mean of	F-Ratio	p-Value	
12	ANOVA Table	Freedom	Squares	Squares			
13	Explained	1	1130247999	1130247999	12.6370	0.0011	
14	Unexplained	34	3040938861	89439378.26			
15							
16		Coefficient	Standard	t-Value	p-Value	Confidence Interval 95%	
17	Regression Table		Error			Lower	Upper
18	Constant	75605.516	6808.611	11.1044	< 0.0001	61768.754	89442.277
19	ProdRuns	655.071	184.275	3.5549	0.0011	280.579	1029.562

Clearly, these two equations are quite different, although each effectively breaks Overhead into a fixed component and a variable component. Equation (11.5) implies that the fixed component of overhead is about $48,621. Bendrix can expect to incur this amount even if zero machine hours are used. The variable component is the 34.7MachHrs term. It implies that the expected overhead increases by about $35 for each extra machine hour. Equation (11.6), on the other hand, breaks overhead down into a fixed component of $75,606 and a variable component of about $655 per each production run.

The difference between these two equations can be attributed to the fact that neither tells the whole story. If the manager's goal is to split overhead into a fixed component and a variable component, then the variable component should include *both* of the measures of work activity (and maybe even others) to give a more complete explanation of overhead. We see how to do this when we reanalyze this example with multiple regression. ■

11.4.2 Standard Error of Estimate

We now reexamine fitted values and residuals to see how they lead to a useful summary measure for a regression equation. In a typical simple regression model, the expression $a + bX$ is the fitted value of Y. Graphically, it is the height of the estimated line above the value X. We often denote it by $\hat{Y}$ (pronounced Y-hat):[4]

$$\hat{Y} = a + bX$$

Then a typical residual, denoted by e, is the difference between the observed value Y and the fitted value $\hat{Y}$ [a restatement of equation (11.2)]:

$$e = Y - \hat{Y}$$

[4]We could write Predicted Y instead of $\hat{Y}$, but the latter notation is more common in statistics literature.

We show some of the fitted values and associated residuals for the Pharmex drugstore example in Figure 11.19. (Recall that these columns are inserted automatically by StatTools's Regression procedure when we request the optional scatterplot of residuals versus fitted values.)

Figure 11.19

Fitted Values and Residuals for Pharmex Example

	A	B	C	D
43	*Graph Data*	**Sales**	**Fit**	**Residual**
44	1	85	83.823	1.177
45	2	103	108.979	-5.979
46	3	102	108.979	-6.979
47	4	109	96.020	12.980
48	5	85	93.733	-8.733
49	6	103	97.545	5.455
50	7	110	101.356	8.644
51	8	86	89.922	-3.922
52	9	92	98.307	-6.307
53	10	87	88.397	-1.397

The magnitudes of the residuals provide a good indication of how useful the regression line is for predicting Y values from X values. However, because there are numerous residuals, it is useful to summarize them with a single numerical measure. This measure, called the **standard error of estimate** and denoted s_e, is essentially the standard deviation of the residuals. It is given by equation (11.7).

Formula for Standard Error of Estimate

$$s_e = \sqrt{\frac{\Sigma e_i^2}{n-2}}$$

(11.7)

Actually, because the average of the residuals from a least squares fit is always 0, this is identical to the standard deviation of the residuals except that we use the denominator $n - 2$ rather than the usual $n - 1$. As we see in more generality later on, the rule is to subtract the number of parameters being estimated from the sample size n to obtain the denominator. Here there are two parameters being estimated: the intercept a and the slope b.

About 2/3 of the fitted Ŷ values are typically within 1 standard error of the actual Y values. About 95% are within 2 standard errors.

The usual empirical rules for standard deviations can be applied to the standard error of estimate. For example, we expect about 2/3 of the residuals to be within 1 standard error of their mean (which is 0). Stated another way, we expect about 2/3 of the observed Y values to be within 1 standard error of the corresponding fitted $\hat{Y}$ values. Similarly, we expect about 95% of the observed Y values to be within 2 standard errors of the corresponding fitted $\hat{Y}$ values.[5]

The standard error of estimate s_e is included in all StatTools regression outputs. Alternatively, it can be calculated directly with Excel's STEYX function in the form

=STEYX(*Y-range,X-range*)

[5]This requires that the residuals be at least approximately normally distributed, a requirement we discuss more fully in the next chapter.

The standard error for the Pharmex data appears in cell E9 of Figure 11.15. Its value, approximately 7.39, indicates the typical error we are likely to make when we use the fitted value (based on the regression line) to predict sales from promotional expenses. More specifically, if we use the regression equation to predict sales for many regions, based on the promotional expenses in each region, then about 2/3 of the predictions will be within 7.39 of the actual sales values, and about 95% of the predictions will be within 2 standard errors, or 14.78, of the actual sales values.

Is this level of accuracy good? One measure of comparison is the standard deviation of the sales variable, namely, 9.90. (This is obtained by the usual STDEV function applied to the observed sales values.) It can be interpreted as the standard deviation of the residuals around a *horizontal* line positioned at the mean value of Sales. This would be the relevant regression line if there were no explanatory variables—that is, if we ignored Promote. In other words, it is a measure of the prediction error we would make if we used the sample mean of Sales as the prediction for *every* region and ignored Promote. The fact that the standard error of estimate, 7.39, is not much less than 9.90 means that the Promote variable adds a relatively small amount to prediction accuracy. We can do nearly as well without it as with it. We would certainly prefer a standard error of estimate *well* below 9.90.

We can often use the standard error of estimate to judge which of several potential regression equations is the most useful. In the Bendrix manufacturing example we estimated two regression lines, one using MachHrs and one using ProdRuns. From Figures 11.17 and 11.18, their standard errors are approximately $8585 and $9457. These imply that MachHrs is a slightly better predictor of overhead. The predictions based on MachHrs will tend to be slightly more accurate than those based on ProdRuns. Of course, we might guess that predictions based on *both* predictors will yield even more accurate predictions, and this is definitely the case, as we see when we discuss multiple regression.

11.4.3 R^2: The Coefficient of Determination

We now discuss another important measure of the goodness of fit of the least squares line: the *coefficient of determination*, or simply R^2. Along with the standard error of estimate s_e, it is the most frequently quoted measure in applied regression analysis. With a value always between 0 and 1, the **coefficient of determination** can be interpreted as the *fraction of variation of the dependent variable explained by the regression line*. (It is often expressed as a percentage, so that we talk about the *percentage* of variation explained by the regression line.)

> The **coefficient of determination (R^2)** is the percentage of variation of the dependent variable explained by the regression.

To see more precisely what this means, we look briefly into the derivation of R^2. In the previous section we suggested that one way to measure the regression equation's ability to predict is to compare the standard error of estimate, s_e, to the standard deviation of the dependent variable, s_Y. The idea is that s_e is (essentially) the standard deviation of the residuals, whereas s_Y is the standard deviation of the residuals that we would obtain from a horizontal regression line at height $\overline{Y}$, the dependent variable's mean. Therefore, if s_e is small compared to s_Y (that is, if s_e/s_Y is small), the regression line has evidently done a good job in explaining the variation of the dependent variable.

The coefficient of determination is based on this idea. R^2 is defined by equation (11.8). (This value is obtained automatically with StatTools's regression procedure, or it can be calculated with Excel's RSQ function.) Equation (11.8) indicates that when the residuals are small, then R^2 will be close to 1, but when they are large, R^2 will be close to 0.

R^2 measures the goodness of a linear fit. The better the linear fit is, the closer R^2 is to 1.

We see from cell C9 of Figure 11.15 that the R^2 measure for the Pharmex drugstore data is 0.453. In words, the single explanatory variable Promote is able to explain only 45.3% of the variation in the Sales variable. This is not particularly good—the same conclusion we made when we based goodness of fit on s_e. There is still 54.7% of the variation left unexplained. Of course, we would like R^2 to be as close to 1 as possible. Usually, the only way to increase it is to use better and/or more explanatory variables.

Analysts often compare equations on the basis of their R^2 values. We see from Figures 11.17 and 11.18 that the R^2 values using MachHrs and ProdRuns as single explanatory variables for the Bendrix overhead data are 39.9% and 27.1%. These provide one more piece of evidence that MachHrs is a slightly better predictor of Overhead than ProdRuns. Of course, they also suggest that the percentage of variation of Overhead explained could be increased by including *both* variables in a single equation. This is true, as we see shortly.

In simple linear regression, R^2 is the square of the correlation between the dependent variable and the explanatory variable.

There is a good reason for the notation R^2. It turns out that R^2 is the square of the correlation between the observed Y values and the fitted $\hat{Y}$ values. This correlation appears in all regression outputs. For the Pharmex data it is 0.673, as seen in cell B9 of Figure 11.15. Aside from rounding, the square of 0.673 is 0.453, the R^2 value right next to it. In the case of simple linear regression, when there is only a single explanatory variable in the equation, the correlation between the Y variable and the fitted $\hat{Y}$ values is the same as the absolute value of the correlation between the Y variable and the explanatory X variable. For the Pharmex data we already saw that the correlation between Sales and Promote is indeed 0.673.

This interpretation of R^2 as the square of a correlation helps to clarify the issue of when a correlation is "large." For example, if the correlation between two variables Y and X is ± 0.8, we know that the regression of Y on X will produce an R^2 of 0.64; that is, the regression with X as the only explanatory variable will explain 64% of the variation in Y. If the correlation drops to ± 0.7, this percentage drops to 49%; if the correlation increases to ± 0.9, the percentage increases to 81%. The point is that before a single variable X can explain a large percentage of the variation in some other variable Y, the two variables must be highly correlated—in *either* a positive or negative direction.

PROBLEMS

Level A

1. Explore the relationship between the selling prices (Y) and the appraised values (X) of the 150 homes in the file **P02_07.xlsx** by estimating a simple linear regression model. Also, compute the standard error of estimate s_e and the coefficient of determination R^2 for the estimated least squares line. Interpret these measures and the least squares line for these data.

   a. Is there evidence of a *linear* relationship between the selling price and appraised value? If so, characterize the relationship (i.e., indicate whether the relationship is a positive or negative one, a strong or weak one, etc.).

   b. For which of the two remaining variables, the size of the home and the number of bedrooms in the home, is the relationship with the home's selling price *stronger*? Justify your choice with additional simple linear regression models.

2. What is the relationship between the number of short-term general hospitals (Y) and the number of general or family physicians (X) in U.S. metropolitan areas? Explore this question by estimating a simple linear regression model using the data in the file **P02_17.xlsx**. Interpret your estimated regression model as well as the coefficient of determination R^2.

3. Motorco produces electric motors for use in home appliances. One of the company's production managers is interested in examining the relationship between the dollars spent per month in inspecting finished motor products (*X*) and the number of motors produced during that month that were returned by dissatisfied customers (*Y*). He has collected the data in the file **P02_18.xlsx** to explore this relationship for the past 36 months. Generate a simple linear regression model using the given data and interpret it for this production manager. Also, compute and interpret s_e and R^2 for these data.

4. The owner of the Original Italian Pizza restaurant chain would like to understand which variable most strongly influences the sales of his specialty, deep-dish pizza. He has gathered data on the monthly sales of deep-dish pizzas at his restaurants and observations on other potentially relevant variables for each of his 15 outlets in central Pennsylvania. These data are provided in the file **P11_04.xlsx**. Estimate a simple linear regression model between the quantity sold (*Y*) and each of the following candidates for the best explanatory variable: average price of deep-dish pizzas, monthly advertising expenditures, and disposable income per household in the areas surrounding the outlets. Which variable is *most* strongly associated with the number of pizzas sold? Be sure to explain your choice.

5. The human resources manager of DataCom, Inc., wants to examine the relationship between annual salaries (*Y*) and the number of years employees have worked at DataCom (*X*). These data have been collected for a sample of employees and are given in the file **P11_05.xlsx**.
   a. Estimate the relationship between *Y* and *X*. Interpret the least squares line.
   b. How well does the estimated simple linear regression model fit the given data? Document your answer.

6. Consider the relationship between the size of the population (*X*) and the average household income level for residents of U.S. towns (*Y*). What do you expect the relationship between these two variables to be? Using the data in the file **P02_24.xlsx**, produce and interpret a simple linear regression model involving these two variables. How well does the estimated model fit the given data?

7. Examine the relationship between the average utility bills for homes of a particular size (*Y*) and the average monthly temperature (*X*). The data in the file **P11_07.xlsx** include the average monthly bill and temperature for each month of the past year.
   a. Use the given data to estimate a simple linear regression model. Interpret the least squares line.
   b. How well does the estimated regression model fit the given data? How might we do a better job of explaining the variation of the average utility bills for homes of a certain size?

8. The U.S. Bureau of Labor Statistics provides data on the year-to-year percentage changes in the wages and salaries of workers in private industries, including both "white-collar" and "blue-collar" occupations. Here we consider selected annual data in the file **P02_56.xlsx**. Is there evidence of a strong relationship between the yearly changes in the wages and salaries of white-collar and blue-collar workers in the United States over the given time period? Answer this question by estimating and interpreting a simple linear regression model.

9. Management of a home appliance store in Charlotte would like to understand the growth pattern of the monthly sales of VCR units over the past 2 years. The managers have recorded the relevant data in the file **P11_09.xlsx**. Have the sales of VCR units been growing linearly over the past 24 months? Using simple linear regression, explain why or why not.

10. Do the sales prices of houses in a given community vary systematically with their sizes (as measured in square feet)? Attempt to answer this question by estimating a simple regression model where the sales price of the house is the dependent variable and the size of the house is the explanatory variable. Use the sample data given in the file **P11_10.xlsx**. Interpret your estimated model and the associated coefficient of determination R^2.

11. The file **P11_11.xlsx** contains annual observations of the American minimum wage. Has the minimum wage been growing at roughly a *constant* rate over this period? Use simple linear regression analysis to address this question. Explain the results you obtain.

12. Based on the data in the file **P02_25.xlsx** from the U.S. Department of Agriculture, explore the relationship between the number of farms (*X*) and the average size of a farm (*Y*) in the United States. Specifically, generate a simple linear regression model and interpret it.

13. Estimate the relationship between monthly electrical power usage (*Y*) and home size (*X*) using the data in the file **P11_13.xlsx**. Interpret your results. How well does a simple linear regression model explain the variation in monthly electrical power usage?

14. The *ACCRA Cost of Living Index* provides a useful and reasonably accurate measure of cost of living differences among a large number of urban areas. Items on which the index is based have been carefully chosen to reflect the different categories of consumer expenditures. The data are in the file **P02_19.xlsx**. Use the given data to estimate simple linear regression models to explore the relationship between the composite index (i.e., dependent variable) and each of the

various expenditure components (i.e., explanatory variable).

a. Which expenditure component has the *strongest* linear relationship with the composite index?

b. Which expenditure component has the *weakest* linear relationship with the composite index?

15. The management of Beta Technologies, Inc., is trying to determine the variable that best explains the variation of employee salaries using a sample of 52 full-time employees in the file **P02_01.xlsx**. Estimate simple linear regression models to identify which of the following has the *strongest* linear relationship with annual salary: the employee's gender, age, number of years of relevant work experience prior to employment at Beta, number of years of employment at Beta, or number of years of postsecondary education. Provide support for your conclusion.

11.5 MULTIPLE REGRESSION

In general, there are two possible approaches to obtaining improved fits. The first is to examine a scatterplot of residuals for nonlinear patterns and then make appropriate modifications to the regression equation. We discuss this approach later in this chapter. The second approach is much more straightforward: We simply add more explanatory variables to the regression equation. In the Bendrix manufacturing example we deliberately included only a single explanatory variable in the equation at a time so that we could keep the equations simple. But because scatterplots indicate that both explanatory variables are also related to Overhead, we ought to try including both in the regression equation. With any luck, the linear fit should improve.

When we include several explanatory variables in the regression equation, we move into the realm of *multiple* regression. Some of the concepts from simple regression carry over naturally to multiple regression, but some change considerably. The following list provides a starting point that we expand on throughout this section.

Characteristics of Multiple Regression

- Graphically, we are no longer fitting a *line* to a set of points. If there are exactly two explanatory variables, then we are fitting a *plane* to the data in three-dimensional space. There is one dimension for the dependent variable and one for each of the two explanatory variables. Although we can imagine a flat plane passing through a swarm of points, it is difficult to graph this on a two-dimensional screen. If there are more than two explanatory variables, then we can only imagine the regression plane; drawing in four or more dimensions is impossible.

- The regression equation is still estimated by the least squares method—that is, by minimizing the sum of squared residuals. However, it is definitely not practical to implement this method by hand. A statistical software package such as StatTools is required.

- Simple regression is actually a special case of multiple regression—that is, an equation with a single explanatory variable can be considered as a "multiple" regression equation. This explains why it is possible to use StatTools's Multiple Regression procedure for simple regression.

- There is a "slope" term for each explanatory variable in the equation. The interpretation of these slope terms is somewhat more difficult than in simple regression, as we discuss in the following subsection.

- The standard error of estimate and R^2 summary measures are almost exactly as in simple regression, as we discuss in Section 11.5.2.

- Many *types* of explanatory variables can be included in the regression equation, as we discuss in Section 11.6. To a large part, these are responsible for the wide applicability of multiple regression in the business world.

11.5.1 Interpretation of Regression Coefficients

A typical slope term measures the expected change in Y when the corresponding X increases by 1 unit.

If Y is the dependent variable and X_1 through X_k are the explanatory variables, then a typical multiple regression equation has the form shown in equation (11.9), where a is again the Y-intercept, and b_1 through b_k are the slopes. Collectively, we refer to a and the b's in equation (11.9) as the **regression coefficients**. The intercept a is the expected value of Y when all of the X's equal 0. (Of course, this makes sense only if it is practical for all of the X's to equal 0, which is seldom the case.) Each slope coefficient is the expected change in Y when this particular X increases by one unit and the other X's in the equation remain constant. For example, b_1 is the expected change in Y when X_1 increases by one unit and the other X's in the equation, X_2 through X_k, remain constant.

General Multiple Regression Equation
$$Y = a + b_1 X_1 + b_2 X_2 + \cdots + b_k X_k \tag{11.9}$$

This extra proviso, "when the other X's in the equation remain constant," is very important for the interpretation of the regression coefficients. In particular, it means that the estimates of the b's depend on which other X's are included in the regression equation. We illustrate these ideas in the following continuation of the Bendrix manufacturing example.

EXAMPLE | 11.2 EXPLAINING OVERHEAD COSTS AT BENDRIX (CONTINUED)

Estimate and interpret the equation for Overhead when both explanatory variables, MachHrs and ProdRuns, are included in the regression equation.

Objective To use StatTools's Regression procedure to estimate the equation for overhead costs at Bendrix as a function of machine hours and production runs.

Solution

To obtain the regression output, we select Regression from the StatTools Regression and Classification dropdown and fill out the resulting dialog box as shown in Figure 11.20. As before, we choose the Multiple option, specify the single D variable and the two I variables, and check any optional graphs we would like to see. (This time we have selected the first and third options.)

The main regression output appears in Figure 11.21. The coefficients in the range B18:B20 indicates that the estimated regression equation is

$$\text{Predicted Overhead} = 3997 + 43.54\text{MachHrs} + 883.62\text{ProdRuns} \tag{11.10}$$

The interpretation of equation (11.10) is that if the number of production runs is held constant, then the overhead cost is expected to increase by \$43.54 for each extra machine hour, and if the number of machine hours is held constant, the overhead cost is expected to increase by \$883.62 for each extra production run. The Bendrix manager can interpret the intercept, \$3997, as the fixed component of overhead. The slope terms involving MachHrs and ProdRuns are the variable components of overhead.

It is interesting to compare equation (11.10) with the separate equations for Overhead involving only a single variable each. From the previous section these are

$$\text{Predicted Overhead} = 48{,}621 + 34.7\text{MachHrs}$$

and

$$\text{Predicted Overhead} = 75{,}606 + 655.1\text{ProdRuns}$$

Figure 11.20

Multiple Regression Dialog Box

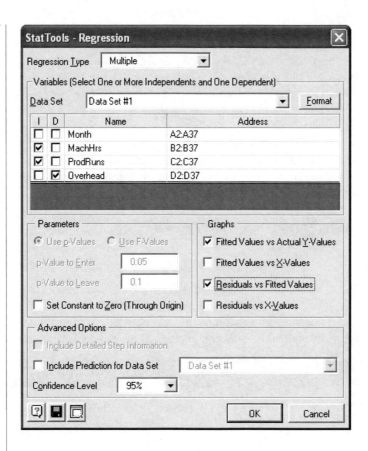

Figure 11.21

Multiple Regression Output for Bendrix Example

	A	B	C	D	E	F	G
7		Multiple	R-Square	Adjusted	StErr of		
8	Summary	R		R-Square	Estimate		
9		0.9308	0.8664	0.8583	4108.993		
10							
11		Degrees of	Sum of	Mean of	F-Ratio	p-Value	
12	ANOVA Table	Freedom	Squares	Squares			
13	Explained	2	3614020661	1807010330	107.0261	< 0.0001	
14	Unexplained	33	557166199.1	16883824.22			
15							
16		Coefficient	Standard	t-Value	p-Value	Confidence Interval 95%	
17	Regression Table		Error			Lower	Upper
18	Constant	3996.678	6603.651	0.6052	0.5492	-9438.551	17431.907
19	MachHrs	43.536	3.589	12.1289	< 0.0001	36.234	50.839
20	ProdRuns	883.618	82.251	10.7429	< 0.0001	716.276	1050.960

Note that the coefficient of MachHrs has increased from 34.7 to 43.5 and the coefficient of ProdRuns has increased from 655.1 to 883.6. Also, the intercept is now lower than either intercept in the single-variable equations. In general, it is difficult to guess the changes that will occur when we introduce more explanatory variables into the equation, but it is likely that changes *will* occur.

The reasoning is that when MachHrs is the only variable in the equation, we are obviously *not* holding ProdRuns constant—we are ignoring it—so in effect the coefficient 34.7 of MachHrs indicates the effect of MachHrs *and* the omitted ProdRuns on Overhead. But when we include both variables, then the coefficient 43.5 of MachHrs indicates the effect of MachHrs only, holding ProdRuns constant. Because the coefficients of MachHrs in the two equations have different *meanings*, it is not surprising that we obtain different numerical estimates of them. ∎

The estimated coefficient of any explanatory variable typically depends on which other explanatory variables are included in the equation.

11.5.2 Interpretation of Standard Error of Estimate and R-Square

The multiple regression output in Figure 11.21 is very similar to simple regression output.[6] In particular, cells C9 and E9 again show R^2 and the standard error of estimate s_e. Also, the square root of R^2 appears in cell B9. We interpret these quantities almost exactly as in simple regression. The standard error of estimate is essentially the standard deviation of residuals, but it is now given by equation (11.11), where n is the number of observations and k is the number of explanatory variables in the equation.

Formula for Standard Error of Estimate in Multiple Regression

$$s_e = \sqrt{\frac{\Sigma e_i^2}{n - k - 1}}$$

(11.11)

Fortunately, we interpret s_e exactly as before. It is a measure of the prediction error we are likely to make when we use the multiple regression equation to predict the dependent variable. In this example, about 2/3 of the predictions should be within 1 standard error, or $4109, of the actual overhead cost. By comparing this with the standard errors from the single-variable equations for Overhead, $8585 and $9457, we see that the multiple regression equation is likely to provide predictions that are more than twice as accurate as the single-variable equations—quite an improvement!

The R^2 value is again the percentage of variation of the dependent variable explained by the combined set of explanatory variables. In fact, it even has the same formula as before [see equation (11.8)]. For the Bendrix data we see that MachHrs and ProdRuns combine to explain 86.6% of the variation in Overhead. This is a big improvement over the single-variable equations that were able to explain only 39.9% and 27.1% of the variation in Overhead. Remarkably, the combination of the two explanatory variables explains a larger percentage than the *sum* of their individual effects. This is not common, but as this example shows, it is possible.

R^2 is always *the square of the correlation between the actual and fitted Y values—in both simple and multiple regression.*

The square root of R^2 shown in cell B9 of Figure 11.21 is again the correlation between the fitted values and the observed values of the dependent variable. For the Bendrix data the correlation between them is 0.931, quite high. A graphical indication of this high correlation can be seen in one of the scatterplots we requested, the plot of fitted versus observed values of Overhead. This scatterplot appears in Figure 11.22. If the regression equation gave *perfect* predictions, then all of the points in this plot would lie on a 45° line—each fitted value would *equal* the corresponding observed value. Although a perfect fit virtually never occurs, the closer the points are to a 45° line, the better the fit is, as indicated by R^2 or its square root.

Although the R^2 value is one of the most frequently quoted values from a regression analysis, it does have one serious drawback: R^2 can only *increase* when extra explanatory variables are added to an equation. This can lead to "fishing expeditions," where an analyst keeps adding variables to an equation, some of which have no conceptual relationship to the dependent variable, just to inflate the R^2 value. To "penalize" the addition of extra variables that do not really belong, an **adjusted** R^2 value is typically listed in regression outputs. This adjusted value appears in cell D9 of Figure 11.21. Although it has no direct interpretation as "percentage of variation explained," it *can* decrease when extra explanatory variables that do not really belong are added to an equation. Therefore, it is a useful index that we can monitor. If we add variables and the adjusted R^2 *decreases*, then the extra variables are essentially not pulling their weight and should probably be omitted. We have much more to say about this issue in the next chapter.

[6]In particular, neither regression output is linked to the data by formulas. If the data change, you must rerun the regression procedure to update the output.

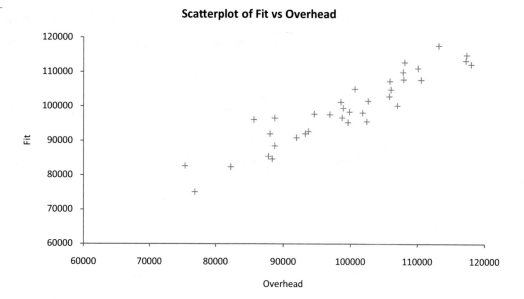

Figure 11.22

Scatterplot of Fitted Values versus Observed Values of Overhead

The **adjusted R^2** is a measure that adjusts R^2 for the number of explanatory variables in the equation. It is used primarily to monitor whether extra explanatory variables really belong in the equation.

PROBLEMS

Level A

16. A trucking company wants to predict the yearly maintenance expense (Y) for a truck using the number of miles driven during the year (X_1) and the age of the truck (X_2, in years) at the beginning of the year. The company has gathered the data given in the file **P11_16.xlsx**. Note that each observation corresponds to a particular truck.

    a. Formulate and estimate a multiple regression model using the given data. Interpret each of the estimated regression coefficients.

    b. Compute and interpret the standard error of estimate s_e and the coefficient of determination R^2 for these data.

17. DataPro is a small but rapidly growing firm that provides electronic data-processing services to commercial firms, hospitals, and other organizations. For each of the past 12 months, DataPro has tracked the number of contracts sold, the average contract price, advertising expenditures, and personal selling expenditures. These data are provided in **P11_17.xlsx**. Assuming that the number of contracts sold is the dependent variable, estimate a multiple regression model with three explanatory variables. Interpret each of the estimated regression coefficients and the coefficient of determination R^2.

18. An antique collector believes that the price received for a particular item increases with its age and with the number of bidders. The file **P11_18.xlsx** contains data on these three variables for 32 recently auctioned comparable items.

    a. Formulate and estimate a multiple regression model using the given data. Interpret each of the estimated regression coefficients. Is the antique collector correct in believing that the price received for the item increases with its age and with the number of bidders?

b. Interpret the standard error of estimate s_e and the coefficient of determination R^2.

19. Stock market analysts are continually looking for reliable predictors of stock prices. Consider the problem of modeling the price per share of electric utility stocks (Y). Two variables thought to influence this stock price are return on average equity (X_1) and annual dividend rate (X_2). The stock price, returns on equity, and dividend rates on a randomly selected day for 16 electric utility stocks are provided in the file **P11_19.xlsx**.
    a. Formulate and estimate a multiple regression model using the given data. Interpret each of the estimated regression coefficients.
    b. Interpret the standard error of estimate s_e, the coefficient of determination R^2, and the adjusted R^2.

20. The manager of a commuter rail transportation system was recently asked by her governing board to determine which factors have a significant impact on the demand for rides in the large city served by the transportation network. The system manager has collected data on variables thought to be possibly related to the number of weekly riders on the city's rail system. The file **P11_20.xlsx** contain these data.
    a. What are the expected signs of the coefficients of the explanatory variables in this multiple regression model? Provide reasoning for each of your stated expectations. (Answer this *before* using regression.)
    b. Formulate and estimate a multiple regression model using the given data. Interpret each of the estimated regression coefficients. Are the signs of the estimated coefficients consistent with your expectations as stated in part **a**?
    c. What proportion of the total variation in the number of weekly riders is *not* explained by this estimated multiple regression model?

21. Consider the enrollment data for *Business Week*'s top U.S. graduate business programs in the file **P02_03.xlsx**. Use these data to estimate a multiple regression model to assess whether there is a systematic relationship between the total number of full-time students and the following explanatory variables: (a) the proportion of female students, (b) the proportion of minority students, and (c) the proportion of international students enrolled at these distinguished business schools.
    a. Interpret the coefficients of your estimated regression model. Do any of these results surprise you? Explain.
    b. How well does your estimated regression model fit the given data?

22. David Savageau and Geoffrey Loftus, the authors of *Places Rated Almanac*, have ranked metropolitan areas in the United States with consideration of the following aspects of life in each area: cost of living, transportation, jobs, education, climate, crime, arts, health, and recreation. The data are in the file **P02_55.xlsx**.
    a. Use multiple regression analysis to explore the relationship between the metropolitan area's overall score and the set of potential explanatory variables.
    b. Interpret each of the estimated coefficients in the regression model. Are the signs of the estimated coefficients consistent with your expectations? If not, can you explain any discrepancies between your findings and expectations?
    c. Does the given set of explanatory variables do a good job of explaining changes in the overall score? Explain why or why not.

Level B

23. The owner of a restaurant in Bloomington, Indiana, has recorded sales data for the past 19 years. He has also recorded data on potentially relevant variables. The entire data set appears in the file **P11_23.xlsx**.
    a. Estimate a simple linear regression model involving annual sales (the dependent variable) and the size of the population residing within 10 miles of the restaurant (the explanatory variable). Interpret R^2.
    b. Add another explanatory variable—annual advertising expenditures—to the regression model in part **a**. Estimate and interpret this expanded model. How does the R^2 value for this multiple regression model compare to that of the simple regression model estimated in part **a**? Explain any difference between the two R^2 values. Interpret the *adjusted* R^2 value for the revised model.
    c. Add one more explanatory variable to the multiple regression model estimated in part **b**. In particular, estimate and interpret the coefficients of a multiple regression model that includes the *previous* year's advertising expenditure. How does the inclusion of this third explanatory variable affect the R^2 and adjusted R^2 values, in comparison to the corresponding values for the model of part **b**? Explain any changes in these values.

24. A regional express delivery service company recently conducted a study to investigate the relationship between the cost of shipping a package (Y), the package weight (X_1), and the distance shipped (X_2). Twenty packages were randomly selected from among the large number received for shipment, and a detailed analysis of the shipping cost was conducted for each package. These sample observations are given in the file **P11_24.xlsx**.
    a. Estimate a simple linear regression model involving shipping cost and package weight. Interpret the slope coefficient of the least squares line as well as the computed value of R^2.

b. Add another explanatory variable—distance shipped—to the regression model in part **a**. Estimate and interpret this expanded model. How does the R^2 value for this multiple regression model compare to that of the simple regression model estimated in part **a**? Explain any difference between the two R^2 values. Interpret the *adjusted* R^2 value for the revised model.

25. Using the sample data given in the file **P11_10.xlsx**, formulate a multiple regression model to predict the sales price of houses in a given community.

a. Add one explanatory variable at a time and estimate each partial regression equation. Report and explain changes in the standard error of estimate s_e, the coefficient of determination R^2, and the adjusted R^2 as each explanatory variable is added to the model.

b. Interpret each of the estimated regression coefficients in the full model.

c. What proportion of the total variation in the sales price is explained by the multiple regression model that includes all four explanatory variables?

11.6 MODELING POSSIBILITIES

Once we move from simple to multiple regression, the floodgates open. All types of explanatory variables are potential candidates for inclusion in the regression equation. In this section we examine several new types of explanatory variables. These include "dummy" variables, interaction variables, and nonlinear transformations. The techniques in this section provide us with many alternative approaches to modeling the relationship between a dependent variable and potential explanatory variables. In many applications these techniques produce much better fits than we could obtain without them.

As the title of this section suggests, these techniques are modeling *possibilities*. They provide a wide variety of explanatory variables to choose from. However, this does not mean that it is wise to include all or even many of these new types of explanatory variables in any particular regression equation. The chances are that only a few, if any, will significantly improve the linear fit. Knowing which explanatory variables to include requires a great deal of practical experience with regression, as well as a thorough understanding of the particular problem to be solved. The material in this section should *not* be an excuse for a mindless fishing expedition.

11.6.1 Dummy Variables

Some potential explanatory variables are categorical and cannot be measured on a quantitative scale. However, these categorical variables are often related to the dependent variable, so we need a way to include them in a regression equation. The trick is to use **dummy** variables, also called **indicator** or **0–1** variables. Dummy variables are variables that indicate the category a given observation is in. If a dummy variable for a given category equals 1, the observation is in that category; if it equals 0, the observation is not in that category.

A **dummy variable** is a variable with possible values 0 and 1. It equals 1 if the observation is in a particular category and 0 if it is not.

Categorical variables are used in two situations. The first and perhaps most common situation is when a categorical variable has only two categories. A good example of this is a gender variable that has the two categories "male" and "female." In this case we need only a *single* dummy variable, and we have the choice of assigning the 1's to either category. If we label the dummy variable Gender, then we can code Gender as 1 for males and 0 for females, or we can code Gender as 1 for females and 0 for males. We just need to be consistent and specify explicitly which coding scheme we are using.

The other situation is when there are more than two categories. A good example of this is when we have quarterly time series data and we want to treat the quarter of the year as a categorical variable with four categories, 1 through 4. Then we can create four dummy variables, Q1 through Q4. For example, Q2 equals 1 for all second-quarter observations and equals 0 for all other observations. Although we can create four dummy variables, we will see that only three of them—*any* three—should be used in a regression equation.

The following example illustrates how we form, use, and interpret dummy variables in regression analysis.

EXAMPLE	**11.3 POSSIBLE GENDER DISCRIMINATION IN SALARY AT FIFTH NATIONAL BANK OF SPRINGFIELD**

The Fifth National Bank of Springfield is facing a gender discrimination suit.[7] The charge is that its female employees receive substantially smaller salaries than its male employees. The bank's employee database is listed in the file **Bank Salaries.xlsx**. For each of its 208 employees, the data set includes the following variables:

- EducLev: education level, a categorical variable with categories 1 (finished high school), 2 (finished some college courses), 3 (obtained a bachelor's degree), 4 (took some graduate courses), 5 (obtained a graduate degree)

- JobGrade: a categorical variable indicating the current job level, the possible levels being 1 through 6 (6 is highest)

- YrsExper: years of experience with this bank

- Age: employee's current age

- Gender: a categorical variable with values "Female" and "Male"

- YrsPrior: number of years of work experience at another bank prior to working at Fifth National

- PCJob: a categorical yes/no variable depending on whether the employee's current job is computer-related

- Salary: current annual salary

Figure 11.23 lists a few of the observations. Do these data provide evidence that females are discriminated against in terms of salary?

Figure 11.23

Selected Data for Bank Example

	A	B	C	D	E	F	G	H	I
1	Employee	EducLev	JobGrade	YrsExper	Age	Gender	YrsPrior	PCJob	Salary
2	1	3	1	3	26	Male	1	No	$32,000
3	2	1	1	14	38	Female	1	No	$39,100
4	3	1	1	12	35	Female	0	No	$33,200
5	4	2	1	8	40	Female	7	No	$30,600
6	5	3	1	3	28	Male	0	No	$29,000
7	6	3	1	3	24	Female	0	No	$30,500
8	7	3	1	4	27	Female	0	No	$30,000
9	8	3	1	8	33	Male	2	No	$27,000
10	9	1	1	4	62	Female	0	No	$34,000
11	10	3	1	9	31	Female	0	No	$29,500
12	11	3	1	9	34	Female	2	No	$26,800
13	12	2	1	8	37	Female	8	No	$31,300
14	13	2	1	9	37	Female	0	No	$31,200
15	14	2	1	10	58	Female	6	No	$34,700
16	15	3	1	4	33	Female	0	No	$30,000

[7]This example and the accompanying data set are based on a real case. Only the bank's name has been changed.

Objective   To use StatTools's Regression procedure to analyze whether the bank discriminates against females in terms of salary.

Solution

A naive approach to this problem compares the average female salary to the average male salary. This can be done with a pivot table, as in Chapter 2, or with a more formal hypothesis test, as in Chapter 10. Using these methods, we find that the average of all salaries is $39,922, the female average is $37,210, the male average is $45,505, and the difference between the male and female averages is statistically significant at any reasonable level of significance. In short, the females definitely earn less. But perhaps there is a reason for this. They might have lower education levels, they might have been hired more recently, they might be working at lower job grades, and so on. The question is whether the difference between female and male salaries is still evident after taking these other attributes into account. This is a perfect task for regression.

We first need to create dummy variables for the various categorical variables. We can do this manually with IF functions or we can use StatTools's Dummy procedure. To do it manually, we can create a dummy variable Female based on Gender in column J by entering the formula

=IF(F45="Female",1,0)

in cell J4 and copying it down. Note that we are coding the females as 1's and the males as 0's. (The quotes are necessary when a text value is used in an IF function.)

StatTools's Dummy procedure is somewhat easier, especially when there are multiple categories. For example, to create five dummies, Ed_1 through Ed_5, for the education levels, we select Dummy from the StatTools Utilities dropdown, select the Create One Dummy Variable for Each Distinct Category option, and select the EducLev variable to base the dummies on. This creates five dummy columns with variable names EducLev=1 through EducLev=5. We can follow the same procedure to create six dummies, JobGrade=1 through JobGrade=6, for the job grade categories.

We can add dummies to effectively collapse categories.

Sometimes we might want to collapse several categories. For example, we might want to collapse the five education categories into three categories: 1, (2,3), and (4,5). The new second category includes employees who have taken undergraduate courses or have completed a bachelor's degree, and the new third category includes employees who have taken graduate courses or have completed a graduate degree. It is easy to do this. We simply add the EducLev=2 and EducLev=3 columns to get the dummy for the new second category, and we add the EducLev=4 and EducLev=5 columns for the new third category.

Once the dummies have been created, we can run a regression analysis with Salary as the dependent variable, using any combination of numerical and dummy explanatory variables. However, there are two rules we must follow:

- We shouldn't use any of the *original* categorical variables, such as EducLev, that the dummies are based on.

- We should always use *one less dummy* than the number of categories for any categorical variable.

Always include one less dummy than the number of categories. The omitted dummy corresponds to the reference category.

This second rule is a technical one. If we violate it, the statistical software will give us an error message. For example, if we want to use education level as an explanatory variable, we should enter only four of the five dummies EducLev=1 through EducLev=5. *Any four of these can be used.* The omitted dummy then corresponds to the **reference** category. As we will see, the interpretation of the dummy variable coefficients are all relative to this reference category. When there are only two categories, as with the gender variable, we typically name the variable with the category, such as Female, that corresponds to the 1's. If we create the dummy variables manually, we probably don't even bother to create a Male dummy. In this case "Male" automatically becomes the reference category.

To explain dummy variables in regression, we proceed in several stages in this example. We first estimate a regression equation with only one explanatory variable, Female. The output appears in Figure 11.24. The resulting equation is

$$\text{Predicted Salary} = 45505 - 8296\text{Female} \tag{11.12}$$

Figure 11.24

Output for Bank Example with a Single Explanatory Variable

	A	B	C	D	E	F	G
7		Multiple	R-Square	Adjusted	StErr of		
8	Summary	R		R-Square	Estimate		
9		0.3465	0.1201	0.1158	10584.3		
10							
11		Degrees of	Sum of	Mean of	F-Ratio	p-Value	
12	ANOVA Table	Freedom	Squares	Squares			
13	Explained	1	3149633845	3149633845	28.1151	< 0.0001	
14	Unexplained	206	23077473386	112026569.8			
15							
16		Coefficient	Standard	t-Value	p-Value	Confidence Interval 95%	
17	Regression Table		Error			Lower	Upper
18	Constant	45505.4	1283.5	35.4533	< 0.0001	42974.9	48036.0
19	Female	-8295.5	1564.5	-5.3024	< 0.0001	-11380.0	-5211.0

To interpret regression equations with dummy variables, it is useful to rewrite the equation for each category.

To interpret this equation, recall that Female has only two possible values, 0 and 1. If we substitute Female=1 into equation (11.12), we obtain

$$\text{Predicted Salary} = 45505 - 8296(1) = 37209$$

Because Female=1 corresponds to females, this equation simply indicates the average female salary. Similarly, if we substitute Female=0 into equation (11.12), we obtain

$$\text{Predicted Salary} = 45505 - 8296(0) = 45505$$

Because Female=0 corresponds to males, this equation indicates the average male salary. Therefore, the interpretation of the −8296 coefficient of the Female dummy variable is straightforward. It is the average female salary relative to the reference (male) category—females get paid $8296 less on average than males.

Obviously, equation (11.12) tells only part of the story. It ignores all information except for gender. We expand this equation by adding the experience variables YrsPrior and YrsExper. The output with the Female dummy variable and these two experience variables appears in Figure 11.25. The corresponding regression equation is

$$\text{Predicted Salary} = 35492 + 988\text{YrsExper} + 131\text{YrsPrior} - 8080\text{Female} \tag{11.13}$$

Figure 11.25

Regression Output with Two Numerical Explanatory Variables Included

	A	B	C	D	E	F	G
7		Multiple	R-Square	Adjusted	StErr of		
8	Summary	R		R-Square	Estimate		
9		0.7016	0.4923	0.4848	8079.4		
10							
11		Degrees of	Sum of	Mean of	F-Ratio	p-Value	
12	ANOVA Table	Freedom	Squares	Squares			
13	Explained	3	12910668018	4303556006	65.9279	< 0.0001	
14	Unexplained	204	13316439212	65276662.81			
15							
16		Coefficient	Standard	t-Value	p-Value	Confidence Interval 95%	
17	Regression Table		Error			Lower	Upper
18	Constant	35491.7	1341.0	26.4661	< 0.0001	32847.6	38135.7
19	YrsExper	988.0	80.9	12.2083	< 0.0001	828.4	1147.6
20	YrsPrior	131.3	180.9	0.7259	0.4687	-225.4	488.1
21	Female	-8080.2	1198.2	-6.7438	< 0.0001	-10442.6	-5717.8

It is again useful to write equation (11.13) in two forms: one for females (substituting Female=1) and one for males (substituting Female=0). After doing the arithmetic, they become

$$\text{Predicted Salary} = 27412 + 988\text{YrsExper} + 131\text{YrsPrior}$$

and

$$\text{Predicted Salary} = 35492 + 988\text{YrsExper} + 131\text{YrsPrior}$$

Except for the intercept term, these equations are identical. We can now interpret the coefficient -8080 of the Female dummy variable as the average salary disadvantage for females relative to males *after controlling for job experience*. Gender discrimination still appears to be a very plausible conclusion. However, note that the R^2 value is only 49.2%. Perhaps there is still more to the story.

We next add education level to the equation by including four of the five education level dummies. Although *any* four could be used, we use EducLev=2 through EducLev=5, so that the lowest level becomes the reference category. (We would expect this to lead to *positive* coefficients for these dummies, which are easier to interpret.) The resulting output appears in Figure 11.26. The estimated regression equation is now

$$\text{Predicted Salary} = 26613 + 1033\text{YrsExper} + 362\text{YrsPrior} - 4501\text{Female}$$

$$+ 160\text{EducLev=2} + 4765\text{EducLev=3} + 7320\text{EducLev=4} + 11770\text{EducLev=5} \qquad \textbf{(11.14)}$$

Figure 11.26

Regression Output with Education Dummies Included

	A	B	C	D	E	F	G
7		Multiple	R-Square	Adjusted	StErr of		
8	*Summary*	R		R-Square	Estimate		
9		0.8030	0.6449	0.6324	6824.4		
10							
11		Degrees of	Sum of	Mean of	F-Ratio	p-Value	
12	*ANOVA Table*	Freedom	Squares	Squares			
13	Explained	7	16912692100	2416098871	51.8787	< 0.0001	
14	Unexplained	200	9314415131	46572075.65			
15							
16		Coefficient	Standard	t-Value	p-Value	Confidence Interval 95%	
17	*Regression Table*		Error			Lower	Upper
18	Constant	26613.4	1794.1	14.8335	< 0.0001	23075.5	30151.2
19	YrsExper	1032.9	69.6	14.8404	< 0.0001	895.7	1170.2
20	YrsPrior	362.2	158.1	2.2908	0.0230	50.4	674.0
21	Female	-4501.3	1085.8	-4.1458	< 0.0001	-6642.3	-2360.3
22	EducLev = 2	160.2	1656.0	0.0968	0.9230	-3105.2	3425.7
23	EducLev = 3	4764.6	1473.4	3.2336	0.0014	1859.1	7670.0
24	EducLev = 4	7319.8	2694.2	2.7169	0.0072	2007.2	12632.5
25	EducLev = 5	11770.2	1510.2	7.7937	< 0.0001	8792.2	14748.2

Now there are two categorical variables involved, gender and education level. However, we can still write a separate equation *for any combination* of categories by setting the dummies to the appropriate values. For example, the equation for females at the fifth education level is found by setting Female and EducLev=5 equal to 1, and setting the other education dummies equal to 0. After terms are combined, this equation is

$$\text{Predicted Salary} = 33882 + 1033\text{YrsExper} + 362\text{YrsPrior}$$

The intercept 33882 is the intercept from equation (11.14), 26613, plus the coefficients of Female and EducLev=5.

We can interpret equation (11.14) as follows. For either gender and any education level, the expected increase in salary for one extra year of experience with Fifth National is $1033; the expected increase in salary for one extra year of prior experience with another bank is $362. The coefficients of the education dummies indicate the average increase in salary an employee can expect relative to the reference (lowest) education level. For example, an employee with education level 4 can expect to earn $7320 more than an employee with education level 1, all else being equal. Finally, the key coefficient, $-\$4501$ for females, indicates the average salary disadvantage for females relative to males, given that they have the same experience levels *and* the same education levels. Note that the R^2 value is now 64.5%, quite a bit larger than when the education dummies were not included. We appear to be getting closer to the truth. In particular, we see that there appears to be gender discrimination in salaries, even after accounting for job experience and education level.

One further explanation for gender differences in salary might be job grade. Perhaps females tend to be in lower job grades, which would help explain why they get lower salaries on average. One way to check this is with a pivot table, as in Figure 11.27, where we put job grade in the row area, gender in the column area, and request counts, displayed as percentages of columns. Clearly, females tend to be concentrated at the lower job grades. For example, 28.85% of all employees are at the lowest job grade, but 34.29% of all females are at this grade and only 17.65% of males are at this grade. The opposite is true at the higher job grades. This certainly helps to explain why females get lower salaries on average.

Figure 11.27

Pivot Table of Job Grade Counts for Bank Data

	A	B	C	D
1				
2				
3	Count of Employee	Gender		
4	JobGrade	Female	Male	Grand Total
5	1	34.29%	17.65%	28.85%
6	2	20.71%	19.12%	20.19%
7	3	25.71%	10.29%	20.67%
8	4	12.14%	16.18%	13.46%
9	5	6.43%	17.65%	10.10%
10	6	0.71%	19.12%	6.73%
11	Grand Total	100.00%	100.00%	100.00%

We can go one step further to see the effect of job grade on salary by including the dummies for job grade in the equation, along with the other variables we have included so far. As with the education dummies, we use the lowest job grade as the reference category and include only the five dummies for the other categories. While we are at it, we include the other two potential explanatory variables to the equation: Age and HasPCJob, a dummy based on the PCJob categorical variable. The regression output for this equation appears in Figure 11.28.

Figure 11.28

Regression Output with Other Variables Added

	A	B	C	D	E	F	G
7		Multiple	R-Square	Adjusted	StErr of		
8	Summary	R		R-Square	Estimate		
9		0.8748	0.7652	0.7482	5648.1		
10							
11		Degrees of	Sum of	Mean of	F-Ratio	p-Value	
12	ANOVA Table	Freedom	Squares	Squares			
13	Explained	14	20070250768	1433589341	44.9390	< 0.0001	
14	Unexplained	193	6156856463	31900810.69			
15							
16		Coefficient	Standard	t-Value	p-Value	Confidence Interval 95%	
17	Regression Table		Error			Lower	Upper
18	Constant	29689.9	2490.0	11.9236	< 0.0001	24778.8	34601.1
19	YrsExper	515.6	98.0	5.2621	< 0.0001	322.3	708.8
20	Age	-9.0	57.7	-0.1553	0.8767	-122.8	104.8
21	YrsPrior	167.7	140.4	1.1943	0.2338	-109.3	444.7
22	Female	-2554.5	1012.0	-2.5242	0.0124	-4550.4	-558.5
23	EducLev = 2	-485.6	1398.7	-0.3472	0.7289	-3244.2	2273.1
24	EducLev = 3	527.9	1357.5	0.3889	0.6978	-2149.6	3205.4
25	EducLev = 4	285.2	2404.7	0.1186	0.9057	-4457.7	5028.1
26	EducLev = 5	2690.8	1620.9	1.6601	0.0985	-506.1	5887.7
27	JobGrade = 2	1564.5	1185.8	1.3194	0.1886	-774.2	3903.2
28	JobGrade = 3	5219.4	1262.4	4.1345	< 0.0001	2729.5	7709.2
29	JobGrade = 4	8594.8	1496.0	5.7451	< 0.0001	5644.2	11545.5
30	JobGrade = 5	13659.4	1874.3	7.2879	< 0.0001	9962.7	17356.1
31	JobGrade = 6	23832.4	2799.9	8.5119	< 0.0001	18310.1	29354.7
32	HasPCJob	4922.8	1473.8	3.3402	0.0010	2016.0	7829.7

As expected, the coefficients of the job grade dummies are all positive, and they increase as the job grade increases—it pays to be in the higher job grades. The effect of age appears to be minimal, and there appears to be a "bonus" of close to $5000 for having a PC-related job. The R^2 value has now increased to 76.5%, and the penalty for being a female has decreased to $2555—still large but not as large as before.

The regression indicates that being in lower job grades implies lower salaries, but it doesn't explain why females are in the lower job grades in the first place.

However, even if this penalty, the coefficient of Female in this last equation, is considered "small," is it convincing evidence against the argument for gender discrimination? We believe the answer is "no." We have used variations in job grades to reduce the penalty for being female. But the remaining question is then, Why are females predominantly in the low job grades? Perhaps this is the real source of gender discrimination. Perhaps management is not advancing the females as quickly as it should, which naturally results in lower salaries for females.

We conclude this example for now, but we will say more about it in the next two subsections. ∎

11.6.2 Interaction Variables

Suppose that we regress a variable Y on a numerical variable X and a dummy variable D. If the estimated equation is of the form

$$\hat{Y} = a + b_1 X + b_2 D \tag{11.15}$$

then, as in the previous section, we can break this equation down into two separate equations:

$$\hat{Y} = (a + b_2) + b_1 X$$

and

$$\hat{Y} = a + b_1 X$$

The first corresponds to $D = 1$, and the second corresponds to $D = 0$. The only difference between these two equations is the intercept term; the slope for each is b_1. Geometrically, they correspond to two *parallel* lines that are a distance b_2 apart. For example, if D corresponds to gender, then there is a female line and a parallel male line. The effect of X on Y is the same for females and males. When X increases by 1 unit, we predict Y to change by b_1 units for both males or females.

In effect, when we include *only* a dummy variable in a regression equation, as in equation (11.15), we are allowing the intercepts of the two lines to differ (by an amount b_2), but we are *forcing* the lines to be parallel. Sometimes we want to allow them to have different slopes, in addition to possibly different intercepts. We can do this with an **interaction** variable. Algebraically, an interaction variable is the *product* of two variables. Its effect is to allow the effect of one of the variables on Y to depend on the value of the other variable.

An **interaction** variable is the product of two explanatory variables. We include such a variable in a regression equation if we believe the effect of one explanatory variable on Y depends on the value of another explanatory variable.

Suppose we create the interaction variable XD (the product of X and D) and then estimate the equation

$$\hat{Y} = a + b_1 X + b_2 D + b_3 XD$$

As usual, we rewrite this equation as two separate equations, depending on whether $D = 0$ or $D = 1$. If $D = 1$, we combine terms to write

$$\hat{Y} = (a + b_2) + (b_1 + b_3)X$$

If $D = 0$, the dummy and interaction variables drop out and we obtain

$$\hat{Y} = a + b_1 X$$

The notation is not important. The important part is that the interaction term, $b_3 XD$, allows the slope of the regression line to differ between the two categories.

The following continuation of the bank discrimination example illustrates one possible use of interaction variables.

EXAMPLE **11.3 POSSIBLE GENDER DISCRIMINATION IN SALARY AT FIFTH NATIONAL BANK OF SPRINGFIELD (CONTINUED)**

Earlier we estimated an equation for Salary using the numerical explanatory variables YrsExper and YrsPrior and the dummy variable Female. If we drop the YrsPrior variable from this equation (for simplicity) and rerun the regression, we obtain the equation

$$\text{Predicted Salary} = 35824 + 981\text{YrsExper} - 8012\text{Female} \qquad \textbf{(11.16)}$$

The R^2 value for this equation is 49.1%. If we decide to include an interaction variable between YrsExper and Female in this equation, what is its effect?

Objective To use multiple regression with an interaction variable to see whether the effect of years of experience on salary is different across the two genders.

Solution

We first need to form an interaction variable that is the product of YrsExper and Female. This can be done in two ways in Excel. We can do it manually by introducing a new variable that contains the product of the two variables involved, or we can use the Interaction item from the StatTools Utilities dropdown. For the latter, we select the Two Numeric Variables option in the Interaction Between dropdown, and we select Female and YrsExper as the variables to be used to create an interaction variable.[8]

Once the interaction variable has been created, we include it in the regression equation in addition to the other variables in equation (11.16). The multiple regression output appears in Figure 11.29. The estimated regression equation is

$$\text{Predicted Salary} = 30430 + 1528\text{YrsExper} + 4098\text{Female}$$

$$- 1248\text{Interaction(YrsExper,Female)}$$

where Interaction(YrsExper,Female) is StatTools's default name for the interaction variable. As in the general discussion, it is useful to write this as two separate equations, one for females and one for males. The female equation (Female=1, so that Interaction(YrsExper,Female) =YrsExper) is

$$\text{Predicted Salary} = (30430 + 4098) + (1528 - 1248)\text{YrsExper}$$

$$= 34528 + 280\text{YrsExper}$$

and the male equation (Female=0, so that Interaction(YrsExper,Female) = 0) is

$$\text{Predicted Salary} = 30430 + 1528\text{YrsExper}$$

---

[8]See the StatTools online help for this data utility. It explains the various options for creating interaction variables.

Figure 11.29

Regression Output with an Interaction Variable

	A	B	C	D	E	F	G
7		Multiple	R-Square	Adjusted	StErr of		
8	*Summary*	R		R-Square	Estimate		
9		0.7991	0.6386	0.6333	6816.3		
10							
11		Degrees of	Sum of	Mean of	F-Ratio	p-Value	
12	*ANOVA Table*	Freedom	Squares	Squares			
13	Explained	3	16748875071	5582958357	120.1620	< 0.0001	
14	Unexplained	204	9478232160	46461922.35			
15							
16		Coefficient	Standard	t-Value	p-Value	Confidence Interval 95%	
17	*Regression Table*		Error			Lower	Upper
18	Constant	30430.0	1216.6	25.0129	< 0.0001	28031.4	32828.7
19	YrsExper	1527.8	90.5	16.8887	< 0.0001	1349.4	1706.1
20	Female	4098.3	1665.8	2.4602	0.0147	813.8	7382.7
21	Interaction(YrsExper,Female)	-1247.8	136.7	-9.1296	< 0.0001	-1517.3	-978.3

Graphically, these equations appear as in Figure 11.30. The *Y*-intercept for the female line is slightly higher—females with no experience with Fifth National tend to start out slightly higher than males—but the slope of the female line is much lower. That is, males tend to move up the salary ladder much more quickly than females. Again, this provides another argument, although a somewhat different one, for gender discrimination against females. By the way, the R^2 value with the interaction variable has increased from 49.1% to 63.9%. The interaction variable has definitely added to the explanatory power of the equation.

Figure 11.30 Nonparallel Female and Male Salary Lines

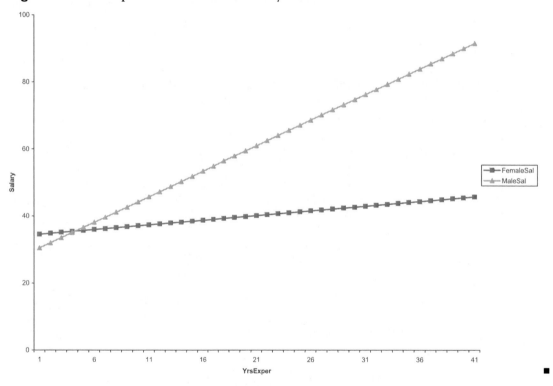

This example illustrates just one possible use of interaction variables. The product of *any* two variables, a numerical and a dummy variable, two dummy variables, or even two numerical variables, can be used. The trick is to interpret the results correctly, and the easiest way to do this is the way we've been doing it—by writing several separate equations and seeing how they differ. To illustrate one further possibility (among many), suppose we include the variables YrsExper, Female, and HighJob in the equation for Salary, along with interactions between Female and YrsExper and between Female and HighJob. Here,

HighJob is a new dummy variable that is 1 for job grades 4 to 6 and is 0 for job grades 1 to 3. (It can be calculated as the sum of the dummies JobGrade=4 through JobGrade=6.) The resulting equation is

$$\text{Predicted Salary} = 28168 + 1261\text{YrsExper} + 9242\text{HighJob} + 6601\text{Female}$$

$$- 1224\text{Interaction(YrsExper,Female)} + 1564\text{Interaction(Female,HighJob)} \quad (11.17)$$

and the R^2 value is now 76.6%.

The interpretation of equation (11.17) is quite a challenge because it is really composed of four separate equations, one for each combination of Female and HighJob. For females in the high job category, the equation becomes

$$\text{Predicted Salary} = (28168 + 9242 + 6601 + 1564) + (1261 - 1224)\text{YrsExper}$$

$$= 45575 + 37\text{YrsExper}$$

and for females in the low job category it is

$$\text{Predicted Salary} = (28168 + 6601) + (1261 - 1224)\text{YrsExper}$$

$$= 34769 + 37\text{YrsExper}$$

Similarly, for males in the high job category, the equation becomes

$$\text{Predicted Salary} = (28168 + 9242) + 1261\text{YrsExper}$$

$$= 37410 + 1261\text{YrsExper}$$

and for males in the low job category it is

$$\text{Predicted Salary} = 28168 + 1261\text{YrsExper}$$

Putting this into words, we can interpret the various coefficients as follows:

Interpretation of Regression Coefficients

- The intercept 28168 is the average *starting* salary (that is, with no experience at Fifth National) for males in the low job category.
- The coefficient 1261 of YrsExper is the expected increase in salary per extra year of experience for males (in either job category).
- The coefficient 9242 of HighJob is the expected salary "premium" for males starting in the high job category instead of the low job category.
- The coefficient 6601 of Female is the expected starting salary premium for females relative to males, given that they start in the low job category.
- The coefficient −1224 of Interaction(YrsExper,Female) is the penalty per extra year of experience for females relative to males—that is, male salaries increase this much more than female salaries each year.
- The coefficient 1564 of Interaction(Female,HighJob) is the extra premium (in addition to the male premium) for females starting in the high job category instead of the low job category.

As we see, there are pros and cons to adding interaction variables. On the plus side, they allow for more complex and interesting models, and they can provide significantly better fits. On the minus side, they can become extremely difficult to interpret correctly. Therefore, we recommend that they be added only when there is good economic and statistical justification for doing so.

11.6.3 Nonlinear Transformations

The general linear regression equation has the form

$$\hat{Y} = a + b_1X_1 + b_2X_2 + \cdots + b_kX_k$$

We typically include nonlinear transformations in a regression equation because of economic considerations or curvature detected in scatterplots.

It is *linear* in the sense that the right-hand side of the equation is a constant plus a sum of products of constants and variables. However, there is no requirement that the dependent variable Y or the explanatory variables X_1 through X_k be *original* variables in the data set. Most often they are, but they are also allowed to be transformations of original variables. We already saw one example of this in the previous section with interaction variables. They are not original variables but are instead products of original (or even transformed) variables. We enter them in the same way as original variables; only the interpretation differs. In this section we look at several nonlinear transformations of variables. These are often used because of curvature detected in scatterplots. They can also arise because of economic considerations. That is, economic theory often leads us to particular nonlinear transformations.

We can transform the dependent variable Y or we can transform any of the explanatory variables, the X's. We can also do both. In either case there are a few nonlinear transformations that are typically used. These include the natural logarithm, the square root, the reciprocal, and the square. The point of any of these is usually to "straighten out" the points in a scatterplot. If several different transformations straighten out the data equally well, then we prefer the one that is easiest to interpret.

We begin with a small example where only the X variable needs to be transformed.

EXAMPLE | **11.4 DEMAND AND COST FOR ELECTRICITY**

The Public Service Electric Company produces different quantities of electricity each month, depending on the demand. The file **Cost of Power.xlsx** lists the number of units of electricity produced (Units) and the total cost of producing these (Cost) for a 36-month period. The data appear in Figure 11.31. How can regression be used to analyze the relationship between Cost and Units?

Figure 11.31

Data for Electric Power Example

	A	B	C
1	Month	Cost	Units
2	1	45623	601
3	2	46507	738
4	3	43343	686
5	4	46495	736
6	5	47317	756
7	6	41172	498
8	7	43974	828
9	8	44290	671
10	9	29297	305
11	10	47244	637
12	11	43185	499
13	12	42658	578

Objective To see whether the cost of supplying electricity is a nonlinear function of demand, and if it is, what form the nonlinearity takes.

Solution

A good place to start is with a scatterplot of Cost versus Units. This appears in Figure 11.32. It indicates a definite positive relationship and one that is nearly linear. However, there is also some evidence of curvature in the plot. The points increase slightly less rapidly as Units increases from left to right. In economic terms, there might be economies of scale, so that the marginal cost of electricity decreases as more units of electricity are produced.

Figure 11.32

Scatterplot of Cost Versus Units for Electricity Example

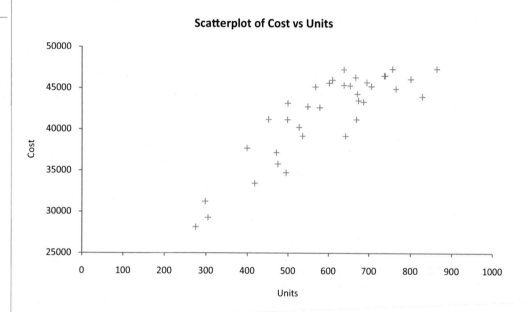

Nevertheless, we first use regression to estimate a *linear* relationship between Cost and Units. The resulting regression equation is

$$\text{Predicted Cost} = 23{,}651 + 30.53\text{Units}$$

The corresponding R^2 and s_e are 73.6% and $2734. We also requested a scatterplot of the residuals versus the fitted values, always a good idea when nonlinearity is suspected. This plot is shown in Figure 11.33. The sign of nonlinearity in this plot is that the residuals to the far left and the far right are all negative, whereas the majority of the residuals in the middle are positive. Admittedly, the pattern is far from perfect—there are several negative residuals in the middle—but the plot does hint at nonlinear behavior.

This negative–positive–negative behavior of residuals suggests a *parabola*—that is, a quadratic relationship with the *square* of Units included in the equation. We first create a new variable (Units)^2 in the data set. This can be done manually (with the formula =C4^2 in

A scatterplot of resid-
uals versus fitted val-
ues often indicates the
need for a nonlinear
transformation.

cell D4, copied down) or with the Transform item in the StatTools Utilities dropdown.[9] This
latter method has the advantage that it allows us to transform several variables simultaneously.
Then we use multiple regression to estimate the equation for Cost with *both* explanatory variables, Units and (Units)^2, included. The resulting equation, as shown in Figure 11.34, is

$$\text{Predicted Cost} = 5793 + 98.35\text{Units} - 0.0600(\text{Units})^2 \qquad \textbf{(11.18)}$$

Note that R^2 has increased to 82.2% and s_e has decreased to \$2281.

Figure 11.33

Residuals from a
Straight-Line Fit

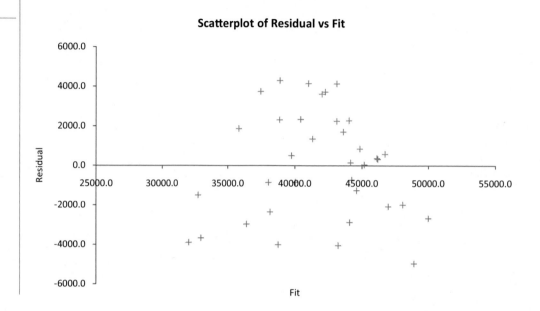

Figure 11.34 Regression Output with Squared Term Included

	A	B	C	D	E	F	G
7		Multiple	R-Square	Adjusted	StErr of		
8	*Summary*	R		R-Square	Estimate		
9		0.9064	0.8216	0.8108	2280.800		
10							
11		Degrees of	Sum of	Mean of	F-Ratio	p-Value	
12	*ANOVA Table*	Freedom	Squares	Squares			
13	Explained	2	790511518.3	395255759.1	75.9808	< 0.0001	
14	Unexplained	33	171667570.7	5202047.597			
15							
16		Coefficient	Standard	t-Value	p-Value	Confidence Interval 95%	
17	*Regression Table*		Error			Lower	Upper
18	Constant	5792.80	4763.06	1.2162	0.2325	-3897.72	15483.31
19	Units	98.350	17.237	5.7058	< 0.0001	63.282	133.419
20	(Units)^2	-0.0600	0.0151	-3.9806	0.0004	-0.0906	-0.0293

[9]StatTools provides four nonlinear transformations: natural logarithm, square, square root, and reciprocal.

One way to see how this regression equation fits the scatterplot of Cost versus Units (in Figure 11.32) is to use Excel's trendline option. To do so, activate the scatterplot, select More Trendline Options from the Trendline dropdown on the Chart Tools Layout ribbon, and select the Polynomial type or order 2, that is, a quadratic. A graph of equation (11.18) is superimposed on the scatterplot, as shown in Figure 11.35. It shows a reasonably good fit, plus an obvious curvature.

Figure 11.35

Quadratic Fit in Electricity Example

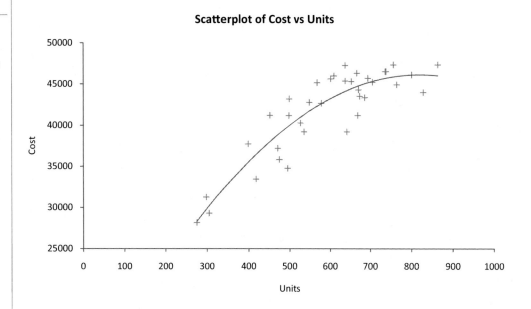

Excel's trendline option allows us to superimpose a number of different curves on a scatterplot.

The main downside to a quadratic regression equation, as in equation (11.18), is that there is no easy interpretation of the coefficients of Units and (Units)^2. For example, we can't conclude from the 98.35 coefficient of Units that Cost increases by 98.35 dollars when Units increases by 1. The reason is that when Units increases by 1, (Units)^2 doesn't stay constant; it *also* increases. All we can say is that the terms in equation (11.18) combine to explain the nonlinear relationship between units produced and total cost.

A final note about this equation concerns the coefficient of (Units)^2, -0.0600. First, the fact that it is negative makes the parabola bend "downward." This produces the decreasing marginal cost behavior, where every extra unit of electricity incurs a smaller cost. Actually, the curve described by equation (11.18) eventually goes *downhill* for large values of Units, but this part of the curve is irrelevant because the company evidently never produces such large quantities. Second, we should not be fooled by the small magnitude of this coefficient. Remember that it is the coefficient of Units *squared*, which is a large quantity. Therefore, the effect of the product -0.0600(Units)^2 is sizable.

There is at least one other possibility we can examine. Rather than a quadratic fit, we can try a logarithmic fit. In this case we create a new variable, Log(Units), the natural logarithm of Units, and then regress Cost against the *single* variable Log(Units). To create the new variable, we can proceed manually with Excel's LN function or we can use the Transform item from StatTools Utilities. Also, we can superimpose a logarithmic curve on the scatterplot of Cost versus Units by using Excel's trendline feature with the logarithmic option. This curve appears in Figure 11.36. To the naked eye, it appears to be similar, and about as good a fit, as the quadratic curve in Figure 11.35.

Figure 11.36

Logarithmic Fit to
Electricity Data

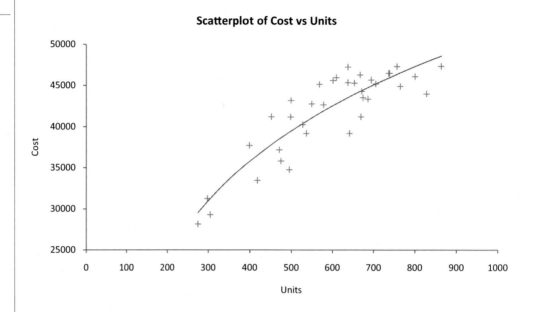

The resulting regression equation is

$$\text{Predicted Cost} = -63{,}993 + 16{,}654\text{Log(Units)} \qquad \textbf{(11.19)}$$

and the R^2 and s_e values are 79.8% and 2393. These latter values indicate that the logarithmic fit is not quite as good as the quadratic fit. However, the advantage of the logarithmic equation is that it is easier to interpret. In fact, one reason logarithmic transformations of variables are used as widely as they are in regression analysis is that they are fairly easy to interpret.

In general, if b is the coefficient of the log of X, then the expected change in Y when X increases by 1% is approximately 0.01 times b.

In the present case, where the log of an *explanatory* variable is used, we can interpret its coefficient as follows. Suppose that Units increases by 1%, for example, from 600 to 606. Then equation (11.19) implies that the expected Cost will increase by approximately

$0.01(16,654) = 166.54$ dollars. In words, every 1% increase in Units is accompanied by an expected \$166.54 increase in Cost. Note that for larger values of Units, a 1% increase represents a larger absolute increase (from 700 to 707 instead of from 600 to 606, say). But each such 1% increase entails the *same* increase in Cost. This is another way of describing the decreasing marginal cost property. ∎

The electricity example has shown two possible nonlinear transformations of the *explanatory* variable (or variables) that we can use. All we need to do is create the transformed X's and run the regression. The interpretation of statistics such as R^2 and s_e is exactly the same as before; only the interpretation of the coefficients of the transformed X's changes. It is also possible to transform the dependent variable Y. Now, however, we must be careful when interpreting summary statistics such as R^2 and s_e, as we explain in the following examples.

A logarithmic transformation of Y is often useful when the distribution of Y values is skewed to the right.

Each of these examples transforms the dependent variable Y by taking its natural logarithm and then using the log of Y as the new dependent variable. This approach is taken in a wide variety of business applications. Essentially, it is often a good option when the distribution of Y is skewed to the right, with a few very large values and many small to medium values. The effect of the logarithm transformation is to spread the small values out and squeeze the large values together, making the distribution more symmetric. This is illustrated in Figures 11.37 and 11.38 for a hypothetical distribution of household incomes. The histogram of incomes in Figure 11.37 is clearly skewed to the right. However, the histogram of the natural log of income in Figure 11.38 is much more nearly symmetric—and, for technical reasons, more suitable for use as the dependent variable in regression.

Figure 11.37

Skewed Distribution of Income

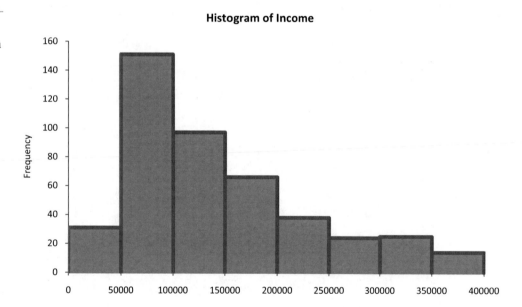

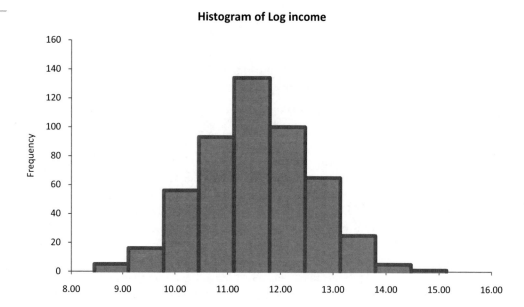

Figure 11.38

Symmetric
Distribution of
Log(Income)

| EXAMPLE | **11.3 POSSIBLE GENDER DISCRIMINATION IN SALARY AT FIFTH NATIONAL BANK OF SPRINGFIELD (CONTINUED)** |

Returning to the bank discrimination example, a glance at the distribution of salaries of the 208 employees shows some skewness to the right—a few employees make substantially more than the majority of employees. Therefore, it might make sense to use the natural logarithm of Salary instead of Salary as the dependent variable. If we do this, how do we interpret the results?

Objective   To reanalyze the bank salary data, now using the logarithm of salary as the dependent variable.

Solution

All of the analyses we did previously with this data set could be repeated with Log(Salary) as the dependent variable. For the sake of discussion, we look only at the regression equation with Female and YrsExper as explanatory variables. After we create the Log(Salary) variable and run the regression, we obtain the output in Figure 11.39. The estimated regression equation is

$$\text{Predicted Log(Salary)} = 10.4907 + 0.0188\text{YrsExper} - 0.1616\text{Female} \quad \textbf{(11.20)}$$

Figure 11.39

Regression Output
with Log of Salary as
Dependent Variable

	A	B	C	D	E	F	G
7		Multiple	R-Square	Adjusted	StErr of		
8	*Summary*	R		R-Square	Estimate		
9		0.6514	0.4243	0.4187	0.1794		
10							
11		Degrees of	Sum of	Mean of		F-Ratio	p-Value
12	*ANOVA Table*	Freedom	Squares	Squares			
13	Explained	2	4.861326452	2.430663226	75.5556	< 0.0001	
14	Unexplained	205	6.59495595	0.032170517			
15							
16		Coefficient	Standard	t-Value	p-Value	Confidence Interval 95%	
17	*Regression Table*		Error			Lower	Upper
18	Constant	10.4907	0.0280	374.8768	< 0.0001	10.4355	10.5458
19	YrsExper	0.0188	0.0018	10.5556	< 0.0001	0.0153	0.0224
20	Female	-0.1616	0.0265	-6.0936	< 0.0001	-0.2139	-0.1093

When logarithm of Y is used in the regression equation, the interpretations of s_e and R^2 are different because the units of the dependent variable are completely different.

The R^2 and s_e values are 42.4% and 0.1794. For comparison, when this same equation was estimated with Salary as the dependent variable, R^2 and s_e were 49.1% and 8.070.

We first interpret R^2 and s_e. Neither is directly comparable to the R^2 or s_e value with Salary as the dependent variable. Recall that R^2 in general is the percentage of the dependent variable explained by the regression equation. The problem here is that the two R^2 values are percentages explained of *different* dependent variables, Log(Salary) and Salary. The fact that one is smaller than the other (42.4% versus 49.1%) does not necessarily mean that it corresponds to a "worse" fit. They simply are not comparable.

The situation is even worse with s_e. Each s_e is a measure of a typical residual, but the residuals in the Log(Salary) equation are in log dollars, whereas the residuals in the Salary equation are in dollars. These units are completely different. For example, the log of $1000 is only 6.91. Therefore, it is no surprise that s_e for the Log(Salary) equation is *much* smaller than s_e for the Salary equation. If we want comparable standard error measures for the two equations, we should take antilogs of fitted values from the Log(Salary) equation to convert them back to dollars, subtract these from the original Salary values, and take the standard deviation of these "residuals." (The EXP function in Excel can be used to take antilogs.) You can check that the resulting standard deviation is 7774.[10] This is somewhat smaller than s_e from the Salary equation, an indication of a slightly *better* fit.

Finally, we interpret equation (11.20) itself. Fortunately, this is fairly easy. When the dependent variable is Log(Y) and a term on the right-hand side of the equation is of the form bX, then whenever X increases by 1 unit, $\hat{Y}$ changes by a constant *percentage*, and this percentage is approximately equal to b (written as a percentage). For example, if $b = 0.035$, then when X increases by one unit, $\hat{Y}$ increases by approximately 3.5%. Applied to equation (11.20), this means that for each extra year of experience with Fifth National, an employee's salary can be expected to increase by about 1.88%. To interpret the Female coefficient, note that the only possible increase in Female is 1 unit (from 0 for male to 1 for female). When this occurs, the expected percentage *decrease* in salary is approximately 16.16%. In other words, equation (11.20) implies that females can expect to make about 16% less than men for comparable years of experience. ■

The coefficient b can now be interpreted as the approximate percentage change in Y when X increases by 1 unit.

We are not necessarily claiming that the bank data are fit better with Log(Salary) as the dependent variable than with Salary—it appears to be a virtual toss-up. However, the lessons from this example are important in general. They are as follows.

1. The R^2 values with Y and Log(Y) as dependent variables are not directly comparable. They are percentages explained of *different* variables.

2. The s_e values with Y and Log(Y) as dependent variables are usually of totally different magnitudes. To make the s_e from the log equation comparable, we need to

---

[10]To make the two "standard deviations" comparable, we use the denominator $n - 3$ in each.

go through the procedure described in the example, so that the residuals are in *original* units.

3. To interpret any term of the form bX in the log equation, we first express b as a percentage. For example, $b = 0.035$ becomes 3.5%. Then when X increases by 1 unit, the expected *percentage* change in Y is approximately this percentage b.

Remember these points, especially the third, when using the logarithm of Y as the dependent variable.

The log transformation of a dependent variable Y is used frequently. This is partly because it induces nice statistical properties (such as making the distribution of Y more symmetric). But an important advantage of this transformation is its ease of interpretation in terms of percentage changes.

Constant Elasticity Relationships A particular type of nonlinear relationship that has firm grounding in economic theory is called a *constant elasticity* relationship. It is also called a *multiplicative* relationship. It has the form shown in equation (11.21).

> **Formula for Multiplicative Relationship**
> $$Y = aX_1^{b_1}X_2^{b_2} \cdots X_k^{b_k}$$
> (11.21)

One property of this type of relationship is that the effect of a change of any explanatory variable X_i on Y depends on the levels of the other X's in the equation. This is not true for the *additive* relationships

$$Y = a + b_1X_1 + b_2X_2 + \cdots + b_kX_k$$

that we have been discussing. For additive relationships, when any X_i increases by one unit, Y changes by b_i units, regardless of the levels of the other X's. Multiplicative relationships are defined in the box.

> In a **multiplicative** (or **constant elasticity**) **relationship**, the dependent variable is expressed as a *product* of explanatory variables raised to powers. When any explanatory variable changes by 1%, the dependent variable changes by a constant *percentage*.

The term *constant elasticity* comes from economics. Economists define the elasticity of Y with respect to X as the percentage change in Y that accompanies a 1% increase in X. Often this is in reference to a demand–price relationship. Then the *price elasticity* is the percentage decrease in demand when price increases by 1%. Usually, the elasticity depends on the current value of X. For example, the price elasticity when the price is $35 might be different than when the price is $50. However, if the relationship is of the form

$$Y = aX^b$$

then the elasticity is *constant*, the same for any value of X. Moreover, it is approximately equal to the exponent b. For example, if $Y = 2X^{-1.5}$, then the constant elasticity is approximately -1.5, so that when X increases by 1%, Y decreases by approximately 1.5%.

The constant elasticity for any X is approximately equal to the exponent of that X.

The constant elasticity property carries over to the multiple-X relationship in equation (11.21). Then each exponent is the approximate elasticity for its X. For example, if $Y = 2X_1^{-1.5}X_2^{0.7}$, then we can make the following statements:

- When X_1 increases by 1%, Y decreases by approximately 1.5%, regardless of the current values of X_1 and X_2.

- When X_2 increases by 1%, Y increases by approximately 0.7%, regardless of the current values of X_1 and X_2.

We can use linear regression to estimate the nonlinear relationship in equation (11.21) by taking natural logarithms of *all* variables. Here we exploit two properties of logarithms: (1) the log of a product is the sum of the logs, and (2) the log of X^b is b times the log of X. Therefore, taking logs of both sides of equation (11.21) gives

$$\text{Log}(Y) = \text{Log}(a) + b_1\text{Log}(X_1) + \cdots + b_k\text{Log}(X_k)$$

This equation is *linear* in the log variables $\text{Log}(Y)$ and $\text{Log}(X_1)$ through $\text{Log}(X_k)$, so it can be estimated in the usual way with multiple regression. We can then interpret the coefficients of the explanatory variables directly as elasticities. The following example illustrates the method.

EXAMPLE | **11.5 FACTORS RELATED TO SALES OF DOMESTIC AUTOMOBILES**

The file **Car Sales.xlsx** contains annual data (1970–1999) on domestic auto sales in the United States. The data are listed in Figure 11.40. The variables are defined as

- Sales: annual domestic auto sales (in number of units)
- PriceIndex: consumer price index of transportation
- Income: real disposable income
- Interest: prime rate of interest

Figure 11.40   Data for Automobile Demand Example

	A	B	C	D	E	F	G	H	I
1	Year	Sales	PriceIndex	Income	Interest				
2	1970	7,115,270	37.5	2630	7.91%				
3	1971	8,676,410	39.5	2745.3	5.72%	Sources: Automotive News, Market			
4	1972	9,321,310	39.9	2874.3	5.25%	Data Book (various issues) for column			
5	1973	9,618,510	41.2	3072.3	8.03%	B, from Economic Report of the			
6	1974	7,448,340	45.8	3051.9	10.81%	President, 2000, for columns C, D, E			
7	1975	7,049,840	50.1	3108.5	7.86%				
8	1976	8,606,860	55.1	3243.5	6.84%				
9	1977	9,104,930	59	3360.7	6.83%				
10	1978	9,304,250	61.7	3527.5	9.06%				
11	1979	8,316,020	70.5	3628.6	12.67%				
12	1980	6,578,360	83.1	3658	15.27%				
13	1981	6,206,690	93.2	3741.1	18.87%				
14	1982	5,756,610	97	3791.7	14.86%				
15	1983	6,795,230	99.3	3906.9	10.79%				
16	1984	7,951,790	103.7	4207.6	12.04%				
17	1985	8,204,690	106.4	4347.8	9.93%				
18	1986	8,222,480	102.3	4486.6	8.33%				
19	1987	7,080,890	105.4	4582.5	8.21%				
20	1988	7,526,334	108.7	4784.1	9.32%				
21	1989	7,014,850	114.1	4906.5	10.87%				
22	1990	6,842,733	120.5	5041.2	10.01%				
23	1991	6,072,255	123.8	5033	8.46%				
24	1992	6,216,488	126.5	5189.3	6.25%				
25	1993	6,674,458	130.4	5261.3	6.00%				
26	1994	7,181,975	134.3	5397.2	7.15%				
27	1995	7,023,843	139.1	5539.1	8.83%				
28	1996	7,139,884	143	5677.7	8.27%				
29	1997	6,907,992	144.3	5854.5	8.44%				
30	1998	6,756,804	141.6	6168.6	8.35%				
31	1999	6,987,208	144.4	6320	8.00%				

Estimate and interpret a multiplicative (constant elasticity) relationship between Sales and PriceIndex, Income, and Interest.

Objective To use logarithms of variables in a multiple regression to estimate a multiplicative relationship for automobile sales as a function of price, income, and interest rate.

Solution

We first take natural logs of all four variables. (This can be done in one step with the StatTools Transform utility or we can use Excel's LN function.) We then use multiple regression, with Log(Quantity) as the dependent variable and Log(PriceIndex), Log(Income), and Log(Interest) as the explanatory variables. The resulting output is shown in Figure 11.41. The corresponding equation for Log(Quantity) is

Predicted Log(Sales) = 14.126 − 0.384Log(PriceIndex) + 0.388Log(Income) − 0.070Log(Interest)

Figure 11.41

Regression Output for Multiplicative Relationship

	A	B	C	D	E	F	G
7		Multiple	R-Square	Adjusted	StErr of		
8	Summary	R		R-Square	Estimate		
9		0.6813	0.4642	0.4023	0.1053		
10							
11		Degrees of	Sum of	Mean of	F-Ratio	p-Value	
12	ANOVA Table	Freedom	Squares	Squares			
13	Explained	3	0.249567775	0.083189258	7.5073	0.0009	
14	Unexplained	26	0.288107728	0.011081066			
15							
16		Coefficient	Standard	t-Value	p-Value	Confidence Interval 95%	
17	Regression Table		Error			Lower	Upper
18	Constant	14.1260	1.9838	7.1206	< 0.0001	10.0482	18.2037
19	Log(PriceIndex)	-0.3837	0.2091	-1.8351	0.0780	-0.8135	0.0461
20	Log(Income)	0.3881	0.3621	1.0720	0.2936	-0.3561	1.1324
21	Log(Interest)	-0.0698	0.0893	-0.7821	0.4412	-0.2534	0.1137

If we like, we can convert this back to original variables, that is, back to multiplicative form, by taking antilogs. The result is

$$\text{Predicted Sales} = 1364048 \text{PriceIndex}^{-0.384} \text{Income}^{0.388} \text{Interest}^{-0.070}$$

where the constant 1364048 is the antilog of 14.126 (and be calculated in Excel with the EXP function).

In either form the equation implies that the elasticities are approximately equal to −0.384, 0.388, and −0.070. When PriceIndex increases by 1%, Sales tends to decrease by about 0.384%; when Income increases by 1%, Sales tends to increase by about 0.388%; and when Interest increases by 1%, Sales tends to decrease by about 0.070%.

Does this multiplicative equation provide a better fit to the automobile data than an additive relationship? Without doing considerably more work, it is difficult to answer this question with any certainty. As we discussed in the previous example, it is *not* sufficient to compare R^2 and s_e values for the two fits. Again, the reason is that one has Log(Sales) as the dependent variable, whereas the other has Sales, so the R^2 and s_e measures aren't comparable. We simply state that the multiplicative relationship provides a reasonably good fit (for example, a scatterplot of its fitted values versus residuals shows no unusual patterns), and it makes sense economically.

Before leaving this example, we note that the results for this data set are not quite as clear as they might appear. (This is often the case with real data.) First, the correlation between Sales and Income, or between Log(Sales) and Log(Income), is negative, not positive.

However, because of multicollinearity, a topic discussed in the next chapter, the regression coefficient of Log(Income) is positive. Second, most of the behavior appears to be driven by the early years. If you rerun the analysis from 1980 on, you will discover almost no relationship between Sales and the other variables. ∎

One final example of a multiplicative relationship is the *learning curve* model. A **learning curve** relates the unit production time (or cost) to the cumulative volume of output since that production process first began. Empirical studies indicate that production times tend to decrease by a relatively constant *percentage* every time cumulative output doubles. To model this phenomenon, let Y be the time required to produce a unit of output, and let X be the *cumulative* amount of output that has been produced. If we assume that the relationship between Y and X is of the form

$$Y = aX^b$$

then it can be shown that whenever X doubles, Y decreases to a *constant* percentage of its previous value. This constant is often called the **learning rate**. For example, if the learning rate is 80%, then each doubling of cumulative production yields a 20% reduction in unit production time. It can be shown that the learning rate satisfies the equation

$$b = \ln(\text{learning rate})/\ln(2) \qquad \textbf{(11.22)}$$

(where "ln" refers to the natural logarithm). So once we estimate b, we can use equation (11.22) to estimate the learning rate.

The following example illustrates a typical application of the learning curve model.

EXAMPLE **11.6 THE LEARNING CURVE FOR PRODUCTION OF A NEW PRODUCT AT PRESARIO**

The Presario Company produces a variety of small industrial products. It has just finished producing 22 batches of a new product (new to Presario) for a customer. The file **Learning Curve.xlsx** contains the times (in hours) to produce each batch. These data are listed in Figure 11.42. Clearly, the times have tended to decrease as Presario has gained more experience in making the product. Does the multiplicative learning model apply to these data, and what does it imply about the learning rate?

Objective To use a multiplicative regression equation to estimate the learning rate for production time.

Solution

One way to check whether the multiplicative learning model is reasonable is to create the log variables Log(Time) and Log(Batch) in the usual way and then see whether a scatterplot of Log(Time) versus Log(Batch) is approximately *linear*. The multiplicative model implies that it should be. Such a scatterplot appears in Figure 11.43, along with a superimposed linear trend line. The fit appears to be quite good.

To estimate the relationship, we regress Log(Time) on Log(Batch). The resulting equation is

$$\text{Predicted Log(Time)} = 4.834 - 0.155\text{Log(Batch)} \qquad \textbf{(11.23)}$$

Figure 11.42

Data for Learning Curve Example

	A	B
1	Batch	Time
2	1	125.00
3	2	110.87
4	3	105.35
5	4	103.34
6	5	98.98
7	6	99.90
8	7	91.49
9	8	93.10
10	9	92.23
11	10	86.19
12	11	82.09
13	12	82.32
14	13	87.67
15	14	81.72
16	15	83.72
17	16	81.53
18	17	80.46
19	18	76.53
20	19	82.06
21	20	82.81
22	21	76.52
23	22	78.45

Figure 11.43

Scatterplot of Log Variables with Linear Trend Superimposed

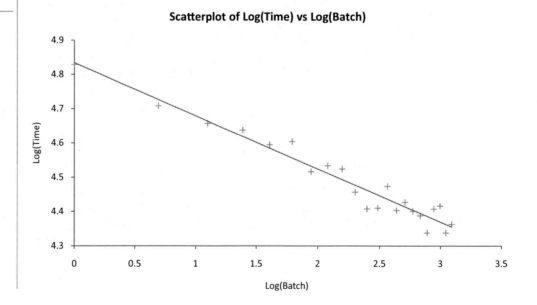

Scatterplot of Log(Time) vs Log(Batch)

There are a couple of ways to interpret this equation. First, because it is based on a multiplicative relationship, we can interpret the coefficient -0.155 as an elasticity. That is, when Batch increases by 1%, Time tends to decrease by approximately 0.155%.

Although this interpretation is correct, it is not as useful as the "doubling" interpretation we discussed previously. We know from equation (11.22) that the estimated learning rate satisfies

$$-0.155 = \ln(\text{learning rate})/\ln(2)$$

Solving for the learning rate (multiply through by $\ln(2)$ and then take antilogs), we find that it is 0.898, or approximately 90%. In words, whenever cumulative production doubles, the time to produce a batch decreases by about 10%.

Presario could use this regression equation to predict future production times. For example, suppose the customer places an order for 15 more batches of the same product. Note that Presario is already partway up the learning curve, that is, these batches are numbers 23 through 37, and the company already has experience producing the product. We can use equation (11.23) to predict the log of production time for each batch, then take their antilogs and sum them to obtain the total production time. The calculations are shown in rows 24 through 39 of Figure 11.44. We enter the batch numbers and calculate their logs in columns A and C. Then we substitute the values of Log(Batch) in column C into equation (11.23) to obtain the predicted values of Log(Time) in column E. Finally, we use Excel's EXP function to calculate the antilogs of these predictions in column B, and we calculate their sum in cell B39. The total predicted time to finish the order is about 1115 hours.

Figure 11.44 Using the Learning Curve Model for Predictions

	A	B	C	D	E	F
21	20	82.81	2.995732274	4.416548827		
22	21	76.52	3.044522438	4.337552145		
23	22	78.45	3.091042453	4.362461479		
24	23	77.324	3.135494216	4.348009995		
25	24	76.816	3.17805383	4.341413654		
26	25	76.332	3.218875825	4.335086627		
27	26	75.869	3.258096538	4.329007785		
28	27	75.426	3.295836866	4.323158388		
29	28	75.003	3.33220451	4.317521744		
30	29	74.596	3.36729583	4.312082919		
31	30	74.205	3.401197382	4.306828497		
32	31	73.829	3.433987204	4.301746382		
33	32	73.466	3.465735903	4.296825631		
34	33	73.117	3.496507561	4.292056313		
35	34	72.779	3.526360525	4.287429384		
36	35	72.453	3.555348061	4.282936587		
37	36	72.137	3.583518938	4.278570366		
38	37	71.832	3.610917913	4.274323782		
39		1115.183	$\longleftarrow$	Predicted time for next 15 batches		

PROBLEMS

Level A

26. In a study of housing demand, a county assessor is interested in developing a regression model to estimate the selling price of residential properties within her jurisdiction. She randomly selects 15 houses and records the selling price in addition to the following values: the size of the house (in hundreds of square feet), the total number of rooms in the house, the age of the house, and an indication of whether the house has an attached garage. These data are stored in the file **P11_26.xlsx**.

  a. Estimate and thoroughly interpret a multiple regression model that includes the four potential explanatory variables.

  b. Evaluate the estimated regression model's goodness of fit.

  c. Use the estimated model to predict the sales price of a 3000-square-foot, 20-year-old home that has 7 rooms but no attached garage.

27. A manager of boiler drums wants to use regression analysis to predict the number of worker-hours needed to erect the drums in future projects. Consequently, data for 36 randomly selected boilers were collected. In addition to worker-hours (Y), the variables measured include boiler capacity, boiler design pressure, boiler type, and drum type. All of these measurements can be found in the file **P11_27.xlsx**.

  a. Formulate an appropriate multiple regression model to predict the number of worker-hours needed to erect boiler drums.

  b. Estimate the formulated model using the given sample data, and interpret the estimated regression coefficients.

  c. According to the estimated regression model, what is the difference between the mean number of worker-hours required for erecting industrial and utility field boilers?

  d. According to the estimated regression model, what is the difference between the mean number of worker-hours required for erecting boilers with steam drums and those with mud drums?

  e. Given the estimated regression model, predict the number of worker-hours needed to erect a utility-field, steam-drum boiler with a capacity of 550,000 pounds per hour and a design pressure of 1400 pounds per square inch.

  f. Given the estimated regression model, predict the number of worker-hours needed to erect an industrial-field, mud-drum boiler with a capacity of 100,000 pounds per hour and a design pressure of 1000 pounds per square inch.

28. Suppose that a regional express delivery service company wants to estimate the cost of shipping a package (Y) as a function of cargo type, where cargo type includes the following possibilities: fragile, semi-fragile, and durable. Costs for 15 randomly chosen packages of approximately the same weight and same distance shipped, but of different cargo types, are provided in the file **P11_28.xlsx**.

  a. Formulate an appropriate multiple regression model to predict the cost of shipping a given package.

  b. Estimate the formulated model using the given sample data, and interpret the estimated regression coefficients.

  c. According to the estimated regression model, which cargo type is the *most* costly to ship? Which cargo type is the *least* costly to ship?

  d. How well does the estimated model fit the given sample data? How can the model's goodness of fit be improved?

  e. Given the estimated regression model, predict the cost of shipping a package with semifragile cargo.

29. The file **P11_11.xlsx** contains annual observations of the American minimum wage. Has the minimum wage been growing at roughly a *constant* rate over this period?

  a. Generate a scatterplot for these data. Comment on the observed behavior of the minimum wage over time.

  b. Formulate and estimate an appropriate regression model to explain the variation of the American minimum age over the given time period. Interpret the estimated regression coefficients.

  c. Analyze the estimated model's residuals. Is your estimated regression model adequate? If not, return to part **b** and revise your model. Continue to revise the model until your results are satisfactory.

30. Formulate a regression model that adequately estimates the relationship between monthly electrical power usage (Y) and home size (X) using the data in the file **P11_13.xlsx**. Interpret your results. How well does your model explain the variation in monthly electrical power usage?

31. An insurance company wants to determine how its annual operating costs depend on the number of home insurance (X_1) and automobile insurance (X_2) policies that have been written. The file **P11_31.xlsx** contains relevant information for 10 branches of the insurance company. The company believes that a multiplicative model might be appropriate because operating costs typically increase by a constant percentage as the number of either type of policy increases by a given percentage. Use the given data to estimate a multiplicative model for this insurance company. Interpret your results. Does a multiplicative model provide a good fit with these data?

32. Suppose that an operations manager is trying to determine the number of labor hours required to produce the ith unit of a certain product. Consider the data provided in the file **P11_32.xlsx**. For example, the second unit produced required 517 labor hours, and the 600th unit required 34 labor hours.

   a. Use the given data to estimate a relationship between the total number of units produced and the labor hours required to produce the last unit in the total set. Interpret your findings.

   b. Use your estimated relationship to predict the number of labor hours that will be needed to produce the 800th unit.

Level B

33. The human resources manager of DataCom, Inc., wants to predict the annual salaries of given employees using the following explanatory variables: the number of years of prior relevant work experience, the number of years of employment at DataCom, the number of years of education beyond high school, the employee's gender, the employee's department, and the number of individuals supervised by the given employee. These data have been collected for a sample of employees and are given in the file **P11_05.xlsx**.

   a. Formulate an appropriate multiple regression model to predict the annual salary of a given DataCom employee.

   b. Estimate the formulated model using the given sample data, and interpret the estimated regression coefficients.

   c. According to the estimated regression model, is there a difference between the mean salaries earned by male and female employees at DataCom? If so, how large is the difference?

   d. According to the estimated regression model, is there a difference between the mean salaries earned by employees in the sales department and those in the advertising department at DataCom? If so, how large is the difference?

   e. According to the estimated regression model, in which department are DataCom employees paid the *highest* mean salary? In which department are DataCom employees paid the *lowest* mean salary?

   f. Given the estimated regression model, predict the annual salary of a female employee who served in a similar department at another company for 10 years prior to coming to work at DataCom. This woman, a graduate of a 4-year collegiate business program, has been supervising 12 subordinates in the purchasing department since joining the organization 5 years ago.

34. Does the rate of violent crime acts vary across different regions of the United States?

   a. Using the data in the file **P11_34.xlsx**, develop and estimate an appropriate regression model to explain the variation in acts of violent crime across the four established regions of the United States. Thoroughly interpret the estimated model. Rank the four regions from highest to lowest according to their mean violent crime rate.

   b. How would you modify the regression model in part **a** to account for possible differences in the violent crime rate across the various subdivisions of the given regions? Estimate your revised model and interpret your findings. Rank the nine subdivisions from highest to lowest according to their mean violent crime rate.

35. Suppose that you are interested in predicting the price of a laptop computer based on its various features. The file **P11_35.xlsx** contains observations on the sales price and a number of potentially relevant variables for a randomly chosen sample of laptop computers.

   a. Formulate a multiple regression model that includes all potential explanatory variables and estimate it with the given sample data.

   b. Interpret the estimated regression equation. Be sure to indicate the impact of each attribute on the computer's sales price. For example, what impact does the monitor type have on the average sales price of a laptop computer?

   c. How well does the estimated regression model fit the data given in the file?

   d. Use the estimated regression equation to predict the price of a laptop computer with the following features: a 60-megahertz processor, a battery that holds its charge for 240 minutes, 32 megabytes of RAM, a DX chip, a color monitor, a mouse pointing device, and a 24-hour, toll-free customer service hotline.

36. Continuing Problem 18, suppose that the antique collector believes that the *rate of increase* of the auction price with the age of the item will be driven upward by a large number of bidders. How would you revise the multiple regression model developed previously to model this feature of the problem?

   a. Estimate your revised model using the data in the file **P11_18.xlsx**.

   b. Interpret each of the estimated coefficients in your revised model.

   c. Does this revised model fit the given data better than the original multiple regression model? Explain why or why not.

37. Continuing Problem 19, revise the multiple regression model developed previously to include an interaction term between the return on average equity (X_1) and annual dividend rate (X_2).

   a. Estimate your revised model using the data provided in the file **P11_19.xlsx**.

   b. Interpret each of the estimated coefficients in your revised model. In particular, how do you interpret the coefficient for the interaction term in the revised model?

c. Does this revised model fit the given data better than does the original multiple regression model? Explain why or why not.

38. Continuing Problem 24, suppose that one of the managers of this regional express delivery service company is trying to decide whether to add an interaction term involving the package weight (X_1) and the distance shipped (X_2) in the multiple regression model developed previously.

a. Why would the manager want to add such a term to the regression equation?

b. Estimate the revised model using the data given in the file **P11_24.xlsx**.

c. Interpret each of the estimated coefficients in your revised model. In particular, how do you interpret the coefficient for the interaction term in the revised model?

d. Does this revised model fit the given data better than the original multiple regression model? Explain why or why not.

11.7 VALIDATION OF THE FIT

The fit from a regression analysis is often overly optimistic. When we use the least squares procedure on a given set of data, we exploit all of the idiosyncrasies of the particular data set to obtain the best possible fit. There is no guarantee that the fit will be as good when the estimated regression equation is applied to *new* data. In fact, it usually isn't. This is particularly important when our goal is to use the regression equation to predict new values of the dependent variable. The usual situation is that we use a given data set to estimate a regression equation. Then we gather new data on the *explanatory* variables and use these, along with the already-estimated regression equation, to predict the new (but unknown) values of the dependent variable.

One way to see whether this procedure will be successful is to split the original data set into two subsets: one subset for estimation and one subset for validation. We estimate the regression equation from the first subset. Then we substitute the values of explanatory variables from the second subset into this equation to obtain predicted values for the dependent variable. Finally, we compare these predicted values with the known values of the dependent variable in the second subset. If the agreement is good, there is reason to believe that the regression equation will predict well for new data.

This validation procedure is fairly simple to perform in Excel. We illustrate it for the Bendrix manufacturing data in Example 11.2. (See the file **Overhead Costs Validation.xlsx**.) There we used 36 monthly observations to regress Overhead on MachHrs and ProdRuns. For convenience, we repeat the regression output in Figure 11.45. In particular, it shows an R^2 value of 86.6% and an s_e value of $4109.

Figure 11.45

Multiple Regression Output for Bendrix Example

	A	B	C	D	E	F	G
7		Multiple	R-Square	Adjusted	StErr of		
8	Summary	R		R-Square	Estimate		
9		0.9308	0.8664	0.8583	4108.993		
10							
11		Degrees of	Sum of	Mean of	F-Ratio	p-Value	
12	ANOVA Table	Freedom	Squares	Squares			
13	Explained	2	3614020661	1807010330	107.0261	< 0.0001	
14	Unexplained	33	557166199.1	16883824.22			
15							
16		Coefficient	Standard	t-Value	p-Value	Confidence Interval 95%	
17	Regression Table		Error			Lower	Upper
18	Constant	3996.678	6603.651	0.6052	0.5492	-9438.551	17431.907
19	MachHrs	43.536	3.589	12.1289	< 0.0001	36.234	50.839
20	ProdRuns	883.618	82.251	10.7429	< 0.0001	716.276	1050.960

Now suppose that this data set is from one of Bendrix's two plants. The company would like to predict overhead costs for the other plant by using data on machine hours and production runs at the other plant. The first step is to see how well the regression from Figure 11.45 fits data from the other plant. We perform this validation on the 36 months of data shown in Figure 11.46. The validation results also appear in this figure.

Figure 11.46

Validation of Bendrix Regression Results

	A	B	C	D	E	F
1	Validation data					
2						
3	Coefficients from regression equation (based on original data)					
4		Constant	MachHrs	ProdRuns		
5		3996.6782	43.5364	883.6179		
6						
7	Comparison of summary measures					
8		Original	Validation			
9	R-square	0.8664	0.7733			
10	StErr of Est	4108.99	5256.50			
11						
12	Month	MachHrs	ProdRuns	Overhead	Fitted	Residual
13	1	1374	24	92414	85023	7391
14	2	1510	35	92433	100663	-8230
15	3	1213	21	81907	75362	6545
16	4	1629	27	93451	98775	-5324
17	5	1858	28	112203	109629	2574
18	6	1763	40	112673	116096	-3423
19	7	1449	44	104091	105960	-1869
20	8	1422	46	104354	106552	-2198
45	33	1534	38	104946	104359	587
46	34	1529	29	94325	96189	-1864
47	35	1389	47	98474	105999	-7525
48	36	1350	34	90857	92814	-1957

To obtain the results in this figure, we proceed as follows.

PROCEDURE FOR VALIDATING REGRESSION RESULTS

1 **Copy old results.** Copy the results from the original regression to the ranges B5:D5 and B9:B10.

2 **Calculate fitted values and residuals.** The fitted values are now the predicted values of overhead for the other plant, based on the original regression equation. We find these by substituting the new values of MachHrs and ProdRuns into the original equation. To do so, enter the formula

=$B$5+SUMPRODUCT($C$5:$D$5,B13:C13)

in cell E13 and copy it down. Then calculate the residuals (prediction errors for the other plant) by entering the formula

=D13-E13

in cell F13 and copying it down.

3 **Calculate summary measures.** We see how well the original equation fits the new data by calculating R^2 and s_e values. Recall that R^2 in general is the square of the correlation between observed and fitted values. Therefore, enter the formula

=CORREL(E13:E48,D13:D48)^2

in cell C9. The s_e value is essentially the average of the squared residuals, but it uses the denominator $n - 3$ (when there are two explanatory variables) rather than $n - 1$. Therefore, enter the formula

=SQRT(SUMSQ((F13:F48)/33)

in cell C10.

The results in Figure 11.46 are typical. The validation results are usually not as good as the original results. The value of R^2 has decreased from 86.6% to 77.3%, and the value of s_e has increased from $4109 to $5257. Nevertheless, Bendrix might conclude that the original regression equation is adequate for making future predictions at either plant.

11.8 CONCLUSION

The material in this chapter has illustrated how to fit an equation to a set of points and how to interpret the resulting equation. We have also discussed two measures, R^2 and s_e, that indicate the goodness of fit of the regression equation. Although the general technique is called *linear* regression, we have seen how it can be used to estimate nonlinear relationships through suitable transformations of variables. We are not finished with our study of regression, however. In the next chapter we make some statistical assumptions about the regression model and then discuss the types of inferences that can be made from regression output. In particular, we discuss the accuracy of the estimated regression coefficients, the accuracy of predictions made from the regression equation, and the general topic of which explanatory variables "belong" in the regression equation.

Summary of Key Terms

Term	Symbol	Explanation	Excel	Page	Equation Number
Regression analysis		A general method for estimating the relationship between a dependent variable and one or more explanatory variables		572	
Dependent (or response) variable	Y	The variable being estimated or predicted in a regression analysis		574	
Explanatory (or independent) variables	$X_1, X_2,$ and so on	The variables used to explain or predict the dependent variable		574	
Simple regression		A regression model with a single explanatory variable	StatTools/ Regression & Classification/ Regression	574	
Multiple regression		A regression model with any number of explanatory variables	StatTools/ Regression & Classification/ Regression	574	
Correlation	r_{XY}	A measure of strength of the linear relationship between two variables X and Y	**=CORREL(range1, range2)**, or StatTools/ Summary Statistics/ Correlation and Covariance	583	11.1

(continued)

Term	Symbol	Explanation	Excel	Page	Equation Number
Fitted value		The predicted value of dependent variable found by substituting explanatory values into the regression equation		585–587	11.2
Residual		The difference between actual and fitted values of dependent variable		585–587	11.2
Least squares line		The regression equation that minimizes the sum of squared residuals	StatTools/ Regression & Classification/ Regression	587	11.3, 11.4
Standard error of estimate	s_e	Essentially, the standard deviation of the residuals; indicates the magnitude of the prediction errors	StatTools/ Regression & Classification/ Regression	591, 592	11.7, 11.11
Coefficient of determination	R^2	The percentage of variation in the response variable explained by the regression model	StatTools/ Regression & Classification/ Regression	593, 594	11.8
Adjusted R^2		A measure similar to R^2, but adjusted for the number of explanatory variables in the equation		600	
Regression coefficients	$b_1, b_2,$ and so on	The coefficients of the explanatory variables in a regression equation	StatTools/ Regression & Classification/ Regression	597	11.9
Dummy variables		Variables coded as 0 or 1, used to capture categorical variables in a regression analysis	StatTools/Data Utilities/ Dummy	602	
Interaction variables		Products of explanatory variables, used when the effect of one on the dependent variable depends on the value of the other	StatTools/Data Utilities/ Interaction	608	
Nonlinear transformations		Variables created to capture nonlinear relationships in a regression model	StatTools/Data Utilities/ Transform	612	
Quadratic model		A regression model with linear and squared explanatory variables	StatTools/ Regression & Classification/ Regression	615	
Model with logarithmic transformations		A regression model using logarithms of Y and/or X's	StatTools/ Regression & Classification/ Regression	616	
Constant elasticity (or multiplicative relationship)		A relationship where Y changes by a constant percentage when any X changes by 1%; requires logarithmic transformations	StatTools/ Regression & Classification/ Regression	620	11.21

(continued)

Term	Symbol	Explanation	Excel	Page	Equation Number
Learning curve		A particular multiplicative relationship used to indicate how cost or time in production decreases through time	StatTools/ Regression & Classification/ Regression	623	11.22
Validation of fit		Checks how well a regression model based on one sample predicts a related sample	StatTools/ Regression & Classification/ Regression	628	

PROBLEMS

Conceptual Exercises

C.1. Consider the relationship between yearly wine consumption (liters of alcohol from drinking wine, per person) and yearly deaths from heart disease (deaths per 100,000 people) in 19 developed countries. Suppose that you read a newspaper article in which the reporter states the following:

Researchers find that the correlation between yearly wine consumption and yearly deaths from heart disease is −0.84. Thus, it is reasonable to conclude that increased consumption of alcohol from wine causes fewer deaths from heart disease in industrialized societies.

Comment on the reporter's interpretation of the correlation measure in this case.

C.2. "It is generally appropriate to delete all outliers in the given data set when producing a scatterplot." Is this statement true or false? Explain your choice.

C.3. How does one interpret the relationship between two numeric variables when the estimated least squares regression line for them is essentially *horizontal* (i.e., flat)?

C.4. Suppose that you generate a scatterplot of residuals versus fitted values of the dependent variable for a given estimated regression model. Furthermore, you find the correlation between the residuals and fitted values to be 0.829. Does this provide a good indication that the estimated regression model is satisfactory? Explain why or why not.

C.5. Suppose that you have generated three alternative multiple regression models to explain the variation in a particular dependent variable. The regression output for each model can be summarized as follows:

	Model 1	Model 2	Model 3
No. of indep. vars.	4	6	9
R^2	0.76	0.77	0.79
Adj. R^2	0.75	0.74	0.73

Which of these models would you select as "best"? Explain your choice.

Level A

39. Many companies manufacture products that are at least partially produced using chemicals (e.g., paint, gasoline, and steel). In many cases, the quality of the finished product is a function of the temperature and pressure at which the chemical reactions take place. Suppose that a particular manufacturer wants to model the quality (Y) of a product as a function of the temperature (X_1) and the pressure (X_2) at which it is produced. The file **P11_39.xlsx** contains data obtained from a carefully designed experiment involving these variables. Note that the assigned quality score can range from a maximum of 100 to a minimum of 0 for each manufactured product.

a. Formulate a multiple regression model that includes the two given explanatory variables. Estimate the model using the given sample data. Does the estimated model fit the data well?

b. Interpret each of the estimated coefficients in the multiple regression model.

c. Consider adding a term to model a possible interaction between the two explanatory models. Reformulate the model and estimate it again using the given data. Does the inclusion of the interaction term improve the model's goodness of fit?

d. Interpret each of the estimated coefficients in the revised model. In particular, how do you interpret the coefficient for the interaction term in the revised model?

40. Suppose that a power company located in southern Alabama wants to predict the peak power load (i.e., the maximum amount of power that must be generated each day to meet demand) as a function of the daily high temperature (X). A random sample of 25 summer days is chosen, and the peak power load and the high temperature are recorded on each day. The file **P11_40.xlsx** contains these observations.

a. Generate a scatterplot for these data. Comment on the observed relationship between the dependent variable and explanatory variable.

b. Formulate and estimate an appropriate regression model to predict the peak power load for this power company. Interpret the estimated regression coefficients.

c. Analyze the estimated model's residuals. Is your estimated regression model adequate? If not, return to part **b** and revise your model. Continue to revise the model until your results are satisfactory.

d. Use the final version of your model to predict the peak power load on a summer day with a high temperature of 100 degrees.

41. Management of a home appliance store in Charlotte would like to understand the growth pattern of the monthly sales of VCR units over the past 2 years. Managers have recorded the relevant data in an Excel spreadsheet, which can be found in the file **P11_09.xlsx**. Have the sales of VCR units been growing *linearly* over the past 24 months?

a. Generate a scatterplot for these data. Comment on the observed behavior of monthly VCR sales at this store over time.

b. Formulate and estimate an appropriate regression model to explain the variation of monthly VCR sales over the given time period. Interpret the estimated regression coefficients.

c. Analyze the estimated model's residuals. Is your estimated regression model adequate? If not, return to part **b** and revise your model. Continue to revise the model until your results are satisfactory.

42. Chipco, a small computer chip manufacturer, wants to be able to forecast monthly operating costs as a function of the number of units produced during a month. They have collected the 16 months of data in the file **P11_42.xlsx**.

a. Determine an equation that can be used to predict monthly production costs from units produced. Are there any outliers?

b. How could the regression line obtained in part **a** be used to determine whether the company was efficient or inefficient during any particular month?

43. The file **P11_43.xlsx** contains data on the following variables for several underdeveloped countries:

- Infant mortality rate
- Per capita GNP
- Percentage of people completing primary school
- Percentage of adults who can read (adult literacy)

Use these data to determine which of the given variables (by itself) best predicts infant mortality. Can you give an explanation for your answer?

44. The file **P11_44.xlsx** contains data that relate the unit cost of producing a fuel pressure regulator to the cumulative number of fuel pressure regulators produced at the Ford plant in Bedford. For example, the 4000th unit cost $13.70 to produce.

a. Fit a learning curve to these data.

b. We would predict that doubling cumulative production reduces the cost of producing a regulator by what amount?

45. The "beta" of a stock is found by running a regression with the explanatory variable being the monthly return on a market index and the dependent variable being the monthly return on the stock. The beta of the stock is then the slope of this regression.

a. Explain why most stocks have a positive beta.

b. Explain why a stock with a beta with absolute value greater than 1 is more volatile than the market and a stock with a beta less than 1 (in absolute value) is less volatile than the market.

c. Use the data in the file **P11_45.xlsx** to estimate the beta for Ford Motor Company.

d. What percentage of the variation in Ford's return is explained by market variation? What percentage is unexplained by market variation?

e. Verify (using Excel's COVAR and VARP functions) that the beta for Ford is given by

$$\frac{\text{Covariance between Ford and Market}}{\text{Variance of Market}}$$

Also, verify that the correlation between Ford return and Market return is the square root of R^2.

46. The file **P11_46.xlsx** contains monthly returns on Anheuser-Busch (AB) and a market index. Use these data to answer the following questions:

a. What percentage of the variation in the return in AB is explained by variation in the market? What percentage is unexplained by variation in the market?

b. Predict the change in AB during a month in which the market goes up by 2%.

c. Use Excel's CORREL functions to determine the correlation between the return on AB and the market. Verify that this correlation between AB and the market is equal to the square root of R^2 from the regression output.

d. Estimate the beta (refer to the previous problem) for AB by using regression. Then verify that it can also be found (using Excel's COVAR and VARP functions) from

$$\frac{\text{Covariance between AB and Market}}{\text{Variance of Market}}$$

47. Investors are interested in knowing whether estimates of stock betas based on past history are good predictors of future betas (refer to Problem 45). How could you use a data set that gives monthly returns on several stocks over a 5-year period to see whether this is true?

48. The file **P11_48.xlsx** contains monthly sales (in thousands) and price of a popular candy bar.

a. Describe the type of relationship between price and sales (linear, nonlinear, strong, weak).

b. What percentage of variation in monthly sales is explained by variation in price? What percentage is unexplained?

c. If the price of the candy bar is 55 cents, predict monthly candy bar sales.

d. Use the regression output to determine the correlation between price and candy bar sales.

e. Are there any outliers?

49. The file **P11_49.xlsx** contains the amount of money spent advertising a product (in thousands of dollars) and the number of units sold (in millions) for 8 months.

a. Assume that the only factor influencing monthly sales is advertising. Fit the following three curves to these data: linear ($Y = a + bX$), exponential ($Y = ab^X$), and multiplicative ($Y = aX^b$). Which equation best fits the data?

b. Interpret the best-fitting equation.

c. Using the best-fitting equation, predict sales during a month in which $60,000 is spent on advertising.

50. Callaway Golf is trying to determine how the price of a set of clubs affects the demand for clubs. The file **P11_50.xlsx** contains the price of a set of clubs (in dollars) and the monthly sales (in millions of sets sold).

a. Assume the only factor influencing monthly sales is price. Fit the following three curves to these data: linear ($Y = a + bX$), exponential ($Y = ab^X$), and multiplicative ($Y = aX^b$). Which equation best fits the data?

b. Interpret your best-fitting equation.

c. Using the best-fitting equation, predict sales during a month in which the price is $470.

51. The number of cars per 1000 people is known for virtually every country in the world. For many countries, however, per capita income is not known. Can you think of a way to estimate per capita income for countries where it is unknown?

52. The file **P11_52.xlsx** contains the cost (in 1990 dollars) of making a 3-minute phone call from London to New York. Use regression to estimate how (or whether) the cost of a London to New York call has declined over time. Based on these data, predict the cost of a 3-minute phone call in the year 2000. (Source: *The Economist*, September 28, 1996)

53. The file **P11_53.xlsx** contains the databit power per chip for computers. Use regression to estimate how databit power per chip has changed over time. (This result is called Moore's law.) Also predict the databit power per chip in the year 2000. Do you think Moore's law can continue indefinitely? (Source: *One World Ready or Not*, by William Greider, 1996)

54. The file **P11_54.xlsx** contains the cost of building (in hundreds of millions of dollars) a plant to produce RAM chips for PCs. Use regression to estimate how (or whether) the cost of building a RAM plant has increased over time. Predict the cost of building a RAM plant in the year 2000. (Source: *One World Ready or Not*, by William Greider, 1996)

55. The file **P11_55.xlsx** contains the unit cost of producing a unit of computer memory, as a function of the number of units of computer memory that have been produced to date. Use regression to analyze how (or whether) the price of a bit of memory has changed as more memory has been produced (Source: *Every Investor's Guide to High-Tech Stocks*, by Michael Murphy, 1998)

56. The Baker Company wants to develop a budget to predict how overhead costs vary with activity levels. Management is trying to decide whether direct labor hours (DLH) or units produced is the better measure of activity for the firm. Monthly data for the preceding 24 months appear in the file **P11_56.xlsx**. Use regression analysis to determine which measure, DLH or Units (or both), should be used for the budget. How would the regression equation be used to obtain the budget for the firm's overhead costs?

57. The auditor of Kiely Manufacturing is concerned about the number and magnitude of year-end adjustments that are made annually when the financial statements of Kiely Manufacturing are prepared. Specifically, the auditor suspects that the management of Kiely Manufacturing is using discretionary write-offs to manipulate the reported net income. To check this, the auditor has collected data from 25 firms that are similar to Kiely Manufacturing in terms of manufacturing facilities and product lines. The cumulative reported third quarter income and the final net income reported are listed in the file **P11_57.xlsx** for each of these 25 firms. If Kiely Manufacturing reported a cumulative third quarter income of $2,500,000 and a preliminary net income of $4,900,000, should the auditor conclude that the relationship between cumulative third quarter income and the annual income for Kiely Manufacturing differs from that of the 25 firms in this sample? Explain why or why not.

Level B

58. An economic development researcher wants to understand the relationship between the size of the monthly home mortgage or rent payment for households in a particular middle-class neighborhood and the following set of household variables: family size, approximate location of the household within the neighborhood, an indication of whether those surveyed own or rent their home, gross annual income of the first household wage earner, gross annual income of the second household wage earner (if applicable), average monthly expenditure on utilities, and the total indebtedness (excluding the value of a home mortgage) of the household. Observations on each of these variables for a large sample of households are recorded in the file **P02_06.xlsx**.

   a. Beginning with *family size*, iteratively add one explanatory variable and estimate the resulting regression equation to explain the variation in the monthly home mortgage or rent payment. If adding any explanatory variable causes the *adjusted R^2* measure to fall, do not include that variable in subsequent versions of the regression model. Otherwise, include the variable and consider adding the next variable in the set. Which variables are included in the final version of your regression model?

   b. Interpret the final estimated regression equation you obtained through the process outlined in part **a**. Also, report and interpret the standard error of estimate s_e, the coefficient of determination R^2, and the adjusted R^2 for the final estimated model.

59. (This problem is based on an actual court case in Philadelphia.) In the 1994 congressional election, the Republican candidate outpolled the Democratic candidate by 400 votes (excluding absentee ballots). The Democratic candidate outpolled the Republican candidate by 500 absentee votes. The Republican candidate sued (and won), claiming that vote fraud must have played a role in the absentee ballot count. The Republican's lawyer ran a regression to predict (based on past elections) how the absentee ballot margin could be predicted from the votes tabulated on voting machines. Selected results are given in the file **P11_59.xlsx**. Show how this regression could be used by the Republican to prove his claim of vote fraud. (*Hint*: Is the 1994 result an outlier?)

60. The file **P11_60.xlsx** contains data on the price of new and used Taurus sedans. All prices for used cars are from 1995. For example, a new Taurus bought in 1985 cost $11,790 and the wholesale used price of that car in 1995 was $1700. A new Taurus bought in 1994 cost $18,680 and it could be sold used in 1995 for $12,600.

   a. You want to predict the resale value (as a percentage of the original price of the vehicle) as a function of the vehicle's age. Find an equation to do this. (You should try at least two different equations and choose the one with the best fit.)

   b. Suppose all police cars are Ford Tauruses. If you were the business manager for the New York Police Department, what use would you make of your findings from part **a**?

61. The data for this problem are fictitious, but they are not far off.) For each of the top 25 business schools, the file **P11_61.xlsx** contains the average salary of a professor. Thus, for Indiana University (number 15 in the rankings), the average salary is $46,000. Use this information and regression to show that IU is doing a great job with its available resources.

62. Suppose the correlation between the average height of parents and the height of their firstborn male child is 0.5.

You are also told that:

- The average height of all parents is 66 inches.
- The standard deviation of the average height of parents is 4 inches.
- The average height of all male children is 70 inches.
- The standard deviation of the height of all male children is 4 inches.

If a mother and father are 73 and 80 inches tall, respectively, how tall do you predict their son to be? Explain why this is called "regression toward the mean."

63. Do increased taxes increase or decrease economic growth? Table 11.1 gives tax revenues as a percentage of Gross Domestic Product (GDP) and the average annual percentage growth in GDP per capita for nine countries during the years 1970 through 1994. Do these data support or contradict the dictum of supply-side economics? (Source: *The Economist*, August 24, 1996)

Table 11.1 Economic Data from Nine Countries

Country	Tax revenues as % of GDP	Average annual growth in GDP per capita
Japan	26%	3.1%
United States	27%	1.6%
Italy	33%	2.5%
Canada	34%	2.0%
Switzerland	30%	1.0%
Britain	36%	1.9%
Germany	38%	2.2%
France	42%	1.9%
Sweden	49%	1.1%

64. For each of the four data sets in the file **P11_64.xlsx**, calculate the least squares line. For which of these data sets would you feel comfortable in using the least squares line to predict Y? (Source: Frederic Anscombe, *The American Statistician*)

65. Suppose we run a regression on a data set of X's and Y's and obtain a least squares line of $Y = 12 - 3X$.

   a. If we double each value of X, what is the new least squares line?

   b. If we triple each value of Y, what is the new least squares line?

   c. If we add 6 to each value of X, what is the new least squares line?

   d. If we subtract 4 from each value of Y, what is the new least squares line?

66. The file **P11_66.xlsx** contains monthly cost accounting data on overhead costs, machine hours, and direct material costs. This problem will help you explore the meaning of R^2 and the relationship between R^2 and correlations.

a. Create a table of correlations between the individual variables.

b. If you ignored the two explanatory variables MachHrs and DirMatCost and predicted each OHCost as the *mean* of all OHCosts, then a typical "error" would be OHCost minus the mean of all OHCosts. Find the sum of squared errors using this form of prediction, where the sum is over all observations.

c. Now run three regressions: (1) OHCost versus MachHrs, (2) OHCost versus DirMatCost, and (3) OHCost versus both MachHrs and DirMatCost. (The first two are simple regressions, the third is a multiple regression.) For each, find the sum of squared residuals, and divide this by the sum of squared errors from part **b**. What is the relationship between this ratio and the associated R^2 for that equation? (Now do you see why R^2 is referred to as the percentage of variation explained?)

d. For the first two regressions in part **c**, what is the relationship between R^2 and the corresponding correlation between the dependent and explanatory variable? For the third regression it turns out that the R^2 can be expressed as a complicated function of all three correlations in part **a**, that is, not just the correlations between the dependent variable and each explanatory variable, but also the correlation between the explanatory variables. Note that this R^2 is not just the sum of the R^2 values from the first two regressions in part **c**. Why do you think this is true, intuitively? However, R^2 for the multiple regression is still the square of a correlation—namely, the correlation between the observed and predicted values of OHCost. Verify that this is the case for these data.

67. The file **P11_67.xlsx** contains hypothetical starting salaries (in $1000's) for MBA students directly after graduation. The file also lists their years of experience prior to the MBA program and their class standing in the MBA program (on a 0–100 scale).

a. Estimate the regression equation with Salary as the dependent variable and Exper and Class as the explanatory variables. What does this equation imply? What does the standard error of estimate s_e tell you? What about R^2?

b. Repeat part **a**, but now include the interaction term Exper*Class (the product) in the equation as well as Exper and Class individually. Answer the same questions as in part **a**. What evidence is there that this extra variable (the interaction variable) is worth including? How do you interpret this regression equation?

68. In a study published in 1985 in *Business Horizons*, Platt and McCarthy employed multiple regression analysis to explain variations in compensations among the CEOs of large companies. Their primary objective was to discover whether levels of compensations are affected more by short-run considerations—"I'll earn more now if my company does well in the short run"—or long-run considerations—"My best method for obtaining high compensation is to stay with my company for a long time." The study used as its dependent variable the total compensation for each of the 100 highest paid CEOs in 1981. This variable was defined as the sum of salary, bonuses, and other benefits (measured in $1000s).

The following potential explanatory variables were considered. To capture short-run effects, the average of the company's previous 5 years' percentage changes in earnings per share (EPS) and the projected percentage change in next year's EPS were used. To capture the long-run effect, age and years as CEO, two admittedly correlated variables, were used. Dummy variables for the CEO's background (finance, marketing, and so on) were also considered. Finally, the researchers considered several nonlinear and interaction terms based on these variables. The best-fitting equation was the following:

$$TotComp = -3493 + 898.7(\text{Years as CEO})$$
$$+ 9.28(\text{Years as CEO})^2 - 17.19(\text{Years as CEO})(\text{Age})$$
$$+ 88.27\text{Age} + 867.4\text{Finance}$$

(The last variable represents a dummy variable, equal to 1 if the CEO had a finance background, 0 otherwise.) The corresponding R^2 was 19.4%.

a. Explain what this equation implies about CEO compensations.

b. The researchers drew the following conclusions. First, it appears that CEOs should indeed concentrate on long-run considerations—namely, those that keep them on their jobs the longest. Second, the absence of the short-run company-related variables from the equations helps to confirm the conjecture that CEOs who concentrate on earning the quick buck for their companies may not be acting in their best self-interest. Finally, the positive coefficient of the dummy variable may imply that financial people possess skills that are vitally important, and firms therefore outbid one another for the best financial talent. Based on the data given, do you agree with these conclusions?

c. Consider a CEO (other than those in the study) who has been in his position for 10 years and has a financial background. Predict his total yearly compensation (in $1000s) if he is 50 years old; if he is 55 years old. Explain why the difference between these two predictions is not 5(88.27), where 88.27 is the coefficient of the Age variable.

69. The Wilhoit Company has observed that there is a linear relationship between indirect labor expense (ILE) and direct labor hours (DLH). Data for direct labor hours and indirect labor expense for 18 months are given in the file **P11_69.xlsx**. At the start of month 7, all cost categories in the Wilhoit Company increased by 10%, and they stayed at this level for months 7 through 12. Then at the start of month 13, another 10% across-the-board increase in all costs occurred, and the company operated at this price level for months 13 through 18.

a. Plot the data. Verify that the relationship between ILE and DLH is approximately linear within each 6-month period. Use regression (three times) to estimate the slope and intercept during months 1 through 6; during months 7 through 12; during months 13 through 18.

b. Use regression to fit a straight line to all 18 data points simultaneously. What values of the slope and intercept do you obtain?

c. Perform a price level adjustment to the data and re-estimate the slope and intercept using all 18 data points. Assuming no cost increases for month 19, what is your prediction for indirect labor expense if there are 35,000 direct labor-hours in month 19?

d. Interpret your results. What causes the difference in the linear relationship estimated in parts **b** and **c**?

70. The Bohring Company manufactures a sophisticated radar unit that is used in a fighter aircraft built by Seaways Aircraft. The first 50 units of the radar unit have been completed, and Bohring is preparing to submit a proposal to Seaways Aircraft to manufacture the next 50 units. Bohring wants to submit a competitive bid, but at the same time, it wants to ensure that all the costs of manufacturing the radar unit are fully covered. As part of this process, Bohring is attempting to develop a standard for the number of labor hours required to manufacture each radar unit. Developing a labor standard has been a continuing problem in the past. The file **P11_70.xlsx** lists the number of labor hours required for each of the first 50 units of production. Bohring accountants want to see whether regression analysis, together with the concept of learning curves, can help solve the company's problem.

The Firm Chair Company manufactures customized wood furniture and sells the furniture in large quantities to major furniture retailers. Jim Bolling has recently been assigned to analyze the company's pricing policy. He has been told that quantity discounts were usually given. For example, for one type of chair, the pricing changed at quantities of 200 and 400—that is, these were the quantity "breaks," where the marginal cost of the next chair changed. For this type of chair, the file **Firm Chair.xlsx** contains the quantity and total price to the customer for 81 orders. Use regression to help Jim discover the pricing structure that Firm Chair evidently used. (*Note:* A linear regression of TotPrice versus Quantity will give you a "decent" fit, but you can do much better by introducing appropriate variables into the regression.) ■

Sales of single-family houses have been brisk in Mid City this year. This has especially been true in older, more established neighborhoods, where housing is relatively inexpensive compared to the new homes being built in the newer neighborhoods. Nevertheless, there are also many families who are willing to pay a higher price for the prestige of living in one of the newer neighborhoods. The file **Mid City.xlsx** contains data on 128 recent sales in Mid City. For each sale, the file shows the neighborhood (1, 2, or 3) in which the house is located, the number of offers made on the house, the square footage, whether the house is made primarily of brick, the number of bathrooms, the number of bedrooms, and the selling price. Neighborhoods 1 and 2 are more traditional neighborhoods, whereas neighborhood 3 is a newer, more prestigious, neighborhood.

Use regression to estimate and interpret the pricing structure of houses in Mid City. Here are some considerations.

1. Is there a "premium" for a brick house, everything else being equal?

2. Is there a premium for a house in neighborhood 3, everything else being equal?

3. Is there an *extra* premium for a brick house in neighborhood 3, in addition to the usual premium for a brick house?

4. For purposes of estimation and prediction, could neighborhoods 1 and 2 be collapsed into a single "older" neighborhood? ■

Howie's Bakery is one of the most popular bakeries in town, and the favorite at Howie's is French bread. Each day of the week, Howie's bakes a number of loaves of French bread, more or less according to a daily schedule. To maintain its fine reputation, Howie's gives away to charity any loaves not sold on the day they are baked. Although this occurs frequently, it is also common for Howie's to run out of French bread on any given day—more demand than supply. In this case, no extra loaves are baked that day; the customers have to go elsewhere (or come back to Howie's the next day) for their French bread. Although French bread at Howie's is always popular, Howie's stimulates demand by running occasional 10% off sales.

Howie's has collected data for 20 consecutive weeks, 140 days in all. These data are listed in the file **Howies Bakery.xlsx**. The variables are Day (Monday–Sunday), Supply (number of loaves baked that day), OnSale (whether French bread is on sale that day), and Demand (loaves actually sold that day). Howie's would like you to see whether regression can be used successfully to estimate Demand from the other data in the file. Howie reasons that if these other variables can be used to predict Demand, then he might be able to determine his daily supply (number of loaves to bake) in a more cost-effective way.

How successful is regression with these data? Is Howie correct that regression can help him determine his daily supply? Is any information "missing" that would be useful? How would you obtain it? How would you use it? Is this extra information *really* necessary? ■

CASE 11.4 INVESTING FOR RETIREMENT

Financial advisors offer many types of advice to customers, but they generally agree that one of the best things people can do is invest as much as possible in tax-deferred retirement plans. Not only are the earnings from these investments exempt from income tax (until retirement), but the investment itself is tax-exempt. This means that if a person invests, say, $10,000 income of his $100,000 income in a tax-deferred retirement plan, he pays income tax that year on only $90,000 of his income. This is probably the best method available to most people for avoiding tax payments. However, which group takes advantage of this attractive investment opportunity: everyone, people with low salaries, people with high salaries, or who?

The file **Retirement Plan.xlsx** lets you investigate this question. It contains data on 194 couples: number of dependent children, combined annual salary of husband and wife, current mortgage on home, average amount of other (nonmortgage) debt, and percentage of combined income invested in tax-deferred retirement plans (assumed to be limited to 15%, which is realistic). Using correlations, scatterplots, and regression analysis, what can you conclude about the tendency to invest in tax-deferred retirement plans in this group of people? ■

Regression Analysis: Statistical Inference

PREDICTING MOVIE REVENUES

In the opener for Chapter 3, we discussed the article by Simonoff and Sparrow (2000) that examined movie revenues for 311 movies released in 1998 and late 1997. We saw that movie revenues were related to several variables, including genre, Motion Picture Association of America (MPAA) rating, country of origin, number of stars in the cast, whether the movie was a sequel, and whether the movie was released during a few "choice" times. In Chapter 3, we were limited to looking at summary measures and charts of the data. Now that we are studying regression, we can look further into the analysis performed by Simonoff and Sparrow. Specifically, they examined whether these variables, plus others, are effective in predicting movie revenues.

The authors actually report the results from three multiple regression models. All of these used the logarithm of the total U.S. gross revenue from the film as the dependent variable. (They used the *logarithm* because the distribution of gross revenues is very positively skewed.) The first model used only the "prerelease" variables listed in the previous paragraph. The values of these variables were all known prior to the movie's release. Therefore, the purpose of this model was to see how well revenues could be predicted *before* the movie was released.

The second model used the variables from model 1, along with two variables that could be observed after the first week of the movie's release: the first weekend gross, and the number of screens the movie opened on. (Actually, the logarithms of these latter two variables were used, again because of positive skewness. Also, the authors found it necessary to run two separate regressions at this stage—one for movies that opened on 10 or fewer screens, and another for movies that opened on more than 10 screens.) The idea here was that the success or failure of many movies depends to a large extent on how they do right after they are released. Therefore, it was expected that this information would add significantly to the predictive power of the regression model.

The third model built on the second by adding an additional explanatory variable: the number of Oscar nominations the movie received for key awards (Best Picture, Best Director, Best Actor, Best Actress, Best Supporting Actor, and Best Supporting Actress). This information is often not known until well after a movie's release, but it was hypothesized that Oscar nominations would lead to a significant increase in a movie's revenues, and that a regression model with this information could lead to very different predictions of revenue.

Simonoff and Sparrow found that the coefficients of the first regression model were in line with the box plots we saw in Figure 3.1 of Chapter 3. For example, the variables that measured the number of "best" actors and actresses were both positive and significant, indicating that star power tends to lead to larger revenues. However, the predictive power of this model was poor. Given its standard error of prediction (and taking into account that the *logarithm* of revenue was the dependent variable), the authors stated that "the predictions of total grosses for an individual movie can be expected to be off by as much as a multiplicative factor of 100 high or low." It appears that there is no way to predict which movies will succeed and which will fail based on prerelease data only.

The second model added considerable predictive power. The regression equations indicated that gross revenue is positively related to first weekend gross and negatively related to the number of opening screens, both of these variables being significant. As for prediction, the factor of 100 mentioned in the previous paragraph decreased to a factor of 10 (for movies with 10 or fewer opening screens) or 2 (for movies with more than 10 opening screens). This is still not perfect—predictions of total revenue made after the movie's first weekend can still be pretty far off—but this additional information about initial success certainly helps.

The third model added only slightly to the predictive power, primarily because so few of the movies (10 out of 311) received Oscar nominations for key awards. However, the predictions for those that did receive nominations increased considerably. For example, the prediction for the multiple Oscar nominee *Saving Private Ryan,* based on the second model, was 194.622 (millions of dollars). Its prediction based on the third model increased to a whopping 358.237. (Interestingly, the prediction for this movie from the first model was only 14.791, and its actual gross revenue was 216.119. Perhaps the reason *Saving Private Ryan* did not make as much as the third model predicted was that the Oscar nominations were announced about 9 months after its release—too long to do much good.)

Simonoff and Sparrow then used their third model to predict gross revenues for 24 movies released in 1999—movies that were not in the data set used to estimate the regression model. They found that 21 out of 24 of the resulting 95% prediction intervals captured the actual gross revenues, which is about what we would expect. However, many of these prediction intervals were extremely wide, and several of the predictions were well above or below the actual revenues. The authors conclude by quoting Tim Noonan, a former movie executive: "Since predicting gross is extremely difficult, you have to serve up a [yearly] slate of movies and know that over time you'll have 3 or 4 to the left and 2 or 3 to the right. You must make sure you are doing things that mitigate your downside risk." ■

12.1 INTRODUCTION

In the previous chapter we learned how to fit a regression equation to a set of points by using the least squares method. The purpose of this regression equation is to provide a good fit to the points in the sample so that we can understand the relationship between a dependent variable and one or more explanatory variables. The entire emphasis of the discussion in the previous chapter was on finding a regression model that fits the observations in the sample. In this chapter we take a slightly different point of view: We assume that the observations in the sample are taken from some larger population. For example, the sample of 50 regions from the Pharmex drugstore example could represent a sample of all the regions where Pharmex does business. If that is the case, then we might be interested in the relationship between variables in the entire population, not just in the sample.

There are two basic problems we discuss in this chapter. The first has to do with a *population regression model*. We want to infer its characteristics—that is, its intercept and slope term(s)—from the corresponding terms estimated by least squares. We also want to know which explanatory variables "belong" in the equation. We have seen that there are typically a large number of *potential* explanatory variables, and it is often not clear which of these do the best job of explaining variation in the dependent variable. In addition, we would like to infer whether there is any population regression equation worth pursuing. It might be that the potential explanatory variables provide very little explanation of the dependent variable, based on the sample data.

The second problem we discuss in this chapter is prediction. We touched on the prediction problem in the previous chapter, primarily in the context of predicting the dependent variable for part of the sample held out for validation purposes. In reality, we had the values of the dependent variable for that part of the sample, so prediction was not really necessary. Now we go beyond the sample and predict values of the dependent variable for *new* observations. There is no way to check the accuracy of these predictions, at least not right away, because the true values of the dependent variable are not yet known. However, we provide prediction intervals to measure the accuracy of the predictions.

12.2 THE STATISTICAL MODEL

To perform statistical inference in a regression context, we must first make several assumptions about the population. Throughout the analysis these assumptions remain exactly that—they are only assumptions, not facts. These assumptions represent an idealization of reality, and as such, they are never likely to be entirely satisfied for the population in any real study. From a practical point of view, all we can ask is that they represent a close approximation to reality. If this is the case, then the analysis in this chapter is valid. But if the assumptions are grossly violated, we should be very suspicious of the statistical inferences that are based on these assumptions. Although we can never be entirely certain of the validity of the assumptions, there are ways to check for gross violations, and we discuss some of these.

Regression Assumptions

1. There is a population regression line. It joins the *means* of the dependent variable for all values of the explanatory variables. For any fixed values of the explanatory variables, the mean of the errors is 0.

2. For any values of the explanatory variables, the standard deviation of the dependent variable is a constant, the same for all such values.

3. For any values of the explanatory variables, the dependent variable is normally distributed.

4. The errors are probabilistically independent.

Because these assumptions are so crucial to the regression analysis that follows, it is important to understand exactly what they mean. Assumption 1 is probably the most important. It implies that for some set of explanatory variables, there is an exact linear relationship in the population between the *means* of the dependent variable and the values of the explanatory variables.

These explanatory variables could be original variables or variables we create, such as dummies, interactions, or nonlinear transformations.

Because of its importance, we discuss assumption 1 in more detail. Let Y be the dependent variable, and assume that there are k explanatory variables, X_1 through X_k. Let $\mu_{Y|X_1,\dots,X_k}$ be the mean of all Y's for any fixed values of the X's. Then assumption 1 implies that there is an exact linear relationship between the mean $\mu_{Y|X_1,\dots,X_k}$ and the X's. Specifically, it implies that there are coefficients α and β_1 through β_k such that the following equation holds for all values of the X's:

Population Regression Line Joining Means

$$\mu_{Y|X_1,\dots,X_k} = \alpha + \beta_1 X_1 + \cdots + \beta_k X_k \qquad \text{(12.1)}$$

We commonly use Greek letters to denote population parameters and regular letters for their sample estimates.

In the terminology of the previous chapter, α is the intercept term, and β_1 through β_k are the slope terms. We use Greek letters for these coefficients to denote that they are *unobservable* population parameters. Assumption 1 implies the existence of a population regression equation and the corresponding α and β's. However, it tells us nothing about the values of these parameters. We still need to estimate them from sample data, and we continue to use the least squares method to do so.

Equation (12.1) says that the *means* of the Y's lie on the population regression line. However, we know from a scatterplot that most *individual* Y's do not lie on this line. The vertical distance from any point to the line is called an **error term**. The error for any point, labeled ϵ, is the difference between Y and $\mu_{Y|X_1,\dots,X_k}$, that is,

$$Y = \mu_{Y|X_1,\dots,X_k} + \epsilon$$

By substituting the assumed linear form for $\mu_{Y|X_1,\dots,X_k}$, we obtain equation (12.2). This equation states that each value of Y is equal to a fitted part plus an error term. The fitted part is the linear expression $\alpha + \beta_1 X_1 + \cdots + \beta_k X_k$. The error term ϵ is sometimes positive, in which case the point is above the regression line, and sometimes negative, in which case the point is below the regression line. The last part of assumption 1 states that these errors average to 0 in the population, so that the positive errors cancel the negative errors.

Population Regression Line with Error Term

$$Y = \alpha + \beta_1 X_1 + \cdots + \beta_k X_k + \epsilon \qquad \text{(12.2)}$$

Note that an error term ϵ is similar to, but not the same as, a residual e. An error term is the vertical distance from a point to the (unobservable) population regression line. A residual is the vertical distance from a point to the estimated regression line. Residuals can be calculated from observed data; error terms cannot.

Assumption 2 concerns variation around the population regression line. Specifically, it states that the variation of the Y's about the regression line is the *same,* regardless of the values of the X's. A technical term for this property is **homoscedasticity**. A simpler term is **constant error variance**. In the Pharmex example (Example 11.1), constant error variance implies that the variation in Sales values is the same regardless of the value of Promote. As another example, recall the Bendrix manufacturing example (Example 11.2). There we related overhead costs (Overhead) to the number of machine hours (MachHrs) and the number of production runs (ProdRuns). Constant error variance implies that overhead costs vary just as much for small values of MachHrs and ProdRuns as for large values—or any values in between.

There are many applications in which assumption 2 is questionable. The variation in Y often increases as X increases—a violation of assumption 2. We saw an example of this in Figure 11.10 (repeated here in Figure 12.1), which is based on the HyTex mail-order data in Example 3.11 from Chapter 3. This scatterplot shows AmountSpent versus Salary for a sample of HyTex's customers. Clearly, the variation in AmountSpent increases as Salary increases, which makes intuitive sense. Customers with small salaries have little disposable income, so they all tend to spend small amounts for mail-order items. Customers with large salaries have more disposable income. Some of them spend a lot of it on mail-order items and some spend only a little of it—hence, a larger variation. Scatterplots with this "fan" shape are not at all uncommon in real studies, and they exhibit a clear violation of assumption 2.[1] We say that the data in this graph exhibit **heteroscedasticity**, or more simply, **nonconstant error variance**. These terms are summarized in the following box.

Homoscedasticity means that the variability of Y values is the same for all X values.
Heteroscedasticity means that the variability of Y values is larger for some X values than for others.

Figure 12.1

Illustration of Nonconstant Error Variance

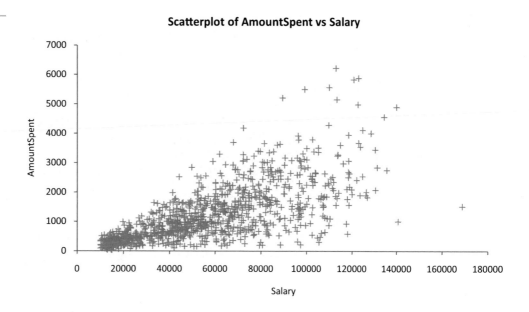

Scatterplot of AmountSpent vs Salary

---

[1]The fan shape in Figure 12.1 is probably the most common form of nonconstant error variance, but it is not the only possible form.

The easiest way to detect nonconstant error variance is through a visual inspection of a scatterplot. We draw a scatterplot of the dependent variable versus an explanatory variable X and see whether the points vary more for some values of X than for others. We can also examine the residuals with a residual plot, where residual values are on the vertical axis and some other variable (Y or one of the X's) is on the horizontal axis. If the residual plot exhibits a fan shape or other evidence of nonconstant error variance, this also indicates a violation of assumption 2.

Assumption 3 states that the errors are normally distributed. We can check this by forming a histogram or a Q-Q plot of the residuals. If assumption 3 holds, then the histogram should be approximately symmetric and bell shaped, and the points in the Q-Q plot should be close to a 45° line. But if there is an obvious skewness, too many residuals more than, say, 2 standard deviations from the mean, or some other nonnormal property, then this indicates a violation of assumption 3.

Finally, assumption 4 requires probabilistic independence of the errors. Intuitively, this assumption means that information on some of the errors provides no information on other errors. For example, if we are told that the overhead costs for months 1 through 4 are all above the regression line (positive residuals), we cannot infer anything about the residual for month 5 if assumption 4 holds.

Assumption 4 (independence of residuals) is usually suspect only for time series data.

For cross-sectional data there is generally little reason to doubt the validity of assumption 4 unless the observations are ordered in some particular way. For cross-sectional data we generally take assumption 4 for granted. However, for time series data, assumption 4 is often violated. This is because of a property called *autocorrelation*. For now, we simply mention that one output given automatically in many regression packages is the *Durbin–Watson statistic*. The Durbin–Watson statistic is one measure of autocorrelation and thus it measures the extent to which assumption 4 is violated. We can usually ignore it in cross-sectional studies, but it is important for time series data. We briefly discuss this Durbin–Watson statistic toward the end of this chapter and in Chapter 13.

One other assumption is important for numerical calculations. We must assume that no explanatory variable is an *exact* linear combination of any other explanatory variables. Another way of stating this is that there is no exact linear relationship between any set of explanatory variables. This would occur, for example, if one variable were an exact multiple of another, or if one variable were equal to the sum of several other variables. More generally, it occurs if one of the explanatory variables can be written as a weighted sum of several of the others.

Exact multicollinearity means that at least one of the explanatory variables is redundant and is not needed in the regression equation.

If such a relationship holds, it means that there is *redundancy* in the data. One of the X's could be eliminated without any loss of information. Here is a simple example. Suppose that MachHrs1 is machine hours measured in hours, and MachHrs2 is machine hours measured in *hundreds* of hours. Then it is clear that these two variables contain exactly the same information, and either of them could (and should) be eliminated.

As another example, suppose that Ad1, Ad2, and Ad3 are the amounts spent on radio ads, television ads, and newspaper ads. Also, suppose that TotAd is the amount spent on radio, television, and newspaper ads combined. Then there is an exact linear relationship among these variables:

$$\text{TotAd} = \text{Ad1} + \text{Ad2} + \text{Ad3}$$

In this case there is no need to include TotAd in the analysis because it contains no information that is not already contained in the variables Ad1, Ad2, and Ad3.

Excel Tip *StatTools issues a warning if it detects an exact linear relationship between explanatory variables in a regression model.*

Generally, it is fairly simple to spot an exact linear relationship such as these, and then to eliminate it by excluding the redundant variable from the analysis. However, if we do *not* spot the relationship and try to run the regression analysis with the redundant variable included, regression packages will typically respond with an error message. If the package interrupts the analysis with an error message containing the words "exact multicollinearity" or "linear dependence," then you should look for a redundant explanatory variable. As an example, the message from StatTools in this case is shown in Figure 12.2. We got it by deliberately entering dummy variables from *each* category of a categorical variable—something we have warned *not* to do.

Figure 12.2

Error Message
from StatTools
Indicating Exact
Multicollinearity

Although this problem can be a nuisance, it is usually caused by an oversight and can be fixed easily by eliminating a redundant variable. A more common and serious problem is **multicollinearity**, where explanatory variables are highly, but not exactly, correlated. A typical example is an employee's years of experience and age. Although these two variables are not equal for all employees, they are likely to be highly correlated. If they are both included as explanatory variables in a regression analysis, the software will not issue any error messages, but the estimates it produces can be unreliable. We discuss multicollinearity in more detail later in this chapter.

12.3 INFERENCES ABOUT THE REGRESSION COEFFICIENTS

In this section we show how to make inferences about the population regression coefficients from sample data. We begin by making the assumptions discussed in the previous section. In particular, the first assumption states that there is a population regression line. Equation (12.2) for this line is repeated here:

$$Y = \alpha + \beta_1 X_1 + \cdots + \beta_k X_k + \epsilon$$

We refer to α and the β's collectively as the **regression coefficients**. Again, Greek letters are used to indicate that these quantities are unknown and unobservable. Actually, there is one other unknown constant in the model: the variance of the error terms. Regression assumption 2 states that these errors have a constant variance, the same for all values of the X's. We label this constant variance σ^2. Equivalently, the common standard deviation of the errors is σ.

This is how it looks in theory. There is a fixed set of explanatory variables, and given these variables, the problem is to estimate α, the β's, and σ. In practice, however, it is not usually this straightforward. In real regression applications the choice of relevant explanatory variables is almost never obvious. There are at least two guiding principles: relevance and data availability. We certainly want variables that are related to the dependent variable. The best situation is when there is an established economic or physical theory to guide us. For example, economic theory suggests that the demand for a product (dependent variable) is related to its price (possible explanatory variable). But there are not enough established theories to cover every situation. We often have to use the available data, plus some trial and error, to determine a *useful* set of explanatory variables. In this sense, it is usually pointless to search for one single "true" population regression equation. Instead, we typically estimate several competing models, each with a different set of explanatory variables, and ultimately select one of them as being the most useful.

Typically, the most challenging part of a regression analysis is deciding which explanatory variables to include in the regression equation.

Deciding which explanatory variables to include in a regression equation is probably the most difficult part of any applied regression analysis. Available data sets frequently offer an overabundance of potential explanatory variables. In addition, it is possible and often useful to create new variables from original variables, such as their logarithms. So where do we stop? Is it best to include every conceivable explanatory variable that might be related to the dependent variable? One overriding principle is **parsimony**—explaining the most with the least. For example, if we can explain a dependent variable just as well (or nearly as well) with two explanatory variables as with 10 explanatory variables, then the principle of parsimony says to use only two. Models with fewer explanatory variables are generally easier to interpret, so we prefer them whenever possible.

> The principle of **parsimony** is to explain the most with the least. It favors a model with fewer explanatory variables, assuming that this model explains the dependent variable almost as well as a model with additional explanatory variables.

Before we can determine which equation has the "best" set of explanatory variables, however, we must be able to estimate the unknown parameters for a given equation. That is, for a given set of explanatory variables X_1 through X_k, we must be able to estimate α, the β's, and σ. We learned how to find point estimates of these parameters in the previous chapter. The estimates of α and the β's are the least squares estimates of the intercept and slope terms. For example, we used the 36 months of overhead data in the Bendrix example to estimate the equation

$$\text{Predicted Overhead} = 3997 + 43.54\text{MachHrs} + 883.62\text{ProdRuns}$$

This implies that the least squares estimates of α, β_1, and β_2 are 3997, 43.54, and 883.62. Furthermore, because the residuals are really estimates of the error terms, the standard error of estimate s_e is an estimate of σ. For the same overhead equation this estimate is $s_e = \$4109$.

However, we know from Chapters 8 and 9 that there is more to statistical estimation than finding point estimates of population parameters. Each potential sample from the population would typically lead to *different* point estimates. For example, if Bendrix estimated the equation for overhead from a different 36-month period, the results would almost certainly be different. Therefore, we now discuss how these point estimates vary from sample to sample.

12.3.1 Sampling Distribution of the Regression Coefficients

The key idea is again sampling distributions. Recall that the sampling distribution of any estimate derived from sample data is the distribution of this estimate over all possible samples. This idea can be applied to the least squares estimate of a regression coefficient. For example, the sampling distribution of b_1, the least squares estimate of β_1, is the distribution of b_1's we would see if we observed many samples and ran a least squares regression on each of them.

Fortunately, mathematicians have used theoretical arguments to find the required sampling distributions. We state the main result as follows. Let β be any of the β's, and let b be the least squares estimate of β. Then if the regression assumptions hold, the standardized value $(b - β)/s_b$ has a t distribution with $n - k - 1$ degrees of freedom, as given in the box. Here, k is the number of explanatory variables included in the equation, and s_b is the estimated standard deviation of the sampling distribution of b.

Sampling Distribution of a Regression Coefficient

If the regression assumptions are valid, the standardized value

$$t = \frac{b - β}{s_b}$$

has a t distribution with $n - k - 1$ degrees of freedom.

This important result can be interpreted as follows. First, the estimate b is *unbiased* in the sense that its mean is β, the true but unknown value of the slope. If we calculated b's from repeated samples, some would underestimate β and others would overestimate β, but on average they would be on target.

Second, the estimated standard deviation of b is labeled s_b. It is usually called the **standard error of b**. This standard error is related to the standard error of estimate s_e, but it is not the same. Generally, the formula for s_b is quite complicated, and it is not shown here, but its value is printed in all standard regression outputs. It measures how much the b's would vary from sample to sample. A small value of s_b is preferred—it means that b is a more accurate estimate of the true coefficient β.

Finally, the shape of the distribution of b is symmetric and bell shaped. The relevant distribution is the t distribution with $n - k - 1$ degrees of freedom.

We have stated this result for a typical coefficient of one of the X's. These are usually the coefficients of most interest. However, exactly the same result holds for the intercept term α. Now we see how to use this result.

EXAMPLE | **12.1 EXPLAINING OVERHEAD COSTS AT BENDRIX**

This example is a continuation of the Bendrix manufacturing example from the previous chapter. As before, the dependent variable is Overhead and the explanatory variables are MachHrs and ProdRuns. What inferences can we make about the regression coefficients?

Objective To use standard regression output to make inferences about the regression coefficients of machine hours and production runs in the equation for overhead costs.

Solution

When we use StatTools's Regression procedure, we obtain the output shown in Figure 12.3. (See the file **Overhead Costs.xlsx**.) This output is practically identical to regression outputs from all other statistical software packages. We have already seen that the estimates of the regression coefficients appear under the label Coefficient in the range B18:B20. These values estimate the true, but unobservable, population coefficients. The next column, labeled Standard Error, shows the s_b's. Specifically, 3.589 is the standard error of the coefficient of MachHrs, and 82.251 is the standard error of the coefficient of ProdRuns.

Figure 12.3 Regression Output for Bendrix Example

	A	B	C	D	E	F	G
7		Multiple	R-Square	Adjusted	StErr of		
8	*Summary*	R		R-Square	Estimate		
9		0.9308	0.8664	0.8583	4108.993		
10							
11		Degrees of	Sum of	Mean of	F-Ratio	p-Value	
12	*ANOVA Table*	Freedom	Squares	Squares			
13	Explained	2	3614020661	1807010330	107.0261	< 0.0001	
14	Unexplained	33	557166199.1	16883824.22			
15							
16		Coefficient	Standard	t-Value	p-Value	Confidence Interval 95%	
17	*Regression Table*		Error			Lower	Upper
18	Constant	3996.678	6603.651	0.6052	0.5492	-9438.551	17431.907
19	MachHrs	43.536	3.589	12.1289	< 0.0001	36.234	50.839
20	ProdRuns	883.618	82.251	10.7429	< 0.0001	716.276	1050.960

The b's represent point estimates of the β's, based on this particular sample. The s_b's indicate the accuracy of these point estimates. For example, the point estimate of β_1, the effect on Overhead of a 1-unit increase in MachHrs, is 43.536. We are about 95% confident that the true β_1 is within 2 standard errors of this point estimate, that is, from approximately 36.357 to 50.715. Similar statements can be made for the coefficient of ProdRuns and the intercept (Constant) term. ■

12.3.2 Confidence Intervals for the Regression Coefficients

As with any population parameters, we can use the sample data to obtain confidence intervals for the regression coefficients. For example, the preceding paragraph implies that an approximate 95% confidence interval for the coefficient of MachHrs extends from approximately 36.357 to 50.715. More precisely, a confidence interval for any β is of the form

$$b \pm t\text{-multiple} \times s_b$$

where the t-multiple depends on the confidence level and the degrees of freedom (here $n - k - 1$). For example, the relevant t-multiple for the Bendrix data, assuming we want a 95% confidence interval, is the value that cuts off probability 0.025 of the t distribution with $36 - 2 - 1 = 33$ degrees of freedom. [It is 2.035 and can be found in Excel with the function TINV(0.05,33).][2] Using this multiple gives a 95% confidence interval from 36.234 to 50.839, as shown in Figure 12.3. StatTools always provides 95% confidence intervals for the regression coefficients automatically.

12.3.3 Hypothesis Tests for the Regression Coefficients

There is another important piece of information in regression outputs: the t-values for the individual regression coefficients. These are shown in the "t-value" column of the regression output in Figure 12.3. The formula for a t-value is simple. It is the ratio of the estimated coefficient to its standard error, as shown in equation (12.3). Therefore, it indicates how many standard errors the regression coefficient is from 0. For example, the t-value for MachHrs is about 12.13, so we know that the regression coefficient of MachHrs, 43.536, is over 12 of its standard errors to the right of 0. Similarly, the coefficient of ProdRuns is more than 10 of its standard errors to the right of 0.

---

[2]StatTools uses its own built-in function to calculate this value, but it is equivalent to TINV.

A *t*-value can be used in an important hypothesis test for the corresponding regression coefficient. To motivate this test, suppose that we want to decide whether a particular explanatory variable belongs in the regression equation. A sensible criterion for making this decision is to check whether the corresponding regression coefficient is 0. If a variable's coefficient is 0, there is no point in including this variable in the equation; the 0 coefficient will cancel its effect on the dependent variable.

Therefore, it is reasonable to test whether a variable's coefficient is 0. This is usually tested versus a *two-tailed* alternative. The null and alternative hypotheses are of the form $H_0{:}\beta = 0$ versus $H_a{:}\beta \neq 0$. If we can reject the null hypothesis and conclude that this coefficient is *not* 0, then we have an argument for including the variable in the regression equation. Conversely, if we cannot reject the null hypothesis, we might decide to eliminate this variable from the equation.

The *t*-value for a variable allows us to run this test easily. We simply compare the *t*-value in the regression output with a tabulated *t*-value and reject the null hypothesis only if the *t*-value from the computer output is greater in magnitude than the tabulated *t*-value. If the test is run at the 5% significance level, for example, then the appropriate tabulated *t*-value can be found in Excel with TINV(0.05,$n - k - 1$), the same *t*-value used previously for confidence intervals.

The test for whether a regression coefficient is 0 can be run by looking at the corresponding p-value: Reject the "equals 0" hypothesis if the p-value is small, say, less than 0.05. It can also be run by looking at the confidence interval for the coefficient: Reject the "equals 0" hypothesis if the confidence interval does not contain the value 0.

Most computer packages, including StatTools, make this test even easier to run by reporting the corresponding *p*-value for the test. This eliminates the need for finding the tabulated *t*-value (or using the TINV function). The *p*-value is interpreted exactly as in Chapter 10. It is the probability (in both tails) of the relevant *t* distribution beyond the listed *t*-value. For example, referring again to Figure 12.3, the *t*-value for MachHrs is 12.13, and the associated *p*-value is less than 0.0001. This means that there is virtually no probability beyond the observed *t*-value. In words, we are still not exactly sure of the true coefficient of MachHrs, but we are virtually sure it is not 0. The same can be said for the coefficient of ProdRuns.

We soon say even more about these *t*-values and how they can help to decide which variables to include or exclude in a regression equation. But we first make the following points about hypothesis tests for regression coefficients.

Hypothesis Tests and Regression Coefficients

1. A *t*-value is usually reported for the intercept (constant) term in the equation, as well as for the other coefficients. However, this information is usually of little relevance. The reason is that there is usually no practical reason for testing whether the intercept is 0. There are rare situations where an intercept equal to 0 has a meaningful interpretation, and in such situations the hypothesis test is relevant.

2. The test of $\beta = 0$ versus a two-tailed alternative at the 5% level, say, can also be run by calculating a 95% confidence interval for β and rejecting the null hypothesis if 0 is not within the confidence interval. That is, if a 95% confidence interval for β extends from a negative number to a positive number, we cannot reject the null hypothesis that $\beta = 0$.

3. The previous test, a two-tailed test of whether a particular β is 0, is only one of many hypothesis tests that can be run. For example, consider a sample of houses that have been sold recently. We would like to regress the selling prices of the houses on their appraised values, as obtained by a professional appraiser. Now, it is pretty clear, even

before the data are observed, that selling prices will be *positively* related to appraised values. Therefore, there isn't much point in testing whether the coefficient of AppraisedValue is 0.

A more interesting test in this example is whether the coefficient of AppraisedValue is less than or greater than 1. If it is less than 1, say, then every extra dollar of appraised value contributes *less than* an extra dollar to the selling price. Therefore, we might run the one-tailed test of $H_0{:}\beta \geq 1$ versus $H_a{:}\beta < 1$. (We could also run a two-tailed test. It just depends on what we're trying to prove.) In this case we would base the test on the test statistic

$$t\text{-value} = \frac{b - 1}{s_b}$$

where b and s_b are the coefficient and standard error of AppraisedValue in the regression output. Its p-value could be calculated in Excel with the function TDIST(ABS(t-value),$n-2$,1). This t-value and the corresponding p-value are *not* reported in computer outputs, but they are easy to obtain.

The point here is that most computer outputs provide the ingredients for a very natural test—whether a given regression coefficient is 0. Virtually no work is needed to perform this test because the t-value and p-value are given in the regression output. But other hypothesis tests on the coefficients are sometimes relevant, and they can be performed easily with Excel functions.

12.3.4 A Test for the Overall Fit: The ANOVA Table

The t-values for the regression coefficients allow us to see which of the potential explanatory variables are useful in explaining the dependent variable. But it is conceivable that *none* of these variables does a very good job. That is, it is conceivable that the entire group of explanatory variables explains only an insignificant portion of the variability of the dependent variable. Although this is the exception rather than the rule in most real applications, it can certainly happen. An indication of this is that we obtain a very small R^2 value. Because R^2 is the square of the correlation between the observed values of the dependent variable and the fitted values from the regression equation, another indication of a lack of fit is that this correlation (the "multiple R") is small. In this section we state a formal procedure for testing the overall fit, or explanatory power, of a regression equation.

Suppose that the dependent variable is Y and the explanatory variables are X_1 through X_k. Then the proposed population regression equation is

$$Y = \alpha + \beta_1 X_1 + \cdots + \beta_k X_k + \epsilon$$

To say that this equation has absolutely no explanatory power means that the same value of Y will be predicted regardless of the values of the X's. In this case it makes no difference which values of the X's we use because they all lead to the same predicted value of Y. But the only way this can occur is if all of the β's are 0. So the formal hypothesis we test in this section is $H_0{:}\beta_1 = \cdots = \beta_k = 0$ versus the alternative that at least one of the β's is not 0. In words, the null hypothesis is that this set of explanatory variables has no power to explain the variation in the dependent variable Y. If we can reject the null hypothesis, as we can in the majority of applications, this means that the explanatory variables *as a group* provide at least some explanatory power. These hypotheses are summarized in the box.

> *Hypotheses for ANOVA Test*
>
> The null hypothesis is that all coefficients of the explanatory variables are 0. The alternative is that at least one of these coefficients is not 0.

At first glance it might appear that we can test this null hypothesis by looking at the individual t-values. If they are all small (statistically insignificant), then we can accept the null hypothesis of no fit; otherwise, we can reject it. However, as we see in the next section, it is possible, because of multicollinearity, to have small t-values even though the variables as a whole have *significant* explanatory power.

The alternative is to use an F test. This is sometimes referred to as the ANOVA (analysis of variance) test because the elements for calculating the required F-value are shown in an ANOVA table.[3] In general, an ANOVA table analyzes different sources of variation. In the case of regression, the variation in question is the variation of the dependent variable Y. The "total variation" of this variable is the sum of squared deviations about the mean and is labeled SST (sum of squares total).

$$SST = \sum (Y_i - \overline{Y})^2$$

The ANOVA table splits this total variation into two parts, the part *explained* by the regression equation, and the part left *unexplained*. The unexplained part is the sum of squared residuals, usually labeled SSE (sum of squared errors):

$$SSE = \sum e_i^2 = \sum (Y_i - \hat{Y}_i)^2$$

The explained part is then the difference between the total and unexplained variation. It is usually labeled SSR (sum of squares due to regression):

$$SSR = SST - SSE$$

The F test is a formal procedure for testing whether the explained variation is "large" compared to the unexplained variation. Specifically, each of these sources of variation has an associated degrees of freedom (df). For the explained variation, $df = k$, the number of explanatory variables. For the unexplained variation, $df = n - k - 1$, the sample size minus the total number of coefficients (including the intercept term). When we divide the explained or unexplained variation by its degrees of freedom, the result is called a mean square, or MS. The two mean squares we need are MSR and MSE, given by

$$MSR = \frac{SSR}{k}$$

and

$$MSE = \frac{SSE}{n - k - 1}$$

Note that MSE is the square of the standard error of estimate, that is,

$$MSE = s_e^2$$

Finally, the ratio of these mean squares is the required F-ratio for the test:

$$F\text{-ratio} = \frac{MSR}{MSE}$$

When the null hypothesis of no explanatory power is true, this F-ratio has an F distribution with k and $n - k - 1$ degrees of freedom. If the F-ratio is small, then the explained variation is small relative to the unexplained variation, and there is evidence that the regression

---

[3]This ANOVA table is similar to the ANOVA table we discussed in the Chapter 10. However, we repeat the necessary material here for those who didn't cover the ANOVA section in Chapter 10.

equation provides little explanatory power. But if the F-ratio is large, then the explained variation is large relative to the unexplained variation, and we can conclude that the equation does have some explanatory power.

As usual, the F-ratio has an associated p-value that allows us to run the test easily. In this case the p-value is the probability to the *right* of the observed F-ratio in the appropriate F distribution. This p-value is reported in most regression outputs, along with the elements that lead up to it. If it is sufficiently small, less than 0.05, say, then we can conclude that the explanatory variables as a whole have at least some explanatory power.

Reject the null hypothesis—and conclude that these X variables have at least some explanatory power—if the F-value in the ANOVA table is large and the corresponding p-value is small.

Although this test is run routinely in most applications, there is often little doubt that the equation has some explanatory power; the only questions are how much, and which explanatory variables provide the best combination. In such cases the F-ratio from the ANOVA table is typically "off the charts" and the corresponding p-value is practically 0. On the other hand, F-ratios, particularly large ones, should not necessarily be used to choose between equations with different explanatory variables included.

For example, suppose that one equation with three explanatory variables has an F-ratio of 54 with an extremely small p-value—obviously very significant. Also, suppose that another equation that includes these three variables plus a few more has an F-ratio of 37 and also has a very small p-value. (When we say small, we mean *small*. These p-values are probably listed as <0.001.) Is the first equation better because its F-ratio is higher? Not necessarily. The two F-ratios imply only that both of these equations have a good deal of explanatory power. It is better to look at their s_e values (or adjusted R^2 values) and their t-values to choose between them.

The ANOVA table is part of the StatTools output for any regression run. It appeared for the Bendrix example in Figure 12.3, which is repeated for convenience in Figure 12.4. The ANOVA table is in rows 12 through 14. We see the degrees of freedom in column B, the sums of squares in column C, the mean squares in column D, the F-ratio in cell E13, and its associated p-value in cell F13. As predicted, this F-ratio is "off the charts," and the p-value is practically 0.

Figure 12.4 Regression Output for Bendrix Example

	A	B	C	D	E	F	G
7		Multiple	R-Square	Adjusted	StErr of		
8	Summary	R		R-Square	Estimate		
9		0.9308	0.8664	0.8583	4108.993		
10							
11		Degrees of	Sum of	Mean of	F-Ratio	p-Value	
12	ANOVA Table	Freedom	Squares	Squares			
13	Explained	2	3614020661	1807010330	107.0261	< 0.0001	
14	Unexplained	33	557166199.1	16883824.22			
15							
16		Coefficient	Standard	t-Value	p-Value	Confidence Interval 95%	
17	Regression Table		Error			Lower	Upper
18	Constant	3996.678	6603.651	0.6052	0.5492	-9438.551	17431.907
19	MachHrs	43.536	3.589	12.1289	< 0.0001	36.234	50.839
20	ProdRuns	883.618	82.251	10.7429	< 0.0001	716.276	1050.960

This information wouldn't be much comfort for the Bendrix manager who is trying to understand the causes of variation in overhead costs. This manager already *knows* that machine hours and production runs are related positively to overhead costs—everyone in the company knows that! What he really wants is a set of explanatory variables that yields a high R^2 and a low s_e. The low p-value in the ANOVA tables does not guarantee these. All it guarantees is that MachHrs and ProdRuns are of "some help" in explaining variations in Overhead.

As this example indicates, the ANOVA table can be used as a screening device. If the explanatory variables do not explain a significant percentage of the variation in the dependent variable, then we can either discontinue the analysis or search for an entirely new set of explanatory variables. But even if the F-ratio in the ANOVA table is extremely significant, there is no guarantee that the regression equation provides a good enough fit for practical uses. This depends on other measures such as s_e and R^2.

PROBLEMS

Level A

1. Explore the relationship between the selling prices (Y) and the appraised values (X) of the 150 homes in the file **P02_07.xlsx** by estimating a simple linear regression model. Construct a 95% confidence interval for the model's slope (i.e., β_1) parameter. What does this confidence interval tell you about the relationship between Y and X for these data?

2. The owner of the Original Italian Pizza restaurant chain would like to predict the sales of his specialty, deep-dish pizza. He has gathered data on the monthly sales of deep-dish pizzas at his restaurants and observations on other potentially relevant variables for each of his 15 outlets in central Pennsylvania. These data are provided in the file **P11_04.xlsx**.
   a. Estimate a multiple regression model between the quantity sold (Y) and the following explanatory variables: average price of deep-dish pizzas, monthly advertising expenditures, and disposable income per household in the areas surrounding the outlets.
   b. Is there evidence of any violations of the key assumptions of regression analysis in this case?
   c. Which of the variables in this model have regression coefficients that are statistically different from 0 at the 5% significance level?
   d. Given your findings in part **c**, which variables, if any, would you choose to remove from the model estimated in part **a**? Explain your decision.

3. The *ACCRA Cost of Living Index* provides a useful and reasonably accurate measure of cost of living differences among a large number of urban areas. Items on which the index is based have been carefully chosen to reflect the different categories of consumer expenditures. The data are in the file **P02_19.xlsx**.
   a. Use multiple regression to explore the relationship between the composite index (dependent variable) and the various expenditure components (explanatory variables).
   b. Is there evidence of any violations of the key assumptions of regression analysis?

   c. Which of the variables in this model have regression coefficients that are statistically different from 0 at the 5% significance level?
   d. Given your findings in part **c**, which variables, if any, would you choose to remove from the model estimated in part **a**? Explain your decision.

4. A trucking company wants to predict the yearly maintenance expense (Y) for a truck using the number of miles driven during the year (X_1) and the age of the truck (X_2, in years) at the beginning of the year. The company has gathered the information given in the file **P11_16.xlsx**. Note that each observation corresponds to a particular truck.
   a. Formulate and estimate a multiple regression model using the given data.
   b. Does autocorrelation, multicollinearity, or heteroscedasticity appear to be a problem?
   c. Construct 95% confidence intervals for the regression coefficients of X_1 and X_2. Based on these interval estimates, which variables, if any, would you choose to remove from the model estimated in part **a**? Explain your decision.

5. Based on the data in the file **P02_25.xlsx** from the U.S. Department of Agriculture, explore the relationship between the number of farms (X) and the average size of a farm (Y) in the United States.
   a. Use the given data to estimate a simple linear regression model.
   b. Test whether there is sufficient evidence to conclude that the slope parameter (i.e., β_1) is *less than* 0. Use a 5% significance level.
   c. Based on your finding in part **b**, is it possible to conclude that a linear relationship exists between the number of farms and the average farm size between 1950 and 2003? Explain.

6. An antique collector believes that the price received for a particular item increases with its age and the number of bidders. The file **P11_18.xlsx** contains data on these three variables for 32 recently auctioned comparable items.
   a. Estimate an appropriate multiple regression model using the given data.

b. Interpret the ANOVA table for this model. In particular, does this set of explanatory variables provide at least some power in explaining the variation in price? Report a p-value for this hypothesis test.

7. Consider the enrollment data for *Business Week*'s top U.S. graduate business programs in the file **P02_03.xlsx**. Use these data to estimate a multiple regression model to assess whether there is a systematic relationship between the total number of full-time students and the following explanatory variables: (a) the proportion of female students, (b) the proportion of minority students, and (c) the proportion of international students enrolled at these distinguished business schools. Next, interpret the ANOVA table for this model. In particular, does this set of explanatory variables provide at least some power in explaining the variation in total full-time enrollment at the top graduate business programs? Report a p-value for this hypothesis test.

8. The U.S. Bureau of Labor Statistics provides data on the year-to-year percentage changes in the wages and salaries of workers in private industries, including both "white-collar" and "blue-collar" occupations. Here we consider these data in the file **P02_56.xlsx**. Is there evidence of a linear relationship between the yearly changes in the wages and salaries of "white-collar" (Y) and "blue-collar" (X) workers in the United States over the given time period? Begin to answer this question by estimating a simple linear regression model.

a. Construct a 95% confidence interval for the model's slope (i.e., β_1) parameter. Interpret this interval estimate to answer the question posed above.

b. Interpret the ANOVA table for this model. In particular, does the explanatory variable included in this simple regression model provide at least some power in explaining the variation in the dependent variable? Report a p-value for this hypothesis test.

c. What is the relationship between the t-ratio for the estimated coefficient of the explanatory variable and the F-ratio found in the ANOVA section of the output? Do these two test statistic values provide the same indication regarding a possible relationship between yearly changes in the wages and salaries of white-collar and blue-collar workers? Explain why or why not.

9. Suppose that a regional express delivery service company wants to estimate the cost of shipping a package (Y) as a function of cargo type, where cargo type includes the following possibilities: fragile, semi-fragile, and durable. Costs for 15 randomly chosen packages of approximately the same weight and same distance shipped, but of different cargo types, are provided in the file **P11_28.xlsx**.

a. Estimate an appropriate multiple regression model to predict the cost of shipping a given package.

b. Interpret the ANOVA table for this model. In particular, do the explanatory variables included in your model formulated in part **a** provide at least some power in explaining the variation in the cost of shipping a package? Report a p-value for this hypothesis test.

10. A simple linear regression with 11 observations yielded the ANOVA table in Table 12.1.
   a. Complete this ANOVA table.
   b. Using $\alpha = 0.05$, test the hypothesis of no linear regression.

Table 12.1 ANOVA Table

Degrees of Freedom	Sum of Squares
Regression	1000
Error	
Total	2500

Level B

11. Consider the relationship between the size of the population (X) and the average household income level (Y) for residents of U.S. towns.
   a. Using the data in the file **P02_24.xlsx**, estimate a regression model involving these two variables.
   b. Does autocorrelation, multicollinearity, or heteroscedasticity appear to be a problem?
   c. Test whether there is sufficient evidence to conclude that the slope parameter (i.e., β_1) is *greater than* 0.0035. Use a 5% significance level.
   d. Based on your finding in part **c**, is it possible to conclude that a linear relationship exists between the size of the population and the average household income level for residents of U.S. towns? Explain.

12. Suppose you find the ANOVA table shown in Table 12.2 for a simple linear regression.
   a. Find the correlation between X and Y. Assume the slope of the least squares line is negative.
   b. Find the p-value for the test of the hypothesis of no linear regression.

Table 12.2 ANOVA Table

Degrees of Freedom	Sum of Squares
SSR	20
SSE	4
SST	100

12.4 MULTICOLLINEARITY

Recall that the coefficient of any variable in a regression equation indicates the effect of this variable on the dependent variable, provided that the other variables in the equation remain constant. Another way of stating this is that the coefficient represents the effect of this variable on the dependent variable *in addition to* the effects of the other variables in the equation. For example, if MachHrs and ProdRuns are included in the equation for Overhead, then the coefficient of MachHrs indicates the *extra* amount MachHrs explains about variation in Overhead, in addition to the amount already explained by ProdRuns. Similarly, the coefficient of ProdRuns indicates the extra amount ProdRuns explains about variation in Overhead, in addition to the amount already explained by MachHrs. Therefore, the relationship between an explanatory variable X and the dependent variable Y is not always accurately reflected in the coefficient of X; it depends on which *other* X's are included or not included in the equation.

This is especially true when there is a linear relationship between two or more *explanatory* variables, in which case we have *multicollinearity*. By definition, **multicollinearity** is the presence of a fairly strong linear relationship between two or more explanatory variables, and it can make estimation difficult.

> **Multicollinearity** occurs when there is a fairly strong linear relationship among a set of explanatory variables.

Consider the following example. It is a rather trivial example, but it is useful for illustrating the potential effects of multicollinearity.

EXAMPLE | 12.2 HEIGHT AS A FUNCTION OF FOOT LENGTH

We want to explain a person's height by means of foot length. The dependent variable is Height, and the explanatory variables are Right and Left, the length of the right foot and the left foot, respectively. What can occur when we regress Height on *both* Right and Left?

Objective To illustrate the problem of multicollinearity when both foot length variables are used in a regression for height.

Solution

Admittedly, there is no need to include both Right and Left in an equation for Height—either one of them would do—but we include them both to make a point. Now, it is likely that there is a large correlation between height and foot size, so we would expect this regression equation to do a good job. For example, the R^2 value will probably be large. But what about the coefficients of Right and Left? Here we have a problem. The coefficient of Right indicates the right foot's effect on Height in addition to the effect of the left foot. This additional effect is probably minimal. That is, after the effect of Left on Height has already been taken into account, the extra information provided by Right is probably minimal. But it goes the other way also. The extra effect of Left, in addition to that provided by Right, is probably also minimal.

To show what can happen numerically, we generated a hypothetical data set of heights and left and right foot lengths. (See the file **Heights.xlsx**.) We did this so that, except for random error, height is approximately 32 plus 3.2 times foot length (all expressed in inches). As shown in Figure 12.5, the correlation between Height and either Right or Left in our data set is quite large, and the correlation between Right and Left is very close to 1.

Figure 12.5

Correlations in Example of Height versus Foot Length

	A	B	C	D
7		Height	Right	Left
8	*Correlation Table*	Data Set #1	Data Set #1	Data Set #1
9	Height	1.000		
10	Right	0.903	1.000	
11	Left	0.900	0.999	1.000

The regression output when both Right and Left are entered in the equation for Height appears in Figure 12.6. This tells a somewhat confusing story. The multiple R and the corresponding R^2 are about what we would expect, given the correlations between Height and either Right or Left in Figure 12.5. In particular, the multiple R is close to the correlation between Height and either Right or Left. Also, the s_e value is quite good. It implies that predictions of height from this regression equation will typically be off by only about 2 inches.

Figure 12.6 Regression Output for Height versus Foot Length Example

	A	B	C	D	E	F	G
7		Multiple	R-Square	Adjusted	StErr of		
8	*Summary*	R		R-Square	Estimate		
9		0.9042	0.8176	0.8140	2.004		
10							
11		Degrees of	Sum of	Mean of	F-Ratio	p-Value	
12	*ANOVA Table*	Freedom	Squares	Squares			
13	Explained	2	1836.384497	918.1922484	228.6003	< 0.0001	
14	Unexplained	102	409.6916079	4.016584391			
15							
16		Coefficient	Standard	t-Value	p-Value	Confidence Interval 95%	
17	*Regression Table*		Error			Lower	Upper
18	Constant	31.760	1.959	16.2087	< 0.0001	27.874	35.647
19	Right	6.823	3.428	1.9901	0.0493	0.023	13.623
20	Left	-3.645	3.441	-1.0592	0.2920	-10.470	3.181

Multicollinearity often causes regression coefficients to have the "wrong" sign, t-values to be too small, and p-values to be too large.

However, the coefficients of Right and Left are not at all what we might expect, given that we generated heights as approximately 32 plus 3.2 times foot length. In fact, the coefficient of Left is the wrong sign—it is *negative*! Besides this "wrong" sign, the tip-off that there is a problem is that the *t*-value of Left is quite small and the corresponding *p*-value is quite large. Judging by this, we might conclude that Height and Left are either not related or are related negatively. But we know from Figure 12.5 that both of these conclusions are wrong. In contrast, the coefficient of Right has the "correct" sign, and its *t*-value and associated *p*-value do imply statistical significance, at least at the 5% level. However, this happened mostly by chance. Slight changes in the data could change the results completely—the coefficient of Right could become negative and insignificant, or both coefficients could become insignificant.

The problem is that although both Right and Left are clearly related to Height, it is impossible for the least squares method to distinguish their *separate* effects. Note that the regression equation does estimate the combined effect fairly well—the sum of the coefficients of Right and Left is $6.823 + (-3.645) = 3.178$. This is close to the coefficient 3.2 we used to

Multicollinearity
typically causes
unreliable estimates
of regression coeffi-
cients, but it does
not generally cause
poor predictions.

generate the data. Also, the estimated intercept 31.760 is close to the intercept 32 we used to generate the data. Therefore, the estimated equation will work well for predicting heights. It just does not have reliable estimates of the individual coefficients of Right and Left.

To see what happens when either Right or Left is excluded from the regression equation, we show the results of *simple* regression. When Right is the only variable in the equation, it becomes

$$\text{Predicted Height} = 31.546 + 3.195\text{Right}$$

The R^2 and s_e values are 81.6% and 2.005, and the *t*-value and *p*-value for the coefficient of Right are now 21.34 and <0.0001—very significant. Similarly, when Left is the only variable in the equation, it becomes

$$\text{Predicted Height} = 31.526 + 3.197\text{Left}$$

The R^2 and s_e values are 81.1% and 2.033, and the *t*-value and *p*-value for the coefficient of Left are 20.99 and and <0.0001—again very significant. Clearly, both of these equations tell almost identical stories, and they are much easier to interpret than the equation with both Right and Left included. The message, therefore, is that when two variables are very highly correlated, only one of them should be included in the regression equation. ■

This example illustrates an extreme form of multicollinearity, where two explanatory variables are very highly correlated. In general, there are various degrees of multicollinearity. In each of them, there is a linear relationship between two or more explanatory variables, and this relationship makes it difficult to estimate the individual effects of the *X*'s on the dependent variable. The symptoms of multicollinearity can be "wrong" signs of the coefficients, smaller-than-expected *t*-values, and larger-than-expected (insignificant) *p*-values. In other words, variables that are really related to the dependent variable can look like they aren't related, based on their *p*-values. The reason is that their effects on *Y* are already explained by other *X*'s in the equation.

Sometimes multicollinearity is easy to spot and treat. For example, it would be silly to include both Right and Left foot length in the equation for Height. They are obviously very highly correlated and only one is needed in the equation for Height. We should exclude one of them—either one—and reestimate the equation. However, multicollinearity is not usually this easy to treat or even diagnose.

Moderate to extreme
multicollinearity poses
a problem in many
regression applications.
Unfortunately, there
are usually no easy
solutions.

Suppose, for example, that we want to use regression to explain variations in salary. Three potentially useful explanatory variables are age, years of experience in the company, and years of experience in the industry. It is very likely that each of these is positively related to salary, and it is also very likely that they are very closely related to each other. However, it isn't clear which, if any, we should exclude from the regression equation. If we include all three, we are likely to find that at least one of them is insignificant (high *p*-value), in which case we might consider excluding it from the equation. If we do so, the s_e and R^2 values will probably not change very much—the equation will provide equally good predicted values—but the coefficients of the variables that remain in the equation could change considerably.

PROBLEMS

Level A

13. Using the data given in **P11_10.xlsx**, estimate a multiple regression equation to predict the sales price of houses in a given community. Employ all available explanatory variables. Is there evidence of multicollinearity in this model? Explain why or why not.

14. Consider the enrollment data for *Business Week*'s top U.S. graduate business programs in the file **P02_03.xlsx**. Use these data to estimate a multiple regression model

to assess whether there is a systematic relationship between the total number of full-time students and the following explanatory variables: (a) the proportion of female students, (b) the proportion of minority students, and (c) the proportion of international students enrolled at these distinguished business schools.

    a. Determine whether each of the regression coefficients for the explanatory variables in this model is statistically different from 0 at the 5% significance level. Summarize your findings.

    b. Is there evidence of multicollinearity in this model? Explain why or why not.

15. The manager of a commuter rail transportation system was recently asked by her governing board to determine the factors that have a significant impact on the demand for rides in the large city served by the transportation network. The system manager has collected data on variables that might be related to the number of weekly riders on the city's rail system. The file **P11_20.xlsx** contains these data.

    a. Estimate a multiple regression model using all of the available explanatory variables. Perform a test of significance for each of the model's regression coefficients. Are the signs of the estimated coefficients consistent with your expectations?

    b. Is there evidence of multicollinearity in this model? Explain why or why not. If multicollinearity appears to be present, explain what you would do to eliminate this problem.

Level B

16. The human resources manager of DataCom, Inc., wants to examine the relationship between annual salaries (Y) and the number of years employees have worked at DataCom (X). These data have been collected for a sample of employees and are given in the file **P11_05.xlsx**.

    a. Estimate the relationship between Y and X using simple linear regression analysis. Is there evidence to support the hypothesis that the coefficient for the number of years employed is statistically different from 0 at the $\alpha = 0.05$ level?

    b. Next, formulate a multiple regression model to explain annual salaries of DataCom employees with X and X^2 as explanatory variables. Estimate this model using the given data. Perform relevant hypothesis tests to determine the significance of the regression coefficients of these two variables. Let $\alpha = 0.05$. Summarize your findings.

    c. How do you explain your findings in part **b** in light of the results found in part **a**?

17. The owner of a restaurant in Bloomington, Indiana, has recorded sales data for the past 19 years. He has also recorded data on potentially relevant variables. The data appear in the file **P11_23.xlsx**.

    a. Estimate a multiple regression equation that includes annual sales as the dependent variable and the following explanatory variables: year, size of the population residing within 10 miles of the restaurant, annual advertising expenditures, and advertising expenditures in the *previous* year.

    b. Which of the explanatory variables have significant effects on sales at the 10% significance level? Do any of these results surprise you? Explain why or why not.

    c. Exclude all insignificant explanatory variables from the full model and estimate the reduced model. Comment on the significance of each remaining explanatory variable. Again, use a 10% significance level.

    d. Based on your analysis of this problem, does multicollinearity appear to be present in the original or revised versions of the model? Provide the reasoning behind your response.

12.5 INCLUDE/EXCLUDE DECISIONS

In this section we make further use of the *t*-values of regression coefficients. In particular, we see how they can be used to make include/exclude decisions for explanatory variables in a regression equation. From Section 12.3 we know that a *t*-value can be used to test whether a population regression coefficient is 0. But does this mean that we should automatically include a variable if its *t*-value is significant and automatically exclude it if its *t*-value is insignificant? The decision is not always this simple.

    The bottom line is that we are always trying to get the best fit possible, and because of the principle of parsimony, we want to use the fewest number of variables. This presents a trade-off, where there are often no easy answers. On the one hand, more variables certainly increase R^2 and they usually reduce the standard error of estimate s_e. On the other hand, fewer variables are better for parsimony. Therefore, we present several guidelines. These guidelines are not hard and fast rules, and they are sometimes contradictory. In real applications there are often several equations that are equally good for all practical purposes, and it is rather pointless to search for a single "true" equation.

Guidelines for Including/Excluding Variables in a Regression Equation

1. Look at a variable's t-value and its associated p-value. If the p-value is above some accepted significance level, such as 0.05, then this variable is a candidate for exclusion.

2. Check whether a variable's t-value is less than 1 or greater than 1 in magnitude. If it is less than 1, then s_e will decrease (and adjusted R^2 will increase) if this variable is excluded from the equation. If it is greater than 1, the opposite will occur. These are mathematical facts. Because of them, some statisticians advocate excluding variables with t-values less than 1 and including variables with t-values greater than 1.

3. Look at t-values and p-values, rather than correlations, when making include/exclude decisions. An explanatory variable can have a fairly high correlation with the dependent variable, but because of *other* variables included in the equation, it might not be needed. This would be reflected in a low t-value and a high p-value, and this variable could possibly be excluded for reasons of parsimony. This often occurs in the presence of multicollinearity.

4. When there is a group of variables that are in some sense logically related, it is sometimes a good idea to include all of them or exclude all of them. In this case, their individual t-values are less relevant. Instead, the "partial F test" discussed in Section 12.7 should be used.

5. Use economic and/or physical theory to decide whether to include or exclude variables, and put less reliance on t-values and/or p-values. The idea is that some variables might really *belong* in an equation because of their theoretical relationship with the dependent variable, and their low t-values, possibly the result of an unlucky sample, should not disqualify them from being in the equation. Similarly, a variable that has no economic or physical relationship with the dependent variable might have a significant t-value just by chance. This does not necessarily mean that it should be included in the equation. We should not use a computer package blindly to hunt for "good" explanatory variables. We should have some idea, before running the package, which variables belong and which do not.

Again, these guidelines can give contradictory signals. Specifically, guideline 2 bases the include/exclude decision on whether the magnitude of the t-value is greater or less than 1. However, analysts who base the decision on statistical significance at the usual 5% level, as in guideline 1, typically exclude a variable from the equation unless its t-value is at least 2 (approximately). This latter approach is more stringent—fewer variables will be retained—but it is probably the more popular approach. However, either approach is likely to result in "similar" equations for all practical purposes.

We illustrate how these guidelines can be used in the following example. It uses a slightly modified version of the data set on HyTex's mail-order customers from Chapter 3.

EXAMPLE **12.3 EXPLAINING SPENDING AMOUNTS AT HYTEX**

The file **Catalog Marketing.xlsx** contains data on 1000 customers who purchased mail-order products from the HyTex Company in the current year. Recall from Example 3.11 in Chapter 3 that HyTex is a direct marketer of stereo equipment, personal computers, and other electronic products. HyTex advertises entirely by mailing catalogs to its customers, and all of its orders are taken over the telephone. The company spends a great deal of money on its catalog mailings, and it wants to be sure that this is paying off in sales. For each customer there are data on the following variables:

- Age: age of the customer at the end of the current year
- Gender: coded as 1 for males, 0 for females

- OwnHome: coded as 1 if customer owns a home, 0 otherwise
- Married: coded as 1 if customer is currently married, 0 otherwise
- Close: coded as 1 if customer lives reasonably close to a shopping area that sells similar merchandise, 0 otherwise
- Salary: combined annual salary of customer and spouse (if any)
- Children: number of children living with customer
- PrevCust: coded as 1 if customer purchased from HyTex during the previous year, 0 otherwise
- PrevSpent: total amount of purchases made from HyTex during the previous year
- Catalogs: number of catalogs sent to the customer this year
- AmountSpent: total amount of purchases made from HyTex this year

Estimate and interpret a regression equation for AmountSpent based on all of these variables.

Objective   To see which potential explanatory variables are useful for explaining current year spending amounts at HyTex with multiple regression.

Solution

First, if you compare this data set to the data set in Chapter 3, you will see that we made the following modifications to simplify the regression analysis.

- Age is now a continuous variable, not a categorical variable with three categories.
- Before, we had a History variable with four categories, depending on how much, if any, the customer purchased from HyTex in the previous year. Now we use the dummy variable PrevCust to indicate whether the customer purchased anything from HyTex in the previous year. We also use the continuous variable PrevSpent for the amount purchased the previous year. Of course, if PrevCust equals 0, so does PrevSpent.

With this much data, 1000 observations, we can certainly afford to set aside part of the data set for validation, as discussed in Section 11.7. Although any split can be used, we decided to base the regression on the first 250 observations and use the other 750 for validation. Therefore, you should select only the range through row 253 when defining the StatTools data set.

We begin by entering all of the potential explanatory variables. Our goal is then to exclude variables that aren't necessary, based on their t-values and p-values. The multiple regression output with all explanatory variables appears in Figure 12.7. It indicates a fairly good fit. The R^2 value is 79.1% and s_e is about \$424. When we consider that the actual amounts spent in the current year vary from a low of under \$50 to a high of over \$5500, with a median of about \$950, a typical prediction error of around \$424 is decent but not great.

From the p-value column, we see that there are three variables, Age, OwnHome, and Married, that have p-values well above 0.05. These are the obvious candidates for exclusion from the equation. We could rerun the equation with all three of these variables excluded, but it is a better practice to exclude one variable at a time. It is possible that when one of these variables is excluded, another one of them will become significant (the Right–Left foot phenomenon).

Actually, this did not happen. We first excluded the variable with the largest p-value, Age, and reran the regression. At this point, OwnHome and Married still had large p-values, and all other variables had small p-values. Next, we excluded Married, the variable with the largest remaining *p*-value, and reran the regression. Now, only OwnHome had a large *p*-value, so we ran one more regression with this variable excluded. The resulting output appears in Figure 12.8. As we see, the R^2 and s_e values of 79.0% and $423 are practically as good as they were with all variables included, and all of the *t*-values are now large (well above 2 in absolute value) and the *p*-values are all small (well below 0.05).

Figure 12.7 Regression Output with All Explanatory Variables Included

	A	B	C	D	E	F	G
7		Multiple	R-Square	Adjusted	StErr of		
8	Summary	R		R-Square	Estimate		
9		0.8893	0.7908	0.7820	423.8584		
10							
11		Degrees of	Sum of	Mean of	F-Ratio	p-Value	
12	ANOVA Table	Freedom	Squares	Squares			
13	Explained	10	162299315.6	16229931.56	90.3390	< 0.0001	
14	Unexplained	239	42937764.53	179655.9186			
15							
16		Coefficient	Standard	t-Value	p-Value	Confidence Interval 95%	
17	Regression Table		Error			Lower	Upper
18	Constant	257.3477	132.9876	1.9351	0.0542	-4.6299	519.3253
19	Age	0.1884	1.7626	0.1069	0.9150	-3.2839	3.6607
20	Gender	-124.0805	55.7627	-2.2252	0.0270	-233.9296	-14.2315
21	OwnHome	62.2752	60.7581	1.0250	0.3064	-57.4145	181.9649
22	Married	49.8426	70.1742	0.7103	0.4782	-88.3964	188.0816
23	Close	-282.7266	71.7762	-3.9390	0.0001	-424.1214	-141.3319
24	Salary	0.0143	0.0017	8.4930	< 0.0001	0.0110	0.0177
25	Children	-155.2858	31.5902	-4.9156	< 0.0001	-217.5166	-93.0550
26	PrevCust	-729.7212	92.3670	-7.9002	< 0.0001	-911.6787	-547.7638
27	PrevSpent	0.4725	0.0782	6.0447	< 0.0001	0.3185	0.6264
28	Catalogs	42.5806	4.3503	9.7880	< 0.0001	34.0108	51.1504

Figure 12.8 Regression Output with Insignificant Variables Excluded

	A	B	C	D	E	F	G
7		Multiple	R-Square	Adjusted	StErr of		
8	Summary	R		R-Square	Estimate		
9		0.8885	0.7895	0.7834	422.5169		
10							
11		Degrees of	Sum of	Mean of	F-Ratio	p-Value	
12	ANOVA Table	Freedom	Squares	Squares			
13	Explained	7	162035109	23147872.71	129.6650	< 0.0001	
14	Unexplained	242	43201971.22	178520.5422			
15							
16		Coefficient	Standard	t-Value	p-Value	Confidence Interval 95%	
17	Regression Table		Error			Lower	Upper
18	Constant	269.8642	108.5596	2.4859	0.0136	56.0219	483.7066
19	Gender	-130.3226	55.2112	-2.3604	0.0190	-239.0784	-21.5668
20	Close	-287.5537	70.8671	-4.0576	< 0.0001	-427.1488	-147.9586
21	Salary	0.0154	0.0014	11.1924	< 0.0001	0.0127	0.0181
22	Children	-158.4511	31.3378	-5.0562	< 0.0001	-220.1809	-96.7214
23	PrevCust	-724.0651	91.5870	-7.9058	< 0.0001	-904.4746	-543.6557
24	PrevSpent	0.4699	0.0777	6.0452	< 0.0001	0.3168	0.6230
25	Catalogs	42.6638	4.3204	9.8751	< 0.0001	34.1535	51.1741

We can interpret this final regression equation as follows:

Interpretation of Regression Equation

- The coefficient of Gender implies that an average male customer spent about $130 less than an average female customer, all other variables being equal. Similarly, an average customer living close to stores with this type of merchandise spent about $288 less than an average customer living far from such stores.

- The coefficient of Salary implies that, on average, about 1.5 cents of every extra salary dollar was spent on HyTex merchandise.

- The coefficient of Children implies that about $158 *less* was spent for every extra child living at home.

- The PrevCust and PrevSpent terms are somewhat more difficult to interpret. First, both of these terms are 0 for customers who didn't purchase from HyTex in the previous year. For those who did, the terms become $-724 + 0.47$PrevSpent. The coefficient 0.47 implies that each extra dollar spent the previous year can be expected to contribute an extra 47 cents in the current year. The -724 literally means that if we compare a customer who didn't purchase from HyTex last year to another customer who purchased only a tiny amount, the latter would be expected to spend about $724 less than the former this year. However, none of the latter customers were in the data set. A look at the data shows that of all customers who purchased from HyTex last year, almost all spent at least $100 and most spent considerably more. In fact, the median amount spent by these customers last year was about $900 (the median of all positive values for the PrevSpent variable). If we substitute this median value into the expression $-724 + 0.47$PrevSpent, we obtain -301. Therefore, this "median" spender from last year can be expected to spend about $301 less this year than the previous year nonspender.

- The coefficient of Catalogs implies that each extra catalog can be expected to generate about $43 in extra spending.

We conclude this example with a couple of cautionary notes. First, when we validate this final regression equation on the other 750 customers, using the procedure from Section 11.7, we find R^2 and s_e values of 71.8% and $522. Actually, these aren't bad. They show only a little deterioration from the values based on the original 250 customers. Second, we haven't tried all possibilities yet. We haven't tried nonlinear or interaction variables, nor have we looked at different coding schemes (such as treating Catalogs as a categorical variable and using dummy variables to represent it); we haven't checked for nonconstant error variance (remember that Figure 12.1 is based on this data set) or looked at the potential effects of outliers. ∎

PROBLEMS

Level A

18. David Savageau and Geoffrey Loftus, the authors of *Places Rated Almanac*, have ranked metropolitan areas in the United States with consideration of the following aspects of life in each area: cost of living, transportation, jobs, education, climate, crime, arts, health, and recreation. The data are in the file **P02_55.xlsx**. Use multiple regression analysis to explore the relationship between the metropolitan areas' overall score and the set of potential explanatory variables. Which explanatory variables should be included in a final version of this regression model? Justify your choices.

19. A manager of boiler drums wants to use regression analysis to predict the number of worker-hours needed to erect the drums in future projects. Consequently, data for 36 randomly selected boilers were collected.

In addition to worker-hours (Y), the variables measured include boiler capacity, boiler design pressure, boiler type, and drum type. All of these measurements are listed in the file **P11_27.xlsx**. Estimate an appropriate multiple regression model to predict the number of worker-hours needed to erect given boiler drums using all available explanatory variables. Which explanatory variables should be included in a final version of this regression model? Justify your choices.

20. An economic development researcher wants to understand the relationship between the size of the monthly home mortgage or rent payment for households in a particular middle-class neighborhood and the following set of household variables: family size, approximate location of the household within the neighborhood, an indication of whether those surveyed own or rent their home, gross annual income of the first household wage earner, gross annual income of the second household wage earner (if applicable), average monthly expenditure on utilities, and the total indebtedness (excluding the value of a home mortgage) of the household. Observations on each of these variables for a large sample of households are recorded in the file **P02_06.xlsx**.

   a. In an effort to explain the variation in the size of the monthly home mortgage or rent payment, estimate a multiple regression model that includes all of the potential household explanatory variables.

   b. Using your regression output, determine which of the explanatory variables should be *excluded* from the regression equation. Explain why you decide to remove each such variable.

21. Managers at Beta Technologies, Inc., have collected current annual salary figures and potentially related data for a random sample of 52 of the company's full-time employees. The data are in the file **P02_01.xlsx**. These data include each selected employee's gender, age, number of years of relevant work experience prior to employment at Beta, the number of years of employment at Beta, and the number of years of postsecondary education.

   a. Estimate a multiple regression model to explain the variation in employee salaries at Beta Technologies using all of the potential explanatory variables.

   b. Using your regression output, determine which of the explanatory variables should be *excluded* from the regression equation. Provide reasoning for your decision to remove each such variable.

22. Stock market analysts are continually looking for reliable predictors of stock prices. Consider the problem of modeling the price per share of electric utility stocks (Y). Two variables thought to influence such a stock price are return on average equity (X_1) and annual dividend rate (X_2). The stock price, returns on equity, and dividend rates on a randomly selected day for 16 electric utility stocks are provided in the file **P11_19.xlsx**.

   a. Estimate a multiple regression model using the given data. Include linear terms as well as an interaction term involving the return on average equity (X_1) and annual dividend rate (X_2).

   b. Which of the three explanatory variables (X_1, X_2, and X_1X_2) should be included in a final version of this regression model? Explain. Does your conclusion make sense in light of your knowledge of corporate finance?

12.6 STEPWISE REGRESSION[4]

Multiple regression represents an improvement over simple regression because it allows any number of explanatory variables to be included in the analysis. Sometimes, however, the large number of potential explanatory variables makes it difficult to know which variables to include. Many statistical packages provide some assistance by including automatic equation-building options. These options estimate a series of regression equations by successively adding (or deleting) variables according to prescribed rules. Generically, the methods are referred to as **stepwise regression**.

Before discussing how stepwise procedures work, consider a naive approach to the problem. We have already looked at correlation tables for indications of linear relationships. Why not simply include all explanatory variables that have large correlations with the dependent variable? There are two reasons for not doing this. First, although a variable is highly correlated with the dependent variable, it might also be highly correlated with other explanatory variables. Therefore, this variable might not be needed in the equation once the other explanatory variables have been included.

Second, even if a variable's correlation with the dependent variable is small, its contribution when it is included with a number of other explanatory variables can be greater

[4]This section can be omitted without any loss of continuity.

than anticipated. Essentially, this variable can have something unique to say about the dependent variable that none of the other variables provides, and this fact might not be apparent from the correlation table.

For these reasons it is sometimes useful to let the computer discover the best combination of variables by means of a stepwise procedure. There are a number of procedures for building equations in a stepwise manner, but they all share a basic idea. Suppose that we have an existing regression equation and we want to add another variable to this equation from a set of variables not yet included. At this point, the variables already in the equation have explained a certain percentage of the variation of the dependent variable. The residuals represent the part still unexplained. Therefore, in choosing the next variable to enter the equation, we pick the one that is most highly correlated with the current residuals. If none of the remaining variables is highly correlated with the residuals, we might decide to quit. This is the essence of stepwise regression. However, besides adding variables to the equation, a stepwise procedure might delete a variable. This is sometimes reasonable because a variable entered early in the procedure might no longer be needed, given the presence of other variables that have entered since.

Stepwise regression (and its variations) can be helpful in discovering a useful regression model, but it should not be used mindlessly.

Many statistical packages have three types of equation-building procedures: *forward, backward,* and *stepwise.* A **forward** procedure begins with no explanatory variables in the equation and successively adds one at a time until no remaining variables make a significant contribution. A **backward** procedure begins with all potential explanatory variables in the equation and deletes them one at a time until further deletion would do more harm than good. Finally, a true **stepwise** procedure is much like a forward procedure, except that it also considers possible deletions along the way. All of these procedures have the same basic objective—namely, to find an equation with a small s_e and a large R^2 (or adjusted R^2). There is no guarantee that they will all produce exactly the same final equation, but in most cases their final results are very similar. The important thing to realize is that the equations estimated along the way, including the final equation, are estimated exactly as before—by least squares. Therefore, none of these procedures produces any new results. They merely take the burden off the user of having to decide ahead of time which variables to include in the equation.

The StatTools add-in implements each of the forward, backward, and stepwise procedures. To use them, we select the dependent variable and a set of *potential* explanatory variables. Then we specify the criterion for adding and/or deleting variables from the equation. This can be done in two ways, with an *F*-value or a *p*-value. We suggest using *p*-values because they are easier to understand, but either method is easy to use. In the *p*-value method, we select a *p*-value such as 0.05. If the regression coefficient for a potential entering variable would have a *p*-value less than 0.05 (if it were entered), then it is a candidate for entering (if the forward or stepwise procedure is used). The procedure selects the variable with the *smallest p*-value as the next entering variable. Similarly, if any currently included variable has a *p*-value greater than some value such as 0.05, then (with the stepwise and backward procedures) it is a candidate for leaving the equation. The methods stop when there are no candidates (according to their *p*-values) for entering or leaving the current equation.

The following continuation of the HyTex mail-order example illustrates these stepwise procedures.

EXAMPLE | **12.3 EXPLAINING SPENDING AMOUNTS AT HYTEX (CONTINUED)**

The analysis of the HyTex mail-order data (for the first 250 customers in the data set) resulted in a regression equation that included all potential explanatory variables except for Age, OwnHome, and Married. We excluded these because their *t*-values were large and their p-values were small (less than 0.05). Do forward, backward, and stepwise procedures produce the same regression equation for the amount spent in the current year?

Objective To use StatTools's Stepwise Regression procedure to analyze the HyTex data.

Solution

Each of these options is found in the StatTools Regression dialog box. It is just a matter of choosing the appropriate option from the Regression Type dropdown list. (See Figure 12.9.) In each, we specify AmountSpent as the dependent variable and select all of the other variables (besides Customer) as *potential* explanatory variables. Once you choose one of the stepwise types, the dialog box changes, as shown in Figure 12.10, to include a Parameters section and enables the Include Detailed Step Information option. We suggest the choices in Figure 12.10 for stepwise regression.

Figure 12.9
Regression Dialog
Box with Regression
Type Options

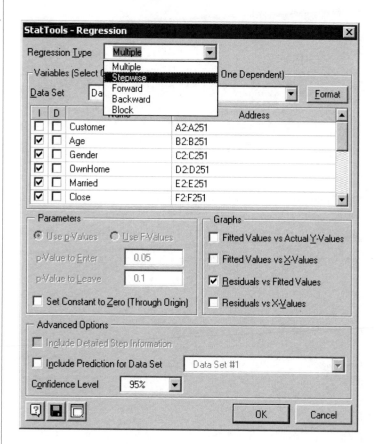

It turns out that each procedure produces a *final* equation that is exactly the same as we obtained previously, with all variables except Age, OwnHome, and Married included. This often happens, but not always. The stepwise and forward procedures add the variables in the order Salary, Catalogs, Children, Close, PrevCust, PrevSpent, and Gender. The backward procedure, which starts with *all* variables in the equation, eliminates variables in the order Age, Married, and OwnHome. A sample of the stepwise output appears in Figure 12.11. At the bottom of the output, we see which variable enters or exits the equation. We also see the usual regression output for the final equation. Again, however, this final equation's output is *exactly* the same as if we used multiple regression with these particular variables.

Figure 12.10
Dialog Box for Stepwise Regression

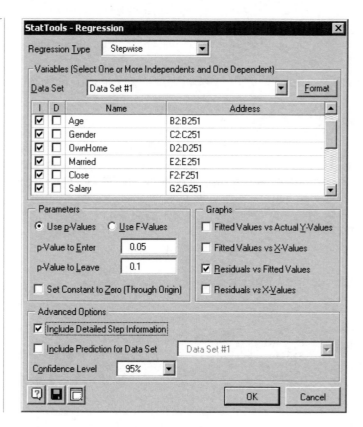

Figure 12.11 Regression Output from Stepwise Procedure

	A	B	C	D	E	F	G
7		Multiple	R-Square	Adjusted	StErr of		
8	Summary	R		R-Square	Estimate		
9		0.8885	0.7895	0.7834	422.5169		
10							
11		Degrees of	Sum of	Mean of	F-Ratio	p-Value	
12	ANOVA Table	Freedom	Squares	Squares			
13	Explained	7	162035109	23147872.71	129.6650	< 0.0001	
14	Unexplained	242	43201971.22	178520.5422			
15							
16		Coefficient	Standard	t-Value	p-Value	Confidence Interval 95%	
17	Regression Table		Error			Lower	Upper
18	Constant	269.8642	108.5596	2.4859	0.0136	56.0219	483.7066
19	Salary	0.0154	0.0014	11.1924	< 0.0001	0.0127	0.0181
20	Catalogs	42.6638	4.3204	9.8751	< 0.0001	34.1535	51.1741
21	Children	-158.4511	31.3378	-5.0562	< 0.0001	-220.1809	-96.7214
22	Close	-287.5537	70.8671	-4.0576	< 0.0001	-427.1488	-147.9586
23	PrevCust	-724.0651	91.5870	-7.9058	< 0.0001	-904.4746	-543.6557
24	PrevSpent	0.4699	0.0777	6.0452	< 0.0001	0.3168	0.6230
25	Gender	-130.3226	55.2112	-2.3604	0.0190	-239.0784	-21.5668
26							
27		Multiple	R-Square	Adjusted	StErr of	Enter or	
28	Step Information	R		R-Square	Estimate	Exit	
29	Salary	0.6624	0.4387	0.4365	681.5285	Enter	
30	Catalogs	0.7718	0.5957	0.5924	579.6088	Enter	
31	Children	0.8256	0.6815	0.6777	515.4461	Enter	
32	Close	0.8540	0.7293	0.7249	476.2003	Enter	
33	PrevCust	0.8670	0.7516	0.7465	457.0666	Enter	
34	PrevSpent	0.8858	0.7847	0.7793	426.4729	Enter	
35	Gender	0.8885	0.7895	0.7834	422.5169	Enter	

Stepwise regression or any of its variations can be very useful for narrowing down the set of all possible explanatory variables to a set that is useful for explaining a dependent variable. However, these procedures should not be used as a substitute for thoughtful analysis. With the availability of such procedures in statistical software packages, there is sometimes a tendency to turn the analysis over to the computer and accept its output. A good analyst does not just collect as much data as possible, throw it into a computer package, and blindly report the results. There should always be some rationale, whether it be based on economic theory, business experience, or common sense, for the variables that we use to explain a given dependent variable. A thoughtless use of stepwise regression can sometimes capitalize on chance to obtain an equation with a reasonably large R^2 but no useful or practical interpretation.

PROBLEMS

Level A

23. Suppose that you are interested in predicting the price of a laptop computer based on its various features. The file **P11_35.xlsx** contains observations on the sales price and a number of potentially relevant variables for a randomly chosen sample of laptop computers. Employ stepwise regression to decide which explanatory variables to include in a regression equation. Use the *p*-value method with a cutoff value of 0.05 for entering and leaving. Summarize your findings.

24. Does the rate of violent crime acts vary across different regions of the United States? Using the data in **P11_34.xlsx** and a stepwise regression procedure, develop an appropriate regression model to explain the variation in acts of violent crime across the United States. Use the *p*-value method with a cutoff value of 0.05 for entering and leaving. Summarize your results.

25. In a study of housing demand, a county assessor is interested in developing a regression model to estimate the selling price of residential properties within her jurisdiction. She randomly selects 15 houses and records the selling price in addition to the following values: the size of the house (in hundreds of square feet), the total number of rooms in the house, the age of the house, and an indication of whether the house has an attached garage. These data are stored in the file **P11_26.xlsx**.
   a. Use stepwise regression to decide which explanatory variables should be included in the assessor's statistical model. Use the *p*-value method with a cutoff value of 0.05 for entering and leaving. Summarize your findings.
   b. How do your results in part **a** change when the critical *p*-value for entering and leaving is increased to 0.10? Explain any differences between the

regression equation obtained here and the one found in part **a**.

26. Continuing Problem 2, employ stepwise regression to evaluate your conclusions regarding the specification of a regression model to predict the sales of deep-dish pizza by the Original Italian Pizza restaurant chain. Sample observations on all potentially relevant variables are provided in **P11_04.xlsx**. Use the *p*-value method with a cutoff value of 0.05 for entering and leaving. Compare your conclusions in Problem 2 with those derived from a stepwise regression procedure in completing this problem.

27. Continuing Problem 3, employ stepwise regression to evaluate your conclusions regarding the specification of a regression model to explain the variation in values of the *ACCRA Cost of Living Index*. Data on potentially relevant expenditure components (i.e., explanatory variables) are provided in the file **P02_19.xlsx**. Use the *p*-value method with a cutoff value of 0.05 for entering and leaving. Compare your conclusions in Problem 3 with those derived from a stepwise regression procedure in completing this problem.

Level B

28. What factors are truly useful in predicting a chief executive officer's annual base salary? Explore this question by employing a stepwise regression procedure on potentially relevant variables for which survey data have been collected and recorded in the file **P02_13.xlsx**. Assess only those variables that make economic sense in predicting CEO base salaries. Also, consider incorporating a set of categorical variables to account for any potential variation in the base salaries that is explained by the CEO's company type. Use the *p*-value method with a cutoff value of 0.10 for entering and leaving. Summarize your findings.

12.7 THE PARTIAL *F* TEST[5]

There are many situations where a set of explanatory variables form a logical group. It is then common to include all of the variables in the equation or exclude all of them. An example of this is when one of the explanatory variables is categorical with more than two categories. In this case we model it by including dummy variables—one less than the number of categories. If we decide that the categorical variable is worth including, we might want to keep all of the dummies. Otherwise, we might exclude all of them. We look at an example of this type subsequently.

For now, consider the following general situation. We have already estimated an equation that includes the variables X_1 through X_j, and we are proposing to estimate a larger equation that includes X_{j+1} through X_k in addition to the variables X_1 through X_j. That is, the larger equation includes all of the variables from the smaller equation, but it also includes $k - j$ extra variables. These extra variables are the ones that form a group. We assume that it makes logical sense to include all of them or none of them.

The complete equation always contains all of the explanatory variables in the reduced equation, plus some more. In other words, the reduced equation is a subset of the complete equation.

In this section we describe a test to determine whether the extra variables provide enough *extra* explanatory power as a group to warrant their inclusion in the equation. The test is called the partial *F* test. The original equation is called the **reduced** equation, and the larger equation is called the **complete** equation. In simple terms, the partial *F* test tests whether the complete equation is significantly better than the reduced equation.[6]

The test itself is intuitive. We use the output from the ANOVA tables of the reduced and complete equations to form an *F*-ratio. This ratio measures how much the sum of squared residuals, *SSE*, *decreases* by including the extra variables in the equation. It *must* decrease by some amount because the sum of squared residuals cannot increase when extra variables are added to an equation. But if it does not decrease sufficiently, then the extra variables might not explain enough to warrant their inclusion in the equation, and we should probably exclude them. The *F*-ratio measures this. If it is sufficiently large, then we can conclude that the extra variables are worth including; otherwise, we can safely exclude them.

To state the test formally, we first state the relevant hypotheses. Let β_{j+1} through β_k be the coefficients of the extra variables in the complete equation. Then the null hypothesis is that these extra variables have no effect on the dependent variable, that is, $H_0: \beta_{j+1} = \cdots = \beta_k = 0$. The alternative is that at least one of the extra variables has an effect on the dependent variable, so that at least one of these β's is not 0. The hypotheses are summarized in the box.

Hypotheses for the Partial* F *Test

The null hypothesis is that the coefficients of all the extra explanatory variables in the complete equation are 0. The alternative is that at least one of these coefficients is not 0.

To run the test, we estimate both the reduced and complete equations and look at the associated ANOVA tables. Let SSE_R and SSE_C be the sums of squared errors from the reduced and complete equations, respectively. Also, let MSE_C be the mean square error for the complete equation. All of these quantities appear in the ANOVA tables. Next, we form the *F*-ratio in equation (12.4).

Test Statistic for Partial* F *Test

$$F\text{-ratio} = \frac{(SSE_R - SSE_C)/(k - j)}{MSE_C} \qquad (12.4)$$

---

[5]This section is somewhat more advanced and can be omitted without any loss of continuity.
[6]StatTools does not run the partial *F* test, but it provides all of the ingredients.

Note that the numerator includes the reduction in sum of squared errors discussed previously. If the null hypothesis is true, then this F-ratio has an F distribution with $k - j$ and $n - k - 1$ degrees of freedom. If it is sufficiently large, we reject H_0. As usual, the best way to run the test is to find the p-value corresponding to this F-ratio. This is the probability beyond the calculated F-ratio in the F distribution with $k - j$ and $n - k - 1$ degrees of freedom. In words, we reject the hypothesis that the extra variables have no explanatory power if this p-value is sufficiently small, less than 0.05, say.

This F-ratio and corresponding p-value are *not* part of the StatTools regression output. However, they are fairly easy to obtain. We run two regressions, one for the reduced equation and one for the complete equation, and we use the appropriate values from their ANOVA tables to calculate the F-ratio in equation (12.4). Then we use Excel's FDIST function in the form FDIST(F-ratio,$k - j$,$n - k - 1$) to calculate the corresponding p-value. The procedure is illustrated in the following example. It uses the bank discrimination data from Example 11.3 of the previous chapter.

EXAMPLE	12.4 POSSIBLE GENDER DISCRIMINATION IN SALARY AT FIFTH NATIONAL BANK OF SPRINGFIELD

Recall from Example 11.3 that Fifth National Bank has 208 employees. The data for these employees are stored in the file **Bank Salaries.xlsx**. In the previous chapter we ran several regressions for Salary to see whether there is convincing evidence of salary discrimination against females. We will continue this analysis here. First, we regress Salary versus the Female dummy, YrsExper, and the interaction between Female and YrsExper, Interaction(YrsExper,Female). This is the reduced equation. Then we'll see whether the JobGrade dummies JobGrade=2 to JobGrade=6 add anything significant to the reduced equation. If so, we then see whether the interactions between the Female dummy and the JobGrade dummies, Interaction(Female,JobGrade=2) to Interaction(Female,JobGrade=6), add anything significant to what we already have. If so, we finally see whether the education dummies EducLev=2 to EducLev=5 add anything significant to what we already have.

Objective To use several partial F tests to see whether various groups of explanatory variables should be included in a regression equation for salary, given that other variables are already in the equation.

Solution

First, note that we created all of the dummies and interaction variables with StatTools's Data Utilities procedures. These could be entered directly with Excel functions, but StatTools makes the process much quicker and easier. Also, note that we have used three sets of dummies, for gender, job grade, and education level. When we use these in a regression equation, the dummy for one category of each should always be excluded; it is the reference category. The reference categories we have used are "male," job grade 1, and education level 1.

The output for the "smallest" equation, using Female, YrsExper, and Interaction(YrsExper,Female) as explanatory variables, appears in Figure 12.12. (We put this output in a sheet called Regression1.) We're off to a good start. These three variables already explain 63.9% of the variation in Salary.

Figure 12.12 Reduced Equation for Bank Example

	A	B	C	D	E	F	G
7		Multiple	R-Square	Adjusted	StErr of		
8	*Summary*	R		R-Square	Estimate		
9		0.7991	0.6386	0.6333	6816.298		
10							
11		Degrees of	Sum of	Mean of	F-Ratio	p-Value	
12	*ANOVA Table*	Freedom	Squares	Squares			
13	Explained	3	16748875071	5582958357	120.1620	< 0.0001	
14	Unexplained	204	9478232160	46461922.35			
15							
16		Coefficient	Standard	t-Value	p-Value	Confidence Interval 95%	
17	*Regression Table*		Error			Lower	Upper
18	Constant	30430.028	1216.574	25.0129	< 0.0001	28031.356	32828.700
19	YrsExper	1527.762	90.460	16.8887	< 0.0001	1349.405	1706.119
20	Female	4098.252	1665.842	2.4602	0.0147	813.776	7382.727
21	Interaction(YrsExper,Female)	-1247.798	136.676	-9.1296	< 0.0001	-1517.277	-978.320

The output for the next equation, which adds the explanatory variables JobGrade=2 to JobGrade=6, appears in Figure 12.13. (We put this output in a sheet called Regression2.) This equation appears to be much better. For example, R^2 has increased to 81.1%. We check whether it is *significantly* better with the partial F test in rows 28 through 32. (This part of the output is not given by StatTools; we have to enter it manually.) The degrees of freedom in cell B29 is 5, the number of *extra* variables. The degrees of freedom in cell B30 is the same as the value in cell B14, the degrees of freedom for *SSE*. Then we calculate the F-ratio in cell B31 with the formula

=((Regression1!C14-Regression2!C14)/Regression2!B29)/Regression2!D14

Figure 12.13 Equation with Job Dummies Added

	A	B	C	D	E	F	G
7		Multiple	R-Square	Adjusted	StErr of		
8	*Summary*	R		R-Square	Estimate		
9		0.9005	0.8109	0.8033	4991.64		
10							
11		Degrees of	Sum of	Mean of	F-Ratio	p-Value	
12	*ANOVA Table*	Freedom	Squares	Squares			
13	Explained	8	21268738998	2658592375	106.7004	< 0.0001	
14	Unexplained	199	4958368233	24916423.28			
15							
16		Coefficient	Standard	t-Value	p-Value	Confidence Interval 95%	
17	*Regression Table*		Error			Lower	Upper
18	Constant	26104.22	1105.44	23.6143	< 0.0001	23924.34	28284.11
19	YrsExper	1070.88	102.01	10.4975	< 0.0001	869.72	1272.05
20	Female	6063.33	1266.32	4.7881	< 0.0001	3566.20	8560.46
21	JobGrade = 2	2596.49	1010.12	2.5705	0.0109	604.58	4588.41
22	JobGrade = 3	6221.39	998.18	6.2328	< 0.0001	4253.03	8189.76
23	JobGrade = 4	11071.95	1172.59	9.4423	< 0.0001	8759.66	13384.25
24	JobGrade = 5	14946.58	1340.25	11.1521	< 0.0001	12303.66	17589.49
25	JobGrade = 6	17097.37	2390.67	7.1517	< 0.0001	12383.07	21811.67
26	Interaction(YrsExper,Female)	-1021.05	118.73	-8.6001	< 0.0001	-1255.17	-786.93
27							
28	Partial F test for including JobGrade dummies						
29	df numerator	5					
30	df denominator	199					
31	F ratio	36.2802					
32	p-value	0.0000					

where Regression1!C14 refers to *SSE* for the reduced equation from the Regression1 sheet. Finally, we calculate the corresponding *p*-value in cell B32 with the formula

=FDIST(B31,B29,B30)

It is practically 0, so there is no doubt that the job grade dummies add significantly to the explanatory power of the equation.

Do the interactions between the Female dummy and the job dummies add anything more? We again use the partial *F* test, but now the previous *complete* equation becomes the new *reduced* equation, and the equation that includes the new interaction terms becomes the new complete equation. The output for this new complete equation appears in Figure 12.14. (We put this output in a sheet called Regression3.) We perform the partial *F* test in rows 34 through 37 exactly as before. For example, the formula for the *F*-ratio in cell B36 is

=((Regression2!C14-Regression3!C14)/Regression3!B34)/Regression3!D14

Figure 12.14 Regression Output with Interaction Terms Added

	A	B	C	D	E	F	G
7		Multiple	R-Square	Adjusted	StErr of		
8	*Summary*	R		R-Square	Estimate		
9		0.9163	0.8396	0.8289	4656.41		
10							
11		Degrees of	Sum of	Mean of	F-Ratio	p-Value	
12	*ANOVA Table*	Freedom	Squares	Squares			
13	Explained	13	22020761739	1693904749	78.1242	< 0.0001	
14	Unexplained	194	4206345492	21682193.26			
15							
16		Coefficient	Standard	t-Value	p-Value	Confidence Interval 95%	
17	*Regression Table*		Error			Lower	Upper
18	Constant	26515.48	1432.40	18.5112	< 0.0001	23690.40	29340.56
19	YrsExper	960.78	104.19	9.2214	< 0.0001	755.28	1166.27
20	Female	4724.46	1735.36	2.7225	0.0071	1301.88	8147.05
21	JobGrade = 2	3341.00	1864.19	1.7922	0.0747	-335.68	7017.67
22	JobGrade = 3	7871.96	2214.94	3.5540	0.0005	3503.49	12240.42
23	JobGrade = 4	10691.89	1956.67	5.4643	< 0.0001	6832.81	14550.97
24	JobGrade = 5	13146.37	1993.14	6.5958	< 0.0001	9215.36	17077.38
25	JobGrade = 6	20979.45	2767.63	7.5803	< 0.0001	15520.95	26437.94
26	Interaction(YrsExper,Female)	-805.99	130.32	-6.1845	< 0.0001	-1063.02	-548.95
27	Interaction(Female,JobGrade = 2)	-943.40	2164.03	-0.4359	0.6634	-5211.44	3324.63
28	Interaction(Female,JobGrade = 3)	-1935.05	2441.44	-0.7926	0.4290	-6750.22	2880.13
29	Interaction(Female,JobGrade = 4)	433.82	2374.97	0.1827	0.8553	-4250.25	5117.90
30	Interaction(Female,JobGrade = 5)	4873.42	2623.16	1.8578	0.0647	-300.16	10047.00
31	Interaction(Female,JobGrade = 6)	-27327.42	5770.02	-4.7361	< 0.0001	-38707.44	-15947.40
32							
33	Partial F test for including Female, JobGrade interactions						
34	df numerator	5					
35	df denominator	194					
36	F ratio	6.9368					
37	p-value	0.0000					

Note how the SSE_R term in equation (12.4) now comes from the Regression2 sheet because this sheet contains the current *reduced* equation. As we see, the terms "reduced" and "complete" are relative. What is complete in one stage becomes reduced in the next stage. In any case, the *p*-value in cell B37 is again extremely small, so there is no doubt that the interaction terms add significantly to what we already had (even though R^2 has increased from 81.1% to only 84.0%).

Finally, we add the education dummies. The resulting output is shown in Figure 12.15. (We put this output in a sheet called Regression4.) Again, we see how the terms reduced and complete are relative. This output now corresponds to the complete equation, and the previous output corresponds to the reduced equation. The formula in cell B40 for the *F*-ratio is now

=((Regression3!C14−Regression4!C14)/Regression4!B38)/Regression4!D14

Figure 12.15 Regression Output with Education Dummies Added

	A	B	C	D	E	F	G
7		Multiple	R-Square	Adjusted	StErr of		
8	*Summary*	R		R-Square	Estimate		
9		0.9205	0.8473	0.8336	4591.42		
10							
11		Degrees of	Sum of	Mean of	F-Ratio	p-Value	
12	*ANOVA Table*	Freedom	Squares	Squares			
13	Explained	17	22221688817	1307158166	62.0060	< 0.0001	
14	Unexplained	190	4005418414	21081149.55			
15							
16			Standard			Confidence Interval 95%	
17	*Regression Table*	Coefficient	Error	t-Value	p-Value	Lower	Upper
18	Constant	26020.52	1678.45	15.5027	< 0.0001	22709.73	29331.31
19	YrsExper	1002.35	104.54	9.5878	< 0.0001	796.14	1208.57
20	Female	4373.78	1724.69	2.5360	0.0120	971.78	7775.78
21	EducLev = 2	-664.78	1120.42	-0.5933	0.5537	-2874.84	1545.29
22	EducLev = 3	612.39	1082.33	0.5658	0.5722	-1522.54	2747.32
23	EducLev = 4	49.13	1961.56	0.0250	0.9800	-3820.11	3918.37
24	EducLev = 5	2808.15	1303.50	2.1543	0.0325	236.97	5379.34
25	JobGrade = 2	2697.31	1875.67	1.4380	0.1521	-1002.51	6397.12
26	JobGrade = 3	6862.57	2249.25	3.0511	0.0026	2425.87	11299.27
27	JobGrade = 4	8745.94	2054.71	4.2565	< 0.0001	4692.97	12798.91
28	JobGrade = 5	10579.59	2180.01	4.8530	< 0.0001	6279.45	14879.72
29	JobGrade = 6	18202.42	2940.22	6.1908	< 0.0001	12402.75	24002.09
30	Interaction(YrsExper,Female)	-760.83	129.87	-5.8584	< 0.0001	-1017.00	-504.66
31	Interaction(Female,JobGrade = 2)	-713.83	2148.35	-0.3323	0.7401	-4951.52	3523.86
32	Interaction(Female,JobGrade = 3)	-1752.87	2430.55	-0.7212	0.4717	-6547.19	3041.46
33	Interaction(Female,JobGrade = 4)	1023.20	2383.88	0.4292	0.6683	-3679.07	5725.47
34	Interaction(Female,JobGrade = 5)	5241.00	2623.06	1.9980	0.0471	66.93	10415.06
35	Interaction(Female,JobGrade = 6)	-29375.22	5753.89	-5.1053	< 0.0001	-40724.94	-18025.50
36							
37	Partial F test for including EducLev dummies						
38	df numerator	4					
39	df denominator	190					
40	F ratio	2.3828					
41	p-value	0.0530					

Its SSE_R value comes from the Regression3 sheet. Note that the increase in R^2 is from 84.0% to only 84.7%. Also, the *p*-value in cell B41 is not extremely small. According to the partial *F* test, it is not quite enough to qualify for statistical significance at the 5% level. Based on this evidence, there is not much to gain from including the education dummies in the equation, so we would probably elect to exclude them.

Note that the results could be very different if we had entered groups in a different order. For example, you might try entering the education dummies, and then interactions between these dummies and Female, *before* entering the job grade dummies. The results will be quite different. Again, remember that because of potential multicollinearity, what is significant can depend on what *other* variables are already in the equation.

Before leaving this example, we make several comments. First, the partial test is *the* formal test of significance for an extra set of variables. Many users look only at the R^2 and/or s_e values to check whether extra variables are doing a "good job." For example, they might cite that R^2 went from 81.1% to 84.0% or that s_e went from 4.992 to 4.656 as evidence that extra variables provide a "significantly" better fit. Although these are important indicators, they are not the basis for a *formal* hypothesis test.

Second, if the partial F test shows that a block of variables is significant, it does not imply that each variable in this block is significant. Some of these variables can have low *t*-values. Consider Figure 12.14, for example. We are able to conclude that the Female/Job interactions as a whole are significant. But three of these interactions, Interaction(Female, JobGrade=2) to Interaction(Female,JobGrade=4), are clearly not significant, and Interaction(Female,JobGrade=5) is borderline. In fact, Interaction(Female,JobGrade=6) is the only one that is clearly significant. Some analysts favor excluding the *individual* variables that aren't significant, whereas others favor keeping the whole block or excluding the whole block. We lean toward the latter but recognize that either approach is valid—and the results are nearly the same either way.

Third, producing all of these outputs and doing the partial F tests is a lot of work. Therefore, a "Block" option is included in StatTools to simplify the analysis. To run the analysis in this example in one step, select the Block option from the Regression Type dropdown list. The dialog box then changes, as shown in Figure 12.16. We select 4 blocks and then check which variables are in which blocks (B1 to B4). Block 1 has Female, YrsExper, and Interaction(YrsExper,Female), block 2 has the job grade dummies, block 3 has the interactions between Female and the job grade dummies, and block 4 has the education dummies. Finally, we specify 0.05 as the *p*-value to enter, which in this case indicates how significant the block *as a whole* must be to enter (for the partial F test).

Figure 12.16

Dialog Box for Block Regression Option

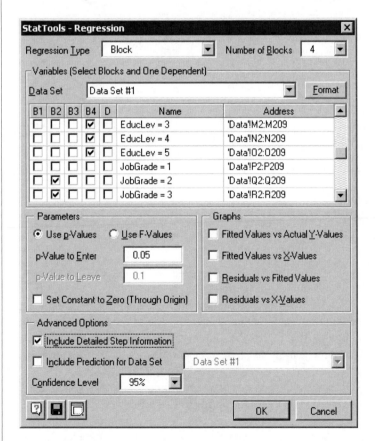

Once we have specified all of this, the regression calculations are done in stages. At each stage, the partial F test checks whether a block is significant. If so, the variables in this block enter and we progress to the next stage. If not, the process ends; neither this block nor any later blocks are entered.

The output from this procedure appears in Figure 12.17. The middle part of the output shows the final regression equation. The output in rows 35 through 38 indicates summary measures after successive blocks have entered. Note that the final block, the education dummies, is not in the final equation. This block did not pass the partial F test at the 5% level.

Figure 12.17 Block Regression Output

	A	B	C	D	E	F	G
7		Multiple	R-Square	Adjusted	StErr of		
8	*Summary*	R		R-Square	Estimate		
9		0.9163	0.8396	0.8289	4656.41		
10							
11		Degrees of	Sum of	Mean of	F-Ratio	p-Value	
12	*ANOVA Table*	Freedom	Squares	Squares			
13	Explained	13	22020761739	1693904749	76.5134	< 0.0001	
14	Unexplained	190	4206345492	22138660.48			
15							
16		Coefficient	Standard	t-Value	p-Value	Confidence Interval 95%	
17	*Regression Table*		Error			Lower	Upper
18	Constant	26515.48	1432.40	18.5112	< 0.0001	23690.03	29340.94
19	YrsExper	960.78	104.19	9.2214	< 0.0001	755.26	1166.29
20	Female	4724.46	1735.36	2.7225	0.0071	1301.42	8147.50
21	Interaction(YrsExper,Female)	-805.99	130.32	-6.1845	< 0.0001	-1063.05	-548.92
22	JobGrade = 2	3341.00	1864.19	1.7922	0.0747	-336.17	7018.16
23	JobGrade = 3	7871.96	2214.94	3.5540	0.0005	3502.92	12241.00
24	JobGrade = 4	10691.89	1956.67	5.4643	< 0.0001	6832.30	14551.48
25	JobGrade = 5	13146.37	1993.14	6.5958	< 0.0001	9214.84	17077.90
26	JobGrade = 6	20979.45	2767.63	7.5803	< 0.0001	15520.23	26438.67
27	Interaction(Female,JobGrade = 2)	-943.40	2164.03	-0.4359	0.6634	-5212.00	3325.20
28	Interaction(Female,JobGrade = 3)	-1935.05	2441.44	-0.7926	0.4290	-6750.86	2880.76
29	Interaction(Female,JobGrade = 4)	433.82	2374.97	0.1827	0.8553	-4250.87	5118.51
30	Interaction(Female,JobGrade = 5)	4873.42	2623.16	1.8578	0.0647	-300.85	10047.68
31	Interaction(Female,JobGrade = 6)	-27327.42	5770.02	-4.7361	< 0.0001	-38708.94	-15945.90
32							
33		Multiple	R-Square	Adjusted	StErr of	Entry	
34	*Step Information*	R		R-Square	Estimate	Number	
35	Block 1	0.7991	0.6386	0.6333	6816.298	1	
36	Block 2	0.9005	0.8109	0.8033	4991.635	2	
37	Block 3	0.9163	0.8396	0.8289	4656.414	3	
38	Block 4	Did Not Enter					

For comparison, we ran the block procedure a second time, changing the order of the blocks. Now block 2 includes the education level dummies, block 3 includes the job grade dummies, and block 4 includes the interactions between Female and the job grade dummies. The regression output appears in Figure 12.18. Note that *all* four blocks enter the equation this time. The implication is that the order of the blocks can make a difference.

Finally, we have concentrated on the partial F test and statistical significance in this example. We don't want you to lose sight, however, of the bigger picture. Once we have decided on a "final" regression equation, say, the one in Figure 12.14, we need to analyze its implications for the problem at hand. In this case the bank is interested in possible salary discrimination against females, so we should interpret this final equation in these terms. We do not go through this exercise again here—we did similar interpretations in the previous chapter. Our point is simply that you shouldn't get so immersed in the details of statistical significance that you lose sight of the original purpose of the analysis!

Figure 12.18 Block Regression Output with Order of Blocks Changed

	A	B	C	D	E	F	G
7		Multiple	R-Square	Adjusted	StErr of		
8	*Summary*	R		R-Square	Estimate		
9		0.9205	0.8473	0.8336	4591.42		
10							
11		Degrees of	Sum of	Mean of	F-Ratio	p-Value	
12	*ANOVA Table*	Freedom	Squares	Squares			
13	Explained	17	22221688817	1307158166	62.0060	< 0.0001	
14	Unexplained	190	4005418414	21081149.55			
15							
16		Coefficient	Standard	t-Value	p-Value	Confidence Interval 95%	
17	*Regression Table*		Error			Lower	Upper
18	Constant	26020.52	1678.45	15.503	< 0.0001	22709.73	29331.31
19	YrsExper	1002.35	104.54	9.588	< 0.0001	796.14	1208.57
20	Female	4373.78	1724.69	2.536	0.0120	971.78	7775.78
21	Interaction(YrsExper,Female)	-760.83	129.87	-5.858	< 0.0001	-1017.00	-504.66
22	EducLev = 2	-664.78	1120.42	-0.593	0.5537	-2874.84	1545.29
23	EducLev = 3	612.39	1082.33	0.566	0.5722	-1522.54	2747.32
24	EducLev = 4	49.13	1961.56	0.025	0.9800	-3820.11	3918.37
25	EducLev = 5	2808.15	1303.50	2.154	0.0325	236.97	5379.34
26	JobGrade = 2	2697.31	1875.67	1.438	0.1521	-1002.51	6397.12
27	JobGrade = 3	6862.57	2249.25	3.051	0.0026	2425.87	11299.27
28	JobGrade = 4	8745.94	2054.71	4.257	< 0.0001	4692.97	12798.91
29	JobGrade = 5	10579.59	2180.01	4.853	< 0.0001	6279.45	14879.72
30	JobGrade = 6	18202.42	2940.22	6.191	< 0.0001	12402.75	24002.09
31	Interaction(Female,JobGrade = 2)	-713.83	2148.35	-0.332	0.7401	-4951.52	3523.86
32	Interaction(Female,JobGrade = 3)	-1752.87	2430.55	-0.721	0.4717	-6547.19	3041.46
33	Interaction(Female,JobGrade = 4)	1023.20	2383.88	0.429	0.6683	-3679.07	5725.47
34	Interaction(Female,JobGrade = 5)	5241.00	2623.06	1.998	0.0471	66.93	10415.06
35	Interaction(Female,JobGrade = 6)	-29375.22	5753.89	-5.105	< 0.0001	-40724.94	-18025.50
36							
37		Multiple	R-Square	Adjusted	StErr of	Entry	
38	*Step Information*	R		R-Square	Estimate	Number	
39	Block 1	0.7991	0.6386	0.6333	6816.30	1	
40	Block 2	0.8552	0.7314	0.7220	5935.25	2	
41	Block 3	0.9028	0.8150	0.8036	4988.13	3	
42	Block 4	0.9205	0.8473	0.8336	4591.42	4	

PROBLEMS

Level A

29. A regional express delivery service company recently conducted a study to investigate the relationship between the cost of shipping a package (Y), the package weight (X_1), and the distance shipped (X_2). Twenty packages were randomly selected from among the large number received for shipment and a detailed analysis of the shipping cost was conducted for each package. These sample observations are given in the file **P11_24.xlsx**.

a. Estimate a multiple regression model involving the two given explanatory variables. Using the ANOVA table, perform and interpret the result of an F test. Use a 5% significance level in making the statistical decision in this case.

b. Is it worthwhile to add the terms X_1^2 and X_2^2 to the regression equation of part **a**? Base your decision here on a partial F test. Once again, employ a 5% significance level in performing this test.

c. Is it worthwhile to add the term X_1X_2 to the most appropriate reduced equation as determined in part **b**? Again, perform a partial F test with a 5% significance level.

d. Based on the previous findings, what regression equation should this company use in predicting the cost of shipping a package? Defend your recommendation.

30. Suppose you are interested in predicting the price of a laptop computer based on its features. The file **P11_35.xlsx** contains observations on the sales price and a number of potentially relevant variables for a randomly chosen sample of laptop computers.

a. Estimate a multiple regression model that predicts the price of a laptop computer using the following quantitative variables: the speed of the computer's CPU, the length of time the computer's battery maintains its charge, and the size of the computer's RAM. Assess this set of explanatory variables with an F test, and report a p-value.

b. Do explanatory variables that model the computer's chip type and monitor type contribute significantly to the prediction of the laptop's sales price? Let the equation estimated in part **a** serve as the reduced equation in a partial F test. Employ a 5% significance level in conducting the appropriate hypothesis test in this case.

c. Do explanatory variables that model the computer's pointing device and the availability of a help line for buyers contribute significantly to the prediction of the laptop's sales price? Let the most appropriate equation found from the analysis in part **b** serve as the reduced equation in a partial F test. Again, employ a 5% significance level in conducting the appropriate hypothesis test in this case.

31. Many companies manufacture products that are at least partially produced using chemicals (for example, paint, gasoline, and steel). In many cases, the quality of the finished product is a function of the temperature and pressure at which the chemical reactions take place. Suppose that a particular manufacturer wants to model the quality (Y) of a product as a function of the temperature (X_1) and the pressure (X_2) at which it is produced. The file **P11_39.xlsx** contains data obtained from a designed experiment involving these variables. Note that the assigned quality score can range from a minimum of 0 to a maximum of 100 for each manufactured product.

a. Estimate a multiple regression model that includes the two given explanatory variables. Assess this set of explanatory variables with an F test, and report a p-value.

b. Conduct a partial F test to decide whether it is worthwhile to add second-order terms (X_1^2, X_2^2, and X_1X_2) to the multiple regression equation estimated in part **a**. Employ a 5% significance level in conducting this hypothesis test.

c. Which regression equation is the most appropriate one for modeling the quality of the given product? Bear in mind that a good statistical model is usually parsimonious.

Level B

32. Continuing Problem 6, we'll refer to the original multiple regression model (i.e., the one that includes the age

of the auctioned item and the number of bidders as explanatory variables) as the *reduced* equation. Suppose now that the antique collector believes that the *rate of increase* of the auction price with the age of the item will be driven upward by a large number of bidders.

a. Revise the multiple regression model developed previously to model this additional feature of the problem. Estimate this larger regression equation, which we call the *complete* equation, using the sample data in the file **P11_18.xlsx**.

b. Perform a partial F test to check whether the complete equation is significantly better than the reduced equation. Use a 5% level of significance.

33. An economic development researcher wants to understand the relationship between the size of the monthly home mortgage or rent payment for households in a particular middle-class neighborhood and the following set of household variables: family size, approximate location of the household within the neighborhood, an indication of whether those surveyed owned or rented their home, gross annual income of the first household wage earner, gross annual income of the second household wage earner (if applicable), average monthly expenditure on utilities, and the total indebtedness (excluding the value of a home mortgage) of the household. Observations on these variables for a large sample of households are recorded in the file **P02_06.xlsx**.

a. To explain the variation in the size of the monthly home mortgage or rent payment, formulate a multiple regression model that includes all of the *quantitative* household variables in the aforementioned set. Estimate this model using the given sample data. Perform an F test of the model's overall significance, and report a p-value.

b. Determine whether the *qualitative* (i.e., categorical) variable that models the location of the household within the neighborhood adds significantly to explaining the variation in the size of the monthly home mortgage or rent payment. Use a 5% significance level in conducting this hypothesis test.

c. Determine whether it is worthwhile to add a variable that models whether the home is owned or rented to the most appropriate regression equation from part **b**. Again, use a 5% significance level in conducting this hypothesis test.

12.8 OUTLIERS

In all of the regression examples we have analyzed to this point, we have ignored the possibility of outliers. Unfortunately, in many real applications we cannot afford to ignore outliers. They are often present, and they can often have a substantial effect on the results. In this section we briefly discuss outliers in the context of regression—how to detect them and what to do about them.

We tend to think of an outlier as an observation that has an extreme value for at least one variable. For example, if salaries in a data set are mostly in the $40,000 to $80,000 range, but one salary is $350,000, then this observation is a clear outlier with respect to salary. However, in a regression context outliers are not always this obvious. In fact, an observation can be considered an outlier for several reasons, and some types of outliers can be difficult to detect. An observation can be an outlier for one or more of the following reasons.

Characteristics of an Outlier

Outliers can come in several forms, as indicated in this list.

1. It has an extreme value for one or more variables.

2. Its value of the dependent variable is much larger or smaller than predicted by the regression line, and its residual is abnormally large in magnitude. An example appears in Figure 12.19. The line in this scatterplot fits most of the points, but it misses badly on the one obvious outlier. This outlier has a large positive residual, but its Y value is not abnormally large. Its Y value is only large relative to points with the same X value that it has.

Figure 12.19 Outlier with a Large Residual

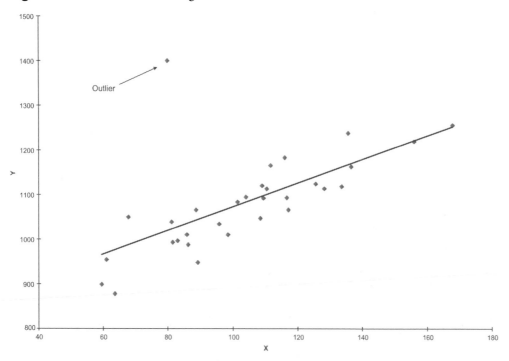

3. Its residual is not only large in magnitude, but this point "tilts" the regression line toward it. An example appears in Figure 12.20. The two lines shown are the regression lines with the outlier and without it. If we keep the outlier, it makes a big difference for the slope and intercept of the regression line. This type of outlier is called an **influential** point, for the obvious reason.

4. Its values of individual explanatory variables are not extreme, but they fall outside the general pattern of the other observations. An example appears in Figure 12.21. Here, we assume that the two variables shown, YrsExper (years of experience) and Rating (an employee's performance rating) are both explanatory variables for some other dependent variable (Salary) that isn't shown in the plot. The obvious outlier does not have an abnormal value of either YrsExper or Rating, but it falls well outside the pattern of most employees.

Figure 12.20

Outlier That Tilts
the Regression Line

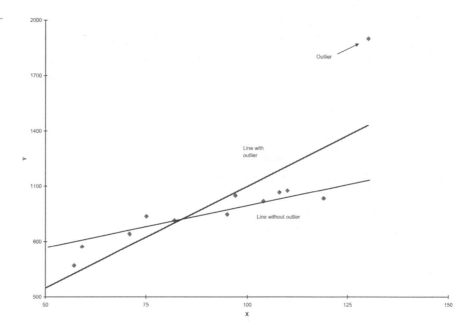

Figure 12.21

Outlier Outside
Pattern of
Explanatory
Variables

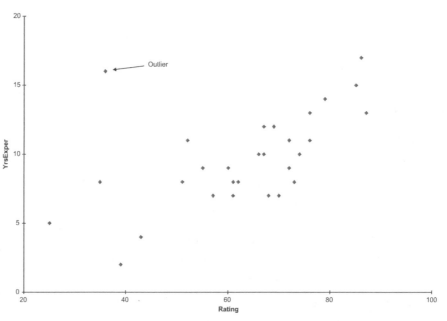

Once we have identified outliers, there is still the thorny problem of what to do with them. In most cases the regression output will look "nicer" if we delete outliers, but this is not necessarily appropriate. If we can argue that the outlier isn't really a member of the relevant population, then it is appropriate and probably best to delete it. But if no such argument can be made, then it is not really appropriate to delete the outlier just to make the analysis come out better. Perhaps the best advice in this case is the advice we gave in the previous chapter. Run the analysis with the outliers and run it again without them. If the key outputs do not change much, then it does not really matter whether the outliers are included or not. If the key outputs do change substantially, then report the results both with and without the outliers, along with a verbal explanation.

We illustrate this procedure in the following continuation of the bank discrimination example.

12.4 Possible Gender Discrimination in Salary at Fifth National Bank of Springfield (continued)

Of the 208 employees at Fifth National Bank, are there any obvious outliers? In what sense are they outliers? Does it matter to the regression results, particularly those concerning gender discrimination, whether the outliers are removed?

Objective To locate possible outliers in the bank salary data, and to see to what extent they affect the regression model.

Solution

There are several places we could look for outliers. An obvious place is the Salary variable. The box plot in Figure 12.22 shows that there are several employees making substantially more in salary than most of the employees. We could consider these outliers and remove them, arguing perhaps that these are senior managers who shouldn't be included in the discrimination analysis. We leave it to you to check whether the regression results are any different with these high-salary employees than without them.

Figure 12.22

Box Plot of Salaries for Bank Data

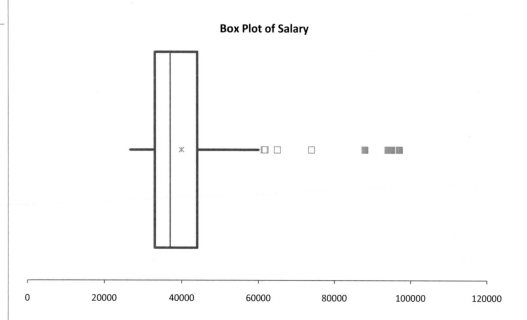

Another place to look is at a scatterplot of the residuals versus the fitted values. This type of plot (offered as an option by StatTools) shows points with abnormally large residuals. For example, we ran the regression with Female, YrsExper, Interaction(YrsExper,Female), and the five job grade dummies, and we obtained the output and scatterplot in Figures 12.23 and 12.24. This scatterplot has several points that could be considered outliers, but we focus on the point identified in the figure. The residual for this point is approximately -21. Given that s_e for this regression is approximately 5, this residual is over four standard errors below 0—quite a lot. When we examine this point more closely, we see that it corresponds to employee 208, who is a 62-year-old female employee in the highest job grade. She has 33 years of experience with Fifth National, she has a graduate degree, and she earns only $30,000. She is clearly an unusual employee, and there are probably special circumstances that can explain her small salary, although we can only guess at what they are.

Figure 12.23 Regression Output with Outlier Included

	A	B	C	D	E	F	G
7		Multiple	R-Square	Adjusted	StErr of		
8	*Summary*	R		R-Square	Estimate		
9		0.9005	0.8109	0.8033	4991.64		
10							
11		Degrees of	Sum of	Mean of	F-Ratio	p-Value	
12	*ANOVA Table*	Freedom	Squares	Squares			
13	Explained	8	21268738998	2658592375	106.7004	< 0.0001	
14	Unexplained	199	4958368233	24916423.28			
15							
16		Coefficient	Standard	t-Value	p-Value	Confidence Interval 95%	
17	*Regression Table*		Error			Lower	Upper
18	Constant	26104.22	1105.44	23.6143	< 0.0001	23924.34	28284.11
19	YrsExper	1070.88	102.01	10.4975	< 0.0001	869.72	1272.05
20	Female	6063.33	1266.32	4.7881	< 0.0001	3566.20	8560.46
21	JobGrade = 2	2596.49	1010.12	2.5705	0.0109	604.58	4588.41
22	JobGrade = 3	6221.39	998.18	6.2328	< 0.0001	4253.03	8189.76
23	JobGrade = 4	11071.95	1172.59	9.4423	< 0.0001	8759.66	13384.25
24	JobGrade = 5	14946.58	1340.25	11.1521	< 0.0001	12303.66	17589.49
25	JobGrade = 6	17097.37	2390.67	7.1517	< 0.0001	12383.07	21811.67
26	Interaction(YrsExper,Female)	-1021.05	118.73	-8.6001	< 0.0001	-1255.17	-786.93

Figure 12.24

Scatterplot of Residuals versus Fitted Values with Outlier Identified

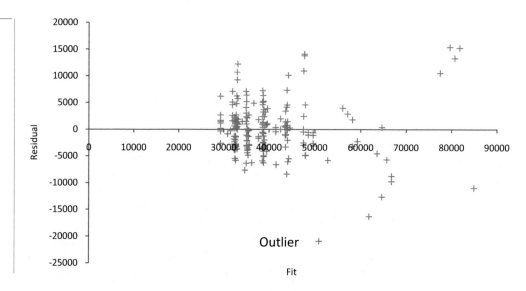

In any case, if we delete this employee and rerun the regression with the same variables, we obtain the output in Figure 12.25.[7] Now, recalling that gender discrimination is the key issue in this example, we compare the coefficients of Female and Interaction(YrsExper,Female) in the two outputs. The coefficient of Female has dropped from 6.063 to 4.353. In words, the Y-intercept for the female regression line used to be about $6000 higher than for the male line; now it is only about $4350 higher. More importantly, the coefficient of Interaction(YrsExper,Female) has changed from -1.021 to -0.721. This coefficient indicates how much less steep the female line for Salary versus YrsExper is than the male line. So a change from -1.021 to -0.721 indicates *less* discrimination against females now than before. In other words, this unusual female employee accounts for a good bit of the discrimination argument—although a strong argument still exists even without her.

Figure 12.25   Regression Output with Outlier Excluded

	A	B	C	D	E	F	G
7		Multiple	R-Square	Adjusted	StErr of		
8	Summary	R		R-Square	Estimate		
9		0.9130	0.8336	0.8269	4685.67		
10							
11		Degrees of	Sum of	Mean of	F-Ratio	p-Value	
12	ANOVA Table	Freedom	Squares	Squares			
13	Explained	8	21780996415	2722624552	124.0064	< 0.0001	
14	Unexplained	198	4347190681	21955508.49			
15							
16		Coefficient	Standard	t-Value	p-Value	Confidence Interval 95%	
17	Regression Table		Error			Lower	Upper
18	Constant	26710.31	1044.02	25.5840	< 0.0001	24651.48	28769.14
19	YrsExper	897.67	101.23	8.8675	< 0.0001	698.04	1097.30
20	Female	4353.11	1232.10	3.5331	0.0005	1923.37	6782.84
21	JobGrade = 2	2717.87	948.49	2.8655	0.0046	847.44	4588.30
22	JobGrade = 3	6257.16	937.02	6.6777	< 0.0001	4409.34	8104.98
23	JobGrade = 4	10983.81	1100.84	9.9777	< 0.0001	8812.93	13154.68
24	JobGrade = 5	15464.47	1261.92	12.2547	< 0.0001	12975.94	17953.00
25	JobGrade = 6	22323.45	2453.01	9.1004	< 0.0001	17486.06	27160.83
26	Interaction(YrsExper,Female)	-720.61	125.15	-5.7578	< 0.0001	-967.41	-473.81

PROBLEMS

Level A

34. The file **P12_34.xlsx** contains the sales, Y, in thousands of dollars per week, for randomly selected fast-food outlets in each of four cities. Furthermore, this data set includes the traffic flow, in thousands of cars, through each of the selected fast-food outlets.

   a. Use the given data to estimate a model for predicting sales as a function of traffic flow. This regression model should account for city-to-city variations that might be due to size or other market conditions. Assume that the level of mean sales will differ from city to city, but that the change in

   mean sales per unit increase in traffic flow will remain the same for all cities (i.e., traffic flow and city factors do not interact).

   b. Perform an F test of the overall significance of the multiple regression model estimated in part **a**, and report a p-value.

   c. How do you explain the result of your statistical hypothesis test in part **b**? What, if anything, would you do to obtain more satisfactory results?

35. A manufacturing firm wants to determine whether a relationship exists between the number of work-hours an employee misses per year (Y) and the employee's annual wages (X). The data provided in the file

---

[7]As it turns out, this employee is the last observation in the data set. An easy way to run the regression (with StatTools) without this employee is to redefine the StatTools data set so that it doesn't include this last row.

P12_35.xlsx are based on a random sample of 15 employees from this organization.

a. Estimate a simple linear regression model using the sample data. How well does the estimated model fit the sample data?

b. Perform an *F* test for the existence of a linear relationship between *Y* and *X*. Use a 5% level of significance.

c. How do you explain the results you have found in parts **a** and **b**?

d. Suppose you learn that the 10th worker in the sample has been fired for missing an excessive number of work-hours during the past year. In light of this information, how would you proceed to estimate the relationship between the number of work-hours an employee misses per year and the employee's annual wages, using the available information? If you decide to revise your estimate of this regression equation, repeat parts **a** and **b**.

Level B

36. Statistician Frank J. Anscombe created a data set to illustrate the importance of doing more than just examining the standard regression output. These data are provided in the file **P12_36.xlsx**.

a. Regress Y_1 on *X*. How well does the estimated model fit the data? Is there evidence of a linear relationship between Y_1 and *X* at the 5% significance level?

b. Regress Y_2 on *X*. How well does the estimated model fit the data? Is there evidence of a linear relationship between Y_2 and *X* at the 5% significance level?

c. Regress Y_3 on *X*. How well does the estimated model fit the data? Is there evidence of a linear relationship between Y_3 and *X* at the 5% significance level?

d. Regress Y_4 on X_4. How well does the estimated model fit the data? Is there evidence of a linear relationship between Y_4 and X_4 at the 5% significance level?

e. Compare these four simple linear regression models (i) in terms of goodness of fit and (ii) in terms of overall statistical significance.

f. How do you explain these findings, considering that each of the regression equations is based on a *different* set of variables?

g. What role, if any, do outliers have on each of these estimated regression models?

12.9 VIOLATIONS OF REGRESSION ASSUMPTIONS

Much of the theoretical research in the area of regression has dealt with violations of the regression assumptions in Section 12.2. There are three issues: how to detect violations of the assumptions, what goes wrong if we ignore violations, and what to do about them if they are detected. Detection is usually relatively easy. We can look at scatterplots, histograms, and time series graphs for visual signs of violations, and there are a number of numerical measures (many not covered here) that have been developed for diagnostic purposes. The second issue, what goes wrong if we ignore violations, depends on the type of violation and its severity. The third issue is the most difficult. There are some relatively easy fixes and some that are well beyond the level of this book. In this section we briefly discuss some of the most common violations and a few possible remedies for them.

12.9.1 Nonconstant Error Variance

The second regression assumption states that the variance of the errors should be *constant* for all values of the explanatory variables. This is a lot to ask, and it is almost always violated to some extent. Fortunately, mild violations do not have much effect on the validity of the regression output, so we can usually ignore them.

A fan shape can cause an incorrect value for the standard error of estimate, so that confidence intervals and hypothesis tests for the regression coefficients are not valid.

However, one particular form of nonconstant error variance occurs fairly often and should be dealt with. This is the "fan shape" we saw in the scatterplot of AmountSpent versus Salary in Figure 12.1. As salaries increase, the variability of amounts spent also increases. Although this fan shape appears in the scatterplot of the dependent variable AmountSpent versus the explanatory variable Salary, it also appears in the scatterplot of residuals versus fitted values when we regress AmountSpent versus Salary. If we ignore this nonconstant error variance, then the standard error of the regression coefficient of Salary is inaccurate, so that a confidence interval for this coefficient or a hypothesis test concerning it can be misleading.

There are at least two ways to deal with this fan-shape phenomenon. The first is to use a different estimation method than least squares. It is called *weighted least squares,* and it is an option available in many statistical software packages. However, it is fairly advanced and it is not available with Excel (or StatTools), so we won't discuss it here.

A logarithmic transformation of Y can sometimes cure the fan-shape problem.

The second method is simpler. When we see a fan shape, where the variability increases from left to right in a scatterplot, we can try a logarithmic transformation of the dependent variable. The reason this often works is that the logarithmic transformation squeezes the large values closer together and pulls the small values farther apart. The scatterplot of the log of AmountSpent versus Salary is in Figure 12.26. Clearly, the fan shape evident in Figure 12.1 is gone.

Figure 12.26

Scatterplot without Fan Shape

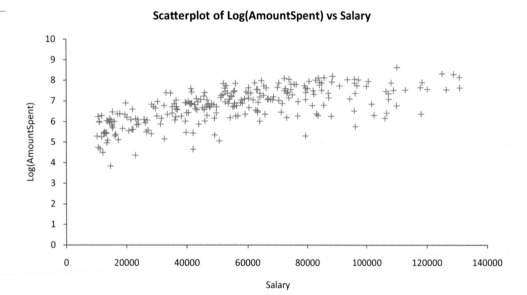

This logarithmic transformation is not a magical cure for all instances of nonconstant error variance. For example, it appears to have introduced some curvature into the plot in Figure 12.26. However, as we discussed in the previous chapter, whenever the distribution of the dependent variable is heavily skewed to the right, as it often is, the logarithmic transformation is worth exploring.

12.9.2 Nonnormality of Residuals

The third regression assumption states that the error terms are normally distributed. We can check this assumption fairly easily by forming a histogram of the residuals. We can even perform a formal test of normality of the residuals by using the procedures discussed in

Section 10.5 of Chapter 10. However, unless the distribution of the residuals is severely nonnormal, the inferences we make from the regression output are still approximately valid. In addition, a form of nonnormality often encountered is skewness to the right, and this can often be remedied by the same logarithmic transformation of the dependent variable that remedies nonconstant error variance.

12.9.3 Autocorrelated Residuals

The fourth regression assumption states that the error terms are probabilistically independent. This assumption is usually valid for cross-sectional data, but it is often violated for time series data. The problem with time series data is that the residuals are often correlated with nearby residuals, a property called **autocorrelation**. The most frequent type of autocorrelation is positive autocorrelation. For example, if residuals separated by 1 month are autocorrelated—called **lag 1 autocorrelation**—in a positive direction, then an overprediction in January, say, will likely lead to an overprediction in February, and an underprediction in January will likely lead to an underprediction in February. If this autocorrelation is large, then serious prediction errors can occur if it isn't dealt with appropriately.

A numerical measure has been developed to check for lag 1 autocorrelation. It is called the **Durbin–Watson statistic** (after the two statisticians who developed it), and it is quoted automatically in the regression output of many statistical software packages. The Durbin–Watson (DW) statistic is scaled to be between 0 and 4. Values close to 2 indicate very little lag 1 autocorrelation, values below 2 indicate positive autocorrelation, and values above 2 indicate negative autocorrelation.

A Durbin–Watson statistic below 2 signals that nearby residuals are positively correlated with one another.

Since *positive* autocorrelation is the usual culprit, the question becomes how much below 2 the DW statistic must be before we should react. There is a formal hypothesis test for answering this question, and a set of tables appears in many statistics texts. Without going into the details, we simply state that when the number of time series observations, n, is about 30 and the number of explanatory variables is fairly small, say, 1 to 5, then any DW statistic less than 1.2 should get our attention. If n increases to around 100, then we shouldn't be concerned unless the DW statistic is below 1.5.

If e_i is the ith residual, then the formula for the DW statistic is

$$\text{DW} = \frac{\sum_{i=2}^{n}(e_i - e_{i-1})^2}{\sum_{i=1}^{n} e_i^2}$$

This is obviously not very attractive for hand calculation, so the StatDurbinWatson function is included in the StatTools add-in. To use it, run any regression and check the option to create a graph of residuals versus fitted values. This automatically creates columns of fitted values and residuals. Then enter the formula

=StatDurbinWatson(*ResidRange*)

in any cell, substituting the actual range of residuals for "ResidRange."

The following continuation of Example 12.1 with the Bendrix manufacturing data—the only time series data set we have analyzed with regression—checks for possible lag 1 autocorrelation.

EXAMPLE | **12.5 EXPLAINING OVERHEAD COSTS AT BENDRIX (CONTINUED)**

Is there any evidence of lag 1 autocorrelation in the Bendrix data when Overhead is regressed on MachHrs and ProdRuns?

Objective   To use the Durbin–Watson statistic to check whether there is any serious autocorrelation in the residuals from the Bendrix regression model for overhead costs.

Solution

We run the usual multiple regression and check that we want a graph of residuals versus fitted values. The results are shown in Figure 12.27. The residuals are listed in column D. Each represents how much the regression overpredicts (if negative) or underpredicts (if positive) the overhead cost for that month. We can check for lag 1 autocorrelation in two ways, with the DW statistic and by examining the time series graph of the residuals in Figure 12.28.

Figure 12.27   Regression Output with Residuals and DW Statistic

	A	B	C	D	E	F
44	*Graph Data*	Overhead	Fit	Residual		Durbin-Watson for residuals
45	1	99798	98391.35059	1406.649409		1.313
46	2	87804	85522.33322	2281.666779		
47	3	93681	92723.59538	957.4046174		
48	4	82262	82428.09201	-166.0920107		
49	5	106968	100227.9028	6740.097234		

Figure 12.28

Time Series Graph of Residuals

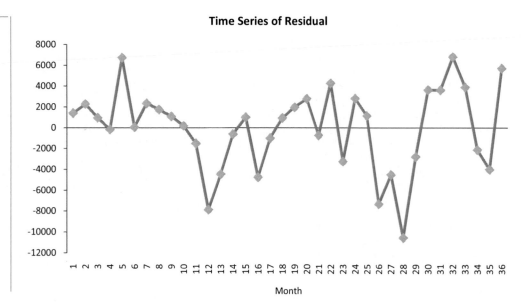

We calculate the DW statistic in cell F45 of Figure 12.27 with the formula

=StatDurbinWatson(D45:D80)

(Remember that StatDurbinWatson is *not* a built-in Excel function. It is available only if StatTools is loaded.) Based on our guidelines for DW values, 1.3131 suggests positive autocorrelation—it is less than 2—but not enough to cause concern.[8] This general conclusion is supported by the time series graph. Serious autocorrelation of lag 1 would tend to show long runs of residuals alternating above and below the horizontal axis—positives would tend to follow positives, and negatives would tend to follow negatives. There is some indication of this behavior in the graph but not an excessive amount. ■

What should we do if the DW statistic signals significant autocorrelation? Unfortunately, the answer to this question would take us much deeper into time series analysis than we can go in this book. Suffice it to say that time series analysis in the context of regression can become very complex, and there are no easy fixes for the autocorrelation that often occurs.

PROBLEMS

Level A

37. Motorco produces electric motors for use in home appliances. One of the company's production managers is interested in examining the relationship between the dollars spent per month in inspecting finished motor products (X) and the number of motors produced during that month that were returned by dissatisfied customers (Y). He has collected the data in the file **P02_18.xlsx** to explore this relationship for the past 36 months.

    a. Generate a simple linear regression model using the given data and interpret it for this production manager.

    b. Conduct an appropriate hypothesis test for the existence of a linear relationship between Y and X in this case, and report a p-value.

    c. Examine the residuals of the estimated regression equation. Do you see evidence of any violations of the assumptions regarding the errors of the regression model?

    d. Conduct a Durbin–Watson test on the model's residuals. Interpret the result of this test for the production manager.

    e. In light of your result in part **d**, do you recommend modifying the original regression model? If so, how would you revise it?

38. Examine the relationship between the average utility bills for homes of a particular size (Y) and the average monthly temperature (X). The data in the file **P11_07.xlsx** include the average monthly bill and temperature for each month of the past year.

    a. Use the given data to estimate a simple linear regression model. How well does the estimated regression model fit the given data?

    b. Conduct an appropriate hypothesis test for the existence of a linear relationship between Y and X, and report a p-value.

    c. Examine the residuals of the estimated regression equation. Do you see evidence of any violations of the assumptions regarding the errors of the regression model?

    d. Conduct a Durbin–Watson test on the model's residuals. Interpret the result of this test.

    e. In light of your result in part **d**, do you recommend modifying the original regression model? If so, how would you revise it?

39. The manager of a commuter rail transportation system was recently asked by her governing board to predict the demand for rides in the large city served by the transportation network. The system manager has collected data on variables thought to be related to the number of weekly riders on the city's rail system. The file **P11_20.xlsx** contains these data.

    a. Estimate a multiple regression model using all of the available explanatory variables.

    b. Conduct and interpret the result of an F test on the given model. Employ a 5% level of significance in conducting this statistical hypothesis test.

    c. Is there evidence of autocorrelated residuals in this model? Explain why or why not.

---

[8]A more formal test, using Durbin–Watson tables, supports this conclusion.

12.10 PREDICTION

Once we have estimated a regression equation from a set of data, we might want to use this equation to predict the value of the dependent variable for *new* observations. As an example, suppose that a retail chain is considering opening a new store in one of several proposed locations. It naturally wants to choose the location that will result in the largest revenues. The problem is that the revenues for the new locations are not yet known. They can be observed only after stores are opened in these locations, and the chain cannot afford to open more than one store at the current time. An alternative is to use regression analysis. Using data from *existing* stores, the chain can run a regression of the dependent variable revenue on several explanatory variables such as population density, level of wealth in the vicinity, number of competitors nearby, ease of access given the existing roads, and so on.

Assuming that the regression equation has a reasonably large R^2 and, even more important, a reasonably small s_e, the chain can then use this equation to predict revenues for the proposed locations. Specifically, it will gather values of the explanatory variables for each of the proposed locations, substitute these into the regression equation, and look at the predicted revenue for each proposed location. All else being equal, the chain will probably choose the location with the highest predicted revenue.

As another example, suppose that we are trying to explain the starting salaries for undergraduate college students. We want to predict the *mean* salary of all graduates with certain characteristics, such as all male marketing majors from state-supported universities. To do this, we first gather salary data from a sample of graduates from various universities. Included in this data set are relevant explanatory variables for each graduate in the sample, such as the type of university, the student's major, GPA, years of work experience, and so on. We then use these data to estimate a regression equation for starting salary and substitute the relevant values of the explanatory variables into the regression equation to obtain the required prediction.

Regression can be used to predict Y for a single observation, or it can be used to predict the mean Y for many observations, all with the same X values.

These two examples illustrate two types of prediction problems in regression. The first problem, illustrated by the retail chain example, is probably the more common of the two. Here we are trying to predict the value of the dependent variable for one or more *individual* members of the population. In this specific example we are trying to predict the future revenue for several potential locations of the new store. In the second problem, illustrated by the salary example, we are trying to predict the *mean* of the dependent variable for all members of the population with certain values of the explanatory variables. In the first problem we are predicting an individual value; in the second problem we are predicting a mean.

The second problem is inherently easier than the first in the sense that the resulting prediction is bound to be more accurate. The reason should be intuitive. Recall that the mean of the dependent variable for any fixed values of the explanatory variables lies on the population regression line. Therefore, if we can accurately estimate this line—that is, if we can accurately estimate the regression coefficients—we can accurately predict the required mean. In contrast, most individual points do *not* lie on the population regression line. Therefore, even if our estimate of the population regression line is perfectly accurate, we still cannot predict exactly where an individual point will fall.

Stated another way, when we predict a mean, there is a single source of error: the possibly inaccurate estimates of the regression coefficients. But when we predict an individual value, there are two sources of error: the inaccurate estimates of the regression coefficients and the inherent variation of individual points around the regression line. This second source of error often dominates the first.

We illustrate these comments in Figure 12.29. For the sake of illustration, the dependent variable is salary and the single explanatory variable is years of experience with the company. Let's suppose that we want to predict either the salary for a particular employee with 10 years of experience or the mean salary of all employees with 10 years of experience. The two lines in this graph represent the population regression line (which in reality is unobservable) and the estimated regression line. For each prediction problem the point prediction—the best guess—is the value above 10 on the estimated regression line. The error in predicting the mean occurs because the two lines in the graph are not the same, that is, the estimated line is not quite correct. The error in predicting the individual value (the point shown in the graph) occurs because the two lines are not the same and also because this point does not lie on the population regression line.

Figure 12.29

Prediction Errors for an Individual Value and a Mean

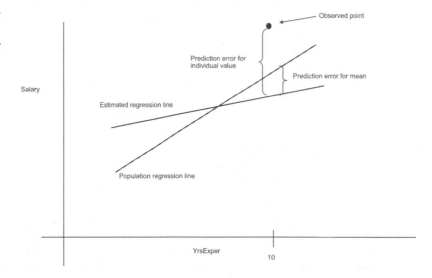

One general aspect of prediction becomes apparent by looking at this graph. If we let X's denote the explanatory variables, predictions for values of the X's close to their means are likely to be more accurate than predictions for X's far from their means. In the graph, the mean years of experience is about 7. (This is approximately where the two lines cross.) Because the slopes of the two lines are different, they get farther apart as YrsExper gets farther away from 7 (on either side). As a result, predictions tend to become less accurate.

It is more difficult to predict for extreme X's than for X's close to the mean. Trying to predict for X's beyond the range of the data set (extrapolation) is quite risky.

This phenomenon shows up as higher standard errors of prediction as the X's get farther away from their means. However, for extreme values of the X's, there is another problem. Suppose, for example, that all values of YrsExper in the data set are between 1 and 15, and we attempt to predict the salary for an employee with 25 years of experience. This is called **extrapolation**; we are attempting to predict beyond the limits of the sample.

The problem here is that there is no guarantee, and sometimes no reason to believe, that the relationship within the range of the sample is valid outside of this range. It is perfectly possible that the effect of years of experience on salary is considerably different in the 25-year range than in the range of the sample. If it is, then extrapolation is bound to yield inaccurate predictions. In general, we should try to avoid extrapolation whenever possible. If we really want to predict the salaries of employees with 25-plus years of experience, then we should include some employees of this type in the original sample.

We now discuss how to make predictions and how to estimate their accuracy, both for individual values and for means. To keep it simple, we first assume that there is a single explanatory variable X. We choose a fixed "trial" value of X, labeled X_0, and predict the value of a single Y or the mean of all Y's when $X = X_0$. For both prediction problems the **point prediction**, or best guess, is found by substituting into the right-hand side of the estimated regression equation. Graphically, this is the height of the estimated regression line above X_0.

To calculate the **point prediction**, substitute the given values of the X's into the estimated regression equation.

The standard error of prediction for a single Y is approximately equal to the standard error of estimate.

To measure the accuracy of these point predictions, we calculate a standard error for each prediction. These standard errors can be interpreted in the usual way. For example, we are about 68% certain that the actual values will be within 1 standard error of the point predictions, and we are about 95% certain that the actual values will be within 2 standard errors of the point predictions. For the individual prediction problem, the standard error is labeled s_{ind} and is given by equation (12.5). As indicated by the approximate equality on the right, when the sample size n is large and X_0 is fairly close to $\overline{X}$, the last two terms inside the square root are relatively small, and this standard error of prediction can be approximated by s_e, the standard error of estimate.

Standard Error of Prediction for a Single Y

$$s_{\text{ind}} = s_e \sqrt{1 + \frac{1}{n} + \frac{(X_0 - \overline{X})^2}{\sum_{i=1}^{n}(X_i - \overline{X})^2}} \simeq s_e \qquad (12.5)$$

For the prediction of the mean, the standard error is labeled s_{mean} and is given by equation (12.6). Here, if X_0 is fairly close to $\overline{X}$, then the last term inside the square root is relatively small, and this standard error of prediction is approximately the expression on the right.

Standard Error of Prediction for the Mean Y

$$s_{\text{mean}} = s_e \sqrt{\frac{1}{n} + \frac{(X_0 - \overline{X})^2}{\sum_{i=1}^{n}(X_i - \overline{X})^2}} \simeq s_e / \sqrt{n} \qquad (12.6)$$

The standard error of prediction for a mean of Y's is approximately equal to the standard error of estimate divided by the square root of the sample size.

These standard errors can be used to calculate a 95% prediction interval for an individual value and a 95% confidence interval for a mean value. Exactly as in Chapter 9, we go out a t-multiple of the relevant standard error on either side of the point prediction. The t-multiple is the value that cuts off 0.025 probability in the right-hand tail of a t distribution with $n - 2$ degrees of freedom.

The term *prediction* interval (rather than confidence interval) is used for an individual value because an individual value of Y is not a population *parameter*. However, the interpretation is basically the same. If we calculate a 95% prediction interval for many members of the population, we expect their actual Y values to fall within the corresponding prediction intervals about 95% of the time.

To see how all of this can be implemented in Excel, we revisit the Bendrix example of predicting overhead expenses.

EXAMPLE | **12.6 PREDICTING OVERHEAD AT BENDRIX**

We have already used regression to analyze overhead expenses at Bendrix, based on 36 months of data. Suppose Bendrix expects the values of MachHrs and ProdRuns for the next three months to be 1430, 1560, 1520, and 35, 45, 40, respectively. What are their point predictions and 95% prediction intervals for Overhead for these three months?

Objective   To predict Overhead at Bendrix for the next three months, given anticipated values of MachHrs and ProdRuns.

Solution

StatTools provides the capability to provide predictions and 95% prediction intervals, but you must set up a second data set to capture the results. This second data set can be placed next to (or below) the original data set. It should have the same variable name headings, plus LowerLimit95 and UpperLimit95 headings, and it should include values of the explanatory variable to be used for prediction. For this example we called the original data set Original Data and the new data set Data for Prediction. The regression dialog box and results in Data for Prediction appear in Figures 12.30 and 12.31. In the dialog box, note that the Prediction option is checked, and the second data set is specified in the corresponding dropdown list.

Figure 12.30

Regression Dialog Box with Predictions Checked

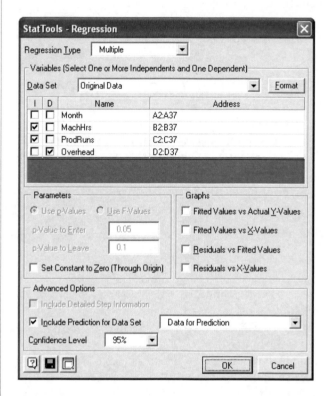

The text box in Figure 12.31 explains how the second data set range should be set up. Initially, you should enter the given values in the Month, MachHrs, and ProdRuns columns. Then when the regression is run (with the Prediction option checked), the values in the Overhead, LowerLimit95, and UpperLimit95 columns will be filled. (If you forget to create LowerLimit95 and UpperLimit95 columns as part of the second data set, StatTools will do it for you.)

The Overhead values in column I are the point predictions for the next three months, and the LowerLimit95 and UpperLimit95 values in column J and K indicate the 95% prediction intervals. We see from the wide prediction intervals how much uncertainty remains. The reason is the relatively large standard error of estimate, s_e. If we could halve the value of s_e, the length of the prediction interval would be only half as large. Contrary to what you might expect, this is not a sample size problem. That is, a larger sample size would almost surely *not* produce a smaller value of s_e. The whole problem is that MachHrs and ProdRuns are not perfectly correlated with Overhead. The only way to decrease s_e and get more accurate predictions is to find other explanatory variables that are more closely related to Overhead.

Figure 12.31 Prediction of Overhead

	F	G	H	I	J	K	L
1	Month	MachHrs	ProdRuns	Overhead	LowerLimit95	UpperLimit95	
2	37	1430	35	97180.35	88700.80	105659.91	
3	38	1560	45	111676.27	103002.95	120349.58	
4	39	1520	40	105516.72	96993.16	114040.28	
5							
6	Above is the data set for prediction. It is best to set this up ahead of						
7	time, entering all of the column headings, entering the values of the explanatory						
8	variables you want to test, and defining this entire range as a new StatTools data						
9	set. The values in the last three columns can be blank or have values, but when						
10	regression is run with the prediction options, they will be filled in or overwritten.						
11							
12							

StatTools provides prediction intervals for individual values, as we have just seen, but it does not provide confidence intervals for the mean of Y, given a set of X's. To obtain such a confidence interval, you can use equation (12.6) to get the required standard error of prediction (for simple regression only), or you can approximate it by $s_e/\sqrt{n}$.

PROBLEMS

Level A

40. The human resources manager of DataCom, Inc., wants to predict the annual salaries of given employees using the following explanatory variables: (a) the number of years of prior relevant work experience, (b) the number of years of employment at DataCom, (c) the number of years of education beyond high school, (d) the employee's gender, (e) the employee's department, and (f) the number of individuals supervised by the given employee. These data have been collected for a sample of employees and are given in the file **P11_05.xlsx**.
   a. Estimate an appropriate multiple regression model to predict the annual salary of a given DataCom employee.
   b. Conduct and interpret the result of an F test from the ANOVA table on the given model. Employ a 5% level of significance in this test.
   c. Given the estimated regression model, predict the annual salary of a male employee who served in a similar department at another company for 5 years prior to coming to work at DataCom. This man, a graduate of a 4-year collegiate business program, has been supervising 6 subordinates in the sales department since joining the organization 7 years ago.

   d. Find a 95% prediction interval for the salary earned by a DataCom employee as characterized in part **c**.
   e. Find a 95% confidence interval for the mean salary earned by all DataCom employees sharing the characteristics provided in part **c**.
   f. How do you explain the difference between the widths of the intervals in parts **d** and **e**?

41. Suppose you are interested in predicting the price of a laptop computer based on its various features. The file **P11_35.xlsx** contains observations on the sales price and on a number of potentially relevant variables for a randomly chosen sample of laptop computers.
   a. Estimate a multiple regression model that includes all available explanatory variables.
   b. Conduct and interpret the result of an F test from the ANOVA table on the given model. Employ a 5% level of significance in this test.
   c. Use the estimated regression equation to predict the price of a laptop computer with the following features: a 50-megahertz processor, a battery that holds its charge for 180 minutes, 20 megabytes of RAM, a DX chip, a color monitor, a trackball pointing device, and a 24-hour, toll-free customer service hotline.
   d. Find a 99% prediction interval for the price of a laptop computer as characterized in part **c**.

e. Find a 99% confidence interval for the average price of all laptop computers sharing the characteristics provided in part **c**.

f. How do you explain the difference between the widths of the intervals in parts **d** and **e**?

42. Suppose that a power company located in southern Alabama wants to predict the peak power load (i.e., *Y*, the maximum amount of power that must be generated each day to meet demand) as a function of the daily high temperature (*X*). A random sample of 25 summer days is chosen, and the peak power load and the high temperature are recorded on each day. The file **P11_40.xlsx** contain these observations.

a. Use the given data to estimate a simple linear regression model. How well does the estimated regression model fit the given data?

b. Conduct an appropriate hypothesis test for the existence of a linear relationship between *Y* and *X*, and report a *p*-value.

c. Examine the residuals of the estimated regression equation. Do you see evidence of any violations of the assumptions regarding the errors of the regression model?

d. Conduct a Durbin–Watson test on the model's residuals. Interpret the result of this test.

e. Given your result in part **d**, do you recommend modifying the original regression model in this case? If so, how would you revise it?

f. Use the final version of your regression model to predict the peak power load on a summer day with a high temperature of 90 degrees.

g. Find a 95% prediction interval for the peak power load on a summer day with a high temperature of 90 degrees.

h. Find a 99% confidence interval for the average peak power load on all summer days with a high temperature of 90 degrees.

12.11 CONCLUSION

In these two chapters on regression, we have seen how useful regression analysis can be for a variety of business applications and how statistical software such as the StatTools add-in in Excel enables us to obtain relevant output—both graphical and numerical—with very little effort. However, we have also seen that there are many concepts that need to be understood well before regression analysis can be used appropriately. Given the user-friendly software currently available, it is all too easy to generate enormous amounts of regression output and then misinterpret or misuse much of it.

At the very least, you should (1) be able to interpret the standard regression output, including statistics on the regression coefficients, summary measures such as R^2 and s_e, and the ANOVA table, (2) know what to look for in the many scatterplots available, (3) know how to use dummy variables, interaction terms, and nonlinear transformations to improve a fit, and (4) be able to spot clear violations of the regression assumptions. However, we haven't covered everything. Indeed, many entire books are devoted exclusively to regression analysis. Therefore, you should recognize when you *don't* know enough to handle a regression problem such as nonconstant error variance or autocorrelation appropriately. In this case you should consult a statistical expert.

Summary of Key Terms

Term	Symbol	Explanation	Excel	Page	Equation Number
Statistical model for regression		A theoretical model, including several assumptions, that must be satisfied, at least approximately, for inferences from regression output to be valid		646	12.1

(continued)

Term	Symbol	Explanation	Excel	Page	Equation Number
Homoscedasticity (and heteroscedasticity)		Equal (and unequal) variance of the dependent variable for different values of the explanatory variables		647	
Autocorrelation of residuals		Lack of independence in the series of residuals, especially relevant for time series data		648	
Parsimony		The concept of explaining the most with the least		650	
Standard error of regression coefficient	s_b	Measures how much the estimates of a regression coefficient vary from sample to sample	StatTools/ Regression & Classification/ Regression	651	
Confidence interval for regression coefficient		An interval likely to contain the population regression coefficient	StatTools/ Regression & Classification/ Regression	652	
t-value for regression coefficient	t	The ratio of the estimate of a regression coefficient to its standard error, used to test whether the coefficient is 0	StatTools/ Regression & Classification/ Regression	653	12.3
Hypothesis test for regression coefficient		Typically, a two-tailed test, where the null hypothesis is that the regression coefficient is 0	StatTools/ Regression & Classification/ Regression	653	
ANOVA table for regression		Used to test whether the explanatory variables, as a whole, have any significant explanatory power	StatTools/ Regression & Classification/ Regression	654	
Multicollinearity		Occurs when there is a fairly strong linear relationship between explanatory variables		659	
Include/exclude decisions		Guidelines for deciding whether to include or exclude potential explanatory variables		662	
Stepwise regression		A class of "automatic" equation-building methods, where variables are added (or deleted) in order of their importance	StatTools/ Regression & Classification/ Regression	667	
Partial F test		Tests whether a set of extra explanatory variables adds any explanatory power to an existing regression equation	Must be done manually	672	12.4
Outliers		Observations that lie outside the general pattern of points and can have a substantial effect on the regression model		680	
Influential point		A point that can "tilt" the regression line		681	

(*continued*)

Term	Symbol	Explanation	Excel	Page	Equation Number
Durbin–Watson statistic		A measure of the autocorrelation between residuals, especially useful for time series data	=StatDurbin Watson(*range*), a StatTools function	688	
Standard errors of prediction	s_{ind}, s_{mean}	Measures of the accuracy of prediction when predicting Y for an individual observation, or predicting the mean of all Y's, for fixed values of the explanatory variables	StatTools/ Regression & Classification/ Regression	693	12.5, 12.6

PROBLEMS

Conceptual Exercises

C.1. Suppose a regression output produces the following 99% confidence interval for one of the regression coefficients:

$[-32.47, -16.88]$

Given this information, should an analyst reject the null hypothesis that this population regression coefficient is equal to 0? Explain your answer.

C.2. Explain why it is not possible to estimate a linear regression model that contains *all* dummy variables associated with a particular categorical explanatory variable.

C.3. Suppose that you are serving as the mentor for a summer intern in your organization. As a first assignment, you direct this undergraduate student to generate a multiple regression model that does a good job of explaining the variation in the monthly sales of one of the products your company manufactures. Shortly thereafter, the intern submits a report that recommends a particular estimated equation. The student tells you that she found the "best" model by enumerating all possible explanatory variables, gathering a random sample for each possible variable, and using a statistical software package that automatically finds a model containing only those variables with statistically significant regression coefficients. What feedback would you give to the intern based on the overall approach she has taken in completing this statistical assignment?

C.4. Distinguish between the test of significance of an individual regression coefficient and the ANOVA test. When, if ever, are these two statistical tests essentially equivalent?

C.5. Which of these intervals based on the same estimated regression equation with fixed values of the explanatory variables would be *wider*: (i) a 95% prediction interval for an individual value of Y or (ii) a 95% confidence interval for the mean value of Y? Explain your answer. How would you interpret the wider of these two intervals in words?

Level A

43. For 12 straight weeks you have observed the sales (in number of cases) of canned tomatoes at Mr. D's. Each week you kept track of the following:
   - Was a promotional notice placed in all shopping carts for canned tomatoes?
   - Was a coupon given for canned tomatoes?
   - Was a price reduction (none, 1, or 2 cents off) given?

   The file **P12_43.xlsx** contains these data.
   a. Use multiple regression to determine how these factors influence sales.
   b. Discuss whether your final equation has any problems with autocorrelation, heteroscedasticity, or multicollinearity.
   c. Predict sales of canned tomatoes during a week in which Mr. D's uses a shopping cart notice, a coupon, and a 1-cent price reduction.

44. The file **P12_44.xlsx** contains data on pork sales. Price is in dollars per hundred pounds, quantity sold is in billions of pounds, per capita income is in dollars, U.S. population is in millions, and GNP is in billions of dollars.
   a. Use the data to develop a regression equation that could be used to predict the quantity of pork sold during future periods. Does heteroscedasticity, autocorrelation, or multicollinearity appear to be a problem?

b. Suppose that during each of the next two quarters, price is 45, U.S. population is 240, GNP is 2620, and per capita income is 10,000. (These are in the units described previously.) Predict the quantity of pork sold during each of the next two quarters.

45. The file **P12_45.xlsx** contains monthly sales (in thousands of dollars) for a photography studio and the price charged per portrait during each month. Suppose we try to predict the current month's sales from last month's sales and the current month's price.
  a. If the price of a portrait during month 21 is $10, predict month 21 sales.
  b. Does autocorrelation, multicollinearity, or heteroscedasticity appear to be a problem?

46. The file **P12_46.xlsx** contains data on a motel chain's revenue and advertising.
  a. Use the data and multiple regression to make predictions for the motel chain's revenues during the next four quarters. Assume that advertising during each of the next four quarters is $50,000.
  b. Does autocorrelation appear to be a problem?

47. The file **P12_47.xlsx** contains the quarterly revenues (in millions of dollars) of Washington Gas and Light for the years 1992 through 1998. We want to use these data to build a multiple regression model that can be used to forecast future revenues.
  a. Which variables should be included in the regression? Explain your rationale for including or excluding variables.
  b. Interpret the coefficients of your final equation.
  c. Make a forecast for revenues during the first quarter of 1999. Also, estimate the probability that 1999 Quarter 1 revenues will be at least $150 million. (*Hint*: Use the standard error of prediction and the fact that the errors are approximately normally distributed.)

48. The file **P11_43.xlsx** contains the following data for several underdeveloped countries:
  ■ Infant mortality rate
  ■ Adult literacy rate
  ■ Percentage of students finishing primary school
  ■ Per capita GNP
  a. Use these data to develop an equation that can be used to predict the infant mortality rate. Justify your equation.
  b. Are there any outliers? If so, what happens if you omit them? *Should* they be omitted?
  c. Interpret the coefficients in your equation.
  d. Does heteroscedasticity or multicollinearity appear to be a problem?
  e. Why is autocorrelation not important in this problem?
  f. Within what amount should 95% of our predictions for the infant mortality rate be accurate?
  g. For a country with a $2000 GNP, 90% adult literacy, and 80% finishing primary school, the regression implies that there is a 1% chance of infant mortality exceeding what value? (*Hint*: Use the standard error of prediction and the fact that the errors are approximately normally distributed.)

49. The file **P12_49.xlsx** contains data on 128 recent home sales in MidCity. For each sale, the file shows the neighborhood (1, 2, or 3) in which the house is located, the number of offers made on the house, the square footage, whether the house is made primarily of brick, the number of bathrooms, the number of bedrooms, and the selling price. Neighborhoods 1 and 2 are more traditional neighborhoods, whereas neighborhood 3 is a newer, more prestigious, neighborhood. For each part below, use StatTools to estimate the relevant regression equation for selling price.
  a. Base this first equation on all variables (other than Home in column A), treating information on brick and neighborhood as categorical and treating all other variables as regular quantitative variables. From this equation, explain what the "premium" is for a house being made of brick, all else being equal. What is the premium for a house being in neighborhood 3, all else being equal? Also, explain the effect of the other variables (besides brick and neighborhood) on price. Are they all significant? (For now, don't eliminate any variables, even if they are insignificant.)
  b. Is there an *extra* premium for a brick house in neighborhood 3, in addition to the usual premium for being brick? Answer by allowing an interaction effect between brick and neighborhood. (This equation should have two extra variables in addition to those in the equation part **a.**)
  c. Starting with the equation in part **b**, remove any variables with p-values greater than 0.1. Explain exactly what this latter equation says about the effect of neighborhood on price. Does it provide much different information than the equation in part **b**?

50. Recall the movie star data from Chapter 2 (in the file **Movie Stars.xlsx**).
  a. Determine an equation to predict salary on the basis of gender, domestic gross, and foreign gross. Make sure all variables in your equation are significant at the 0.15 level.
  b. Interpret the coefficients in your equation.
  c. Does your equation exhibit any autocorrelation, heteroscedasticity, or multicollinearity?
  d. Identify and interpret any outliers.

51. You are trying to determine how the marketing mix influences the sale of Cornpone cereal. The file **P12_51.xlsx** contains the following information for 17 consecutive weeks. (*Note*: Weekly sales are in millions of boxes.)
  ■ Was price cut during the week?
  ■ Was there a prize in the package?
  ■ Was there a coupon in the package?

a. Use these data to determine an equation that can be used to predict weekly Cornpone sales. (Ignore any possible effect of trend.) Make sure all variables in your equation are significant at the 0.15 level.

b. Interpret the coefficients in your equation.

c. Are there any outliers?

d. Is either multicollinearity or autocorrelation a problem?

e. During a week in which there is a price cut and both a prize and a coupon are in the package, what is the probability that sales will be less than 50 million boxes? You may assume that heteroscedasticity and autocorrelation are not problems. (*Hint*: Use the standard error of prediction and the fact that the errors are approximately normally distributed.)

52. The belief that larger majorities for a president in a presidential election help the president's party increase its representation in the House and Senate is called the "coat-tail" effect. The file **P12_52.xlsx** gives the percentage by which each president since 1948 won the election and the number of seats in the House and Senate gained (or lost) during each election. Are these data consistent with the idea of presidential coat-tails? (Source: *Wall Street Journal*, September 10, 1996)

53. The file **P12_53.xlsx** lists the U.S. unemployment rate, the percentage growth in the U.S. economy (in real terms), and the percentage growth in prices for years 1960 through 2001. Determine how changes in unemployment, economic growth, and price changes are related. (Source: *Wall Street Journal Almanac*)

54. The file **P12_54.xlsx** contains the golf handicap and an index of their company's stock performance over the last 3 years for 50 CEOs. A higher index indicates a better stock performance, whereas a lower handicap indicates better golfing ability. For example, Jerry Choate, the CEO of Allstate, has a 10.1 golf handicap, and his company's stock performance index is 83. (The maximum possible stock performance index is 100.) The May 31, 1998, *New York Times* reported that these data indicate that better golfers make better CEOs. What do you think?

55. When potential workers apply for a job that requires extensive manual assembly of small intricate parts, they are initially given three different tests to measure their manual dexterity. The ones who are hired are then periodically given a performance rating on a 0 to 100 scale that combines their speed and accuracy in performing the required assembly operations. The file **P12_55.xlsx** lists the test scores and performance ratings for a randomly selected group of employees. It also lists their seniority (months with the company) at the time of the performance rating.

a. Look at a matrix of correlations. Can you say with certainty (based only on these correlations) that the R^2 value for the regression will be at least 35%? Why or why not?

b. Is there any evidence (from the correlation matrix) that multicollinearity will be a problem? Why or why not?

c. Run the regression of JobPerf versus all four independent variables. List the equation, the value of R^2, and the value of s_e. Do all of the coefficients have the signs you would expect? Briefly explain.

d. Referring to the equation in part **c**, if a worker (outside of the 80 in the sample) has 15 months of seniority and test scores of 57, 71, and 63, give a prediction and an approximate 95% prediction interval for this worker's JobPerf score.

e. One of the *t*-values for the coefficients in part **c** is less than 1. Explain briefly why this occurred. Does it mean that this variable is not related to JobPerf?

f. Arguably, the three test measures provide overlapping (or redundant) information. For the sake of parsimony (explaining "the most with the least"), it might be sensible to regress JobPerf versus only two explanatory variables, Sen and AvgTest, where AvgTest is the average of the three test scores— that is, AvgTest = (Test1 + Test2 + Test3)/3. Run this regression and report the same measures as in part **c**: the equation itself, R^2, and s_e. Would you argue that this equation is "just as good as" the equation in part **c**? Explain briefly.

56. Nicklaus Electronics manufactures electronic components used in the computer and space industries. The annual rate of return on the market portfolio and the annual rate of return on Nicklaus Electronics stock for the last 36 months are shown in the file **P12_56.xlsx**. The company wants to calculate the "systematic risk" of its common stock. (It is systematic in the sense that it represents the part of the risk that Nicklaus shares with the market as a whole.) The rate of return Y_t in period t on a security is hypothesized to be related to the rate of return m_t on a market portfolio by the equation

$$Y_t = a + bm_t + e_t$$

Here, a is the risk-free rate of return, b is the security's systematic risk, and e_t is an error term. Using the data available, estimate the systematic risk of the common stock of Nicklaus Electronics. Would you say that Nicklaus stock is a "risky" investment? Why or why not?

57. The auditor of Kaefer Manufacturing uses regression analysis during the analytical review stage of the firm's annual audit. The regression analysis attempts to uncover relationships that exist between various account balances. Any such relationship is subsequently used as a preliminary test of the reasonableness of the reported account balances. The auditor wants to determine whether a relationship exists between the balance of accounts receivable at the end of the month and that month's sales. The file **P12_57.xlsx** contains data on these two accounts for the last 36 months. It also shows the sales levels 2 months before month 1.

  a. Is there any statistical evidence to suggest a relationship between the monthly sales level and accounts receivable?
  b. Referring to part **a**, would the relationship be described any better by including this month's sales and the previous month's sales (called lagged sales) in the equation for accounts receivable? What about adding the sales from more than a month ago to the equation? For this problem, why might it make accounting sense to include lagged sales variables in the equation? How do you interpret their coefficients?
  c. During month 37, which is a fiscal year-end month, the sales were $1,800,000. The reported accounts receivable balance was $3,000,000. Does this reported amount seem consistent with past experience? Explain.

58. A company gives prospective managers four separate tests for judging their potential. For a sample of 30 managers, the test scores and the subsequent job effectiveness ratings (JobEff) given 1 year later are listed in the file **P12_58.xlsx**.

  a. Look at scatterplots and the table of correlations for these five variables. Does it appear that a multiple regression equation for JobEff, with the test scores as explanatory variables, will be successful? Can you foresee any problems in obtaining accurate estimates of the individual regression coefficients?
  b. Estimate the regression equation that includes all four test scores, and find 95% confidence intervals for the coefficients of the explanatory variables. How can you explain the negative coefficient of Test3, given that the correlation between JobEff and Test3 is positive?
  c. Can you reject the null hypothesis that these test scores, as a whole, have no predictive ability for job effectiveness at the 1% level? Why or why not?
  d. If a new prospective manager has test scores of 83, 74, 65, and 77, what do you predict his job effectiveness rating will be in 1 year? What is the standard error of this prediction?

Level B

59. Confederate Express is attempting to determine how its monthly shipping costs depend on the number of units shipped during a month. The file **P12_59.xlsx** contains the number of units shipped and total shipping costs for the last 15 months.

  a. Use regression to determine a relationship between units shipped and monthly shipping costs.

  b. Plot the errors for the predictions in order of time sequence. Is there any unusual pattern?
  c. We have been told that there was a trucking strike during months 11 through 15, and we believe that this might have influenced shipping costs. How could the answer to part **a** be modified to account for the effects of the strike? After accounting for the effects of the strike, does the unusual pattern in part **b** disappear?

60. You are trying to determine the effects of three packaging displays (A, B, and C) on sales of toothpaste. The file **P12_60.xlsx** contains the number of cases of toothpaste sold for 9 consecutive weeks. The type of store (GR = grocery, DI = discount, and DE = department store) and the store location (U = urban, S = suburban, and R = rural) are also listed.

  a. Run a multiple regression to determine how the type of store, display, and store location influence sales. Which potential explanatory variables should be included in the equation? Explain your rationale for including or excluding variables.
  b. What type of store, store location, and display appears to maximize sales?
  c. For the type of store in your part **b** answer, estimate the probability that 80 or more cases of toothpaste will be sold during a week. (*Hint*: Use the standard error of prediction and the fact that the errors are approximately normally distributed.)
  d. Does multicollinearity or autocorrelation seem to be a problem?

61. You want to determine the variables that influence bus usage in major American cities. For 24 cities, the following data are listed in the file **P12_61.xlsx**:

  ■ Bus travel (annual, in thousands of hours)
  ■ Income (average per capita income)
  ■ Population (in thousands)
  ■ Land area (in square miles)

  a. Use these data to fit the multiplicative equation

  $$BusTravel = \alpha Income^{\beta_1} Population^{\beta_2} LandArea^{\beta_3}$$

  b. Are all variables significant at the 0.05 level?
  c. Interpret the values of β_1, β_2, and β_3.

62. The file **P12_62.xlsx** contains data on 80 managers at a large (fictitious) corporation. The variables are Salary (current annual salary), YrsExper (years of experience in the industry), YrsHere (years of experience with this company), and MglLevel (current level in the company, coded 1 to 4). You want to regress Salary on the potential explanatory variables. What is the "best" ways to do so? Specifically, how should you handle Mg1Level? Also, should you include both YrsExper and YrsHere or only one of these, and if only one, which one? Present your results, and explain them and your reasoning behind them.

63. Mattel has assigned you to analyze the factors influencing Barbie sales. The number of Barbie dolls sold (in millions) during the last 23 years is given in the file **P12_63.xlsx**. Year 23 is last year, year 22 is the year before that, and so on. The following factors are thought to influence Barbie sales:

- Was there a recession?
- Were Barbies on sale at Christmas?
- Was there an upward trend over time?

a. Determine an equation that can be used to predict annual Barbie sales. Make sure that all variables in your equation are significant at the 0.15 level.

b. Interpret the coefficients in your equation.

c. Are there any outliers?

d. Is heteroscedasticity or autocorrelation a problem?

e. During the current year (year 24), a recession is predicted and Barbies will be put on sale at Christmas. There is a 1% chance that sales of Barbies will exceed what value? You may assume here that heteroscedasticity and autocorrelation are not a problem. (*Hint:* Use the standard error of prediction and the fact that the errors are approximately normally distributed.)

64. The capital asset pricing model (CAPM) is a cornerstone of finance. To apply the CAPM, we assume that each stock has a risk measure (called the beta of the stock) associated with it. Then the CAPM asserts that

- The expected return on $1 invested in a stock is a linear function of the stock's beta.
- $1 invested in a stock with a 0 beta will earn an annual return equal to the risk-free interest rate (r_f) on 90-day treasury bills.
- $1 invested in a stock with a beta of 1 will yield an annual return equal to the annual return (r_m) on the market portfolio.

a. Formulate a population regression model incorporating these features of the CAPM. The explanatory variable is the stock's beta and the dependent variable is the annual return on $1 invested in the stock.

b. Given the data in Table 12.3, test the adequacy of the model developed in part **a**. Assume $r_f = 0.09$ and $r_m = 0.18$.

Table 12.3   Stock Returns and Betas

Company	Beta	Annual Return
AT&T	0.56	0.14
IBM	1.07	0.19
GM	0.76	0.16
Polaroid	2.17	0.28
Chrysler	1.04	0.18

65. How does inflation in a country affect changes in exchange rates? The file **P12_65.xlsx** contains the following information for 11 countries.

- Ratio of percentage increase in prices in local country to percentage increase in U.S. prices from 1973 to 1995.
- Ratio of 1995 units of local currency per dollar to 1973 units of local currency per dollar.

Use these data to explain how inflation affects exchange rates. Do you have an explanation for these results? (Source: *The Economist,* January 20, 1996)

66. The file **P12_66.xlsx** shows the "yield curve" (at monthly intervals). For example, in January 1985 the annual rate on a 3-month T-bill was 7.76% and the annual rate on a 30-year government bond was 11.45%. Use regression to determine which interest rates tend to move together most closely. (Source: International Investment and Exchange Database Developed by Craig Holden, Indiana University School of Business)

67. The Keynesian school of macroeconomics believes that increased government spending leads to increased growth. The file **P12_67.xlsx** contains the following annual data:

- Government spending as percentage of GDP (gross domestic product)
- Percentage annual growth in annual GDP

Are these data consistent with the Keynesian school of economics? (Source: *Wall Street Journal*)

68. The June 1997 issue of *Management Accounting* gave the following rule for predicting your current salary if you are a managerial accountant. Take $31,865. Next, add $20,811 if you are top management, add $3604 if you are senior management, or subtract $11,419 if you are entry management. Then add $1105 for every year you have been a managerial accountant. Add $7600 if you have a master's degree or subtract $12,467 if you have no college degree. Add $11,257 if you have a professional certification. Finally, add $8667 if you are male.

a. How do you think the journal derived this method of estimating an accountant's current salary? Be specific.

b. How could a managerial accountant use this information to determine whether he or she is significantly underpaid?

69. Suppose you are trying to use regression to predict the current salary of a major league baseball player. What variables might you use?

70. The file **P12_70.xlsx** contains sample data on annual sales for Prozac, a drug produced by Eli Lilly. For each year, the file lists the price per day of therapy (DOT) charged for Prozac and total Prozac sales (in millions of DOT) for the year. Assuming that price is the only factor influencing Prozac sales, determine the number of DOT of Prozac that Lilly should produce for the year to ensure that there is only a 1% chance that Lilly runs out of Prozac. Assume the current price of Prozac is $1.75. (*Hint:* Use the standard error of prediction and the fact that the errors are approximately normally distributed.)

71. A business school committee was charged with studying admissions criteria to the school. Until that time, only juniors were admitted. Part of the committee's task was to see whether freshman courses would be equally good predictors of success as freshman and sophomore courses combined. Here, we take "success" to mean doing well in A-core (a combination of the junior level finance, marketing, and production courses, F301, M301, and P301). The file **P12_71.xlsx** contains data on 250 students who had just completed A-core. For each student, the file lists their grades in the following courses:

- M118 (freshman)—finite math
- M119 (freshman)—calculus
- K201 (freshman)—computers
- W131 (freshman)—writing
- E201, E202 (sophomore)—micro- and macroeconomics
- L201 (sophomore)—business law
- A201, A202 (sophomore)—accounting
- E270 (sophomore)—statistics
- A-core (junior)—finance, marketing, and production

Except for A-core, each value is a grade point for a specific course (such as 3.7 for an A−). For A-core, each value is the average grade point for the three courses comprising A-core.

a. The A-core grade point is the eventual dependent variable in a regression analysis. Look at the correlations between all variables. Is multicollinearity likely to be a problem? Why or why not?

b. Run a multiple regression using all of the potential explanatory variables. Now, eliminate the variables as follows. (This is a reasonable variation of the procedures discussed in the chapter.) Look at 95% confidence intervals for their coefficients (as usual, not counting the intercept term). Any variable whose confidence interval contains the value 0 is a candidate for exclusion. For all such candidates, eliminate the variable with the *t*-value lowest in magnitude. Then rerun the regression, and use the same procedure to possibly exclude another variable. Keep doing this until 95% confidence intervals of the coefficients of all remaining variables do *not* include 0. Report this final equation, its R^2 value, and its standard error of estimate s_e.

c. Give a quick summary of the properties of the equation in part **b**. Specifically, (i) do the variables have the "correct" signs, (ii) which courses tend to be the best predictors, (iii) are the predictions from

this equation likely to be much good, and (iv) are there any obvious violations of the regression assumptions?

d. Redo part **b**, but now use as your potential explanatory variables only courses taken in the freshman year. As in part **b**, report the final equation, its R^2, and its standard error of estimate s_e.

e. Briefly, do you think there is enough predictive power in the freshman courses, relative to the freshman and sophomore courses combined, to change to a sophomore admit policy? (Answer only on the basis of the regression results; don't get into other merits of the argument.)

72. The file **P12_72.xlsx** has data on several countries. The variables are listed here.

- Country: name of country
- GNPCapita: GNP per capita
- PopGrowth: average annual percentage change in population, 1980–1990
- Calorie: daily per capita calorie content of food used for domestic consumption
- LifeExp: average life expectancy of newborn given current mortality conditions
- Fertility: births per woman given current fertility rates

With data such as these, cause and effect are difficult to determine. For example, does low LifeExp cause GNPCapita to be low, or vice versa? Therefore, the purpose of this problem is to experiment with the following sets of dependent and explanatory variables. In each case, look at scatterplots (and use economic reasoning) to find and estimate the best form of the equation, using only linear and logarithmic variables. Then interpret precisely what each equation is saying.

a. Dependent: LifeExp; Explanatories: Calorie, Fertility

b. Dependent: LifeExp; Explanatories: GNPCapita, PopGrowth

c. Dependent: GNPCapita; Explanatories: PopGrowth, Calorie, Fertility

73. Suppose that an economist has been able to gather data on the relationship between demand and price for a particular product. After analyzing scatterplots and using economic theory, the economist decides to estimate an equation of the form $Q = aP^b$, where Q is quantity demanded and P is price. An appropriate regression analysis is then performed, and the estimated parameters turn out to be $a = 1000$ and $b = -1.3$. Now consider two scenarios: (1) the price increases from $10 to $12.50; (2) the price increases from $20 to $25.

a. Do you expect the percentage decrease in demand to be the same in scenario (1) as in scenario (2)? Why or why not?

b. What is the expected percentage decrease in demand in scenario (1); in scenario (2)? Be as exact as possible. (*Hint*: Remember from economics that an elasticity shows directly what happens for a "small" percentage change in price. These changes aren't that small, so you'll have to do some calculating.)

74. A human resources analyst believes that in a particular industry, the wage rate ($/hr) is related to seniority by an equation of the form $W = ae^{bS}$, where W equals wage rate and S equals seniority (in years). However, the analyst suspects that both parameters, a and b, might depend on whether the workers belong to a union. Therefore, the analyst gathers data on a number of workers, both union and nonunion, and estimates the following equation with regression:

$$\ln(W) = 2.14 + 0.027S + 0.12U + 0.006SU$$

Here $\ln(W)$ is the natural log of W, U is 1 for union workers and 0 for nonunion workers, and SU is the product of S and U.

a. According to this model, what is the predicted wage rate for a nonunion worker with 0 years of seniority? What is it for a union worker with 0 years of seniority?

b. Explain exactly what this equation implies about the predicted effect of seniority on wage rate for a nonunion worker; for a union worker.

75. A company has recorded its overhead costs, machine hours, and labor hours for the past 60 months. The data are in the file **P12_75.xlsx**. The company decides to use regression to explain its overhead hours linearly as a function of machine hours and labor hours. However, recognizing good statistical practice, it decides to estimate a regression equation for the first 36 months, then validate this regression with the data from the last 24 months. That is, it will substitute the values of machine and labor hours from the last 24 months into the regression equation that is based on the first 36 months and see how well it does.

a. Run the regression for the first 36 months. Explain briefly why the coefficient of labor hours is not significant.

b. For this part, use the regression equation from part **a** with both variables still in the equation (even though one was insignificant). Fill in the fitted and residual columns for months 37 through 60. Then do relevant calculations to see whether the R^2 (or multiple R) and the standard error of estimate s_e are as good for these 24 months as they are for the first 36 months. Explain your results briefly. (*Hint*: Remember the meaning of the multiple R and the standard error of estimate.)

76. Pernavik Dairy produces and sells a wide range of dairy products. Because most of the dairy's costs and prices are set by a government regulatory board, most

of the competition between the dairy and its competitors takes place through advertising. The controller of Pernavik has developed the sales and advertising levels for the last 52 weeks. These appear in the file **P12_76.xlsx**. Note that the advertising levels for the 3 weeks prior to week 1 are also listed. The controller wonders whether Pernavik is spending too much money on advertising. He argues that the company's contribution-margin ratio is about 10%. That is, 10% of each sales dollar goes toward covering fixed costs. This means that each advertising dollar has to generate at least $10 of sales or the advertising is not cost-effective. Use regression to determine whether advertising dollars are generating this type of sales response. (*Hint*: It is very possible that the sales value in any week is affected not only by advertising this week, but also by advertising levels in the past 1, 2, or 3 weeks. These are called "lagged" values of advertising. Try regression models with lagged values of advertising included, and see whether you get better results.)

77. The Pierce Company manufactures drill bits. The production of the drill bits occurs in lots of 1000 units. Due to the intense competition in the industry and the correspondingly low prices, Pierce has undertaken a study of the manufacturing costs of each of the products it manufactures. One part of this study concerns the overhead costs associated with producing the drill bits. Senior production personnel have determined that the number of lots produced, the direct labor hours used, and the number of production runs per month might help to explain the behavior of overhead costs. The file **P12_77.xlsx** contains the data on these variables for the past 36 months.

a. See how well you can predict overhead costs on the basis of these variables with a linear regression equation. Why might you be disappointed with the results?

b. A production supervisor believes that labor hours and the number of production run setups affect overhead because Pierce uses a lot of supplies when it is working on the machines and because the machine setup time for each run is charged to overhead. As he says, "When the rate of production increases, we use overtime until we can train the additional people that we require for the machines. When the rate of production falls, we incur idle time until the surplus workers are transferred to other parts of the plant. So it would seem to me that there will be an additional overhead cost whenever the level of production changes. I would also say that because of the nature of this rescheduling process, the bigger the change in production, the greater the effect of the change in production on the increase in overhead." How might you use this information to find a better regression equation than in part **a**? (*Hint*: Develop a new explanatory variable, and use the fact that the number of lots produced in the month preceding month 1 was 5964.)

78. Danielson Electronics manufactures color television sets for sale in a highly competitive marketplace. Recently Ron Thomas, the marketing manager of Danielson Electronics, has been complaining that the company is losing market share because of a poor-quality image, and he has asked that the company's major product, the 25-inch console model, be redesigned to incorporate a higher quality level. The company general manager, Steve Hatting, is considering the request to improve the product quality but is not convinced that consumers will be willing to pay the additional expense for improved quality.

As the company controller, you are in charge of determining the cost effectiveness of improving the quality of the television sets. With the help of the marketing staff, you have obtained a summary of the average retail price of the company's television set and the prices of 29 competitive sets. In addition, you have obtained from *The Shoppers' Guide,* a magazine that evaluates and reports on various consumer products, a quality rating of the television sets produced by Danielson Electronics and its competitors. The file **P12_78.xlsx** summarizes these data. According to *The Shoppers' Guide,* the quality rating, which varies from 0 to 10 (10 being the highest level of quality), considers such factors as the quality of the picture, the frequency of repair, and the cost of repairs. Discussions with the product design group suggest that the cost of manufacturing this type of television set is $125 + Q^2$, where Q is the quality rating.

   a. Regress AvgPrice versus QualityRating. Does the regression equation imply that customers are willing to pay a premium for quality? Explain.
   b. Given the results from part **a**, is there a preferred level of quality for this product? Assume that the quality level will affect only the price charged and not the level of sales of the product.
   c. How might you answer part **b** if the level of sales is also affected by the quality level (or alternatively, if the level of sales is affected by price)?

79. The file **P12_79.xlsx** contains data on gasoline consumption and several economic variables. The variables are gasoline consumption for passenger cars (GasUsed), service station price excluding taxes (SSPrice), retail price of gasoline including state and federal taxes (RPrice), Consumer Price Index for all items (CPI), Consumer Price Index for public transportation (CPIT), number of registered passenger cars (Cars), average miles traveled per gallon (MPG), and real per capita disposable income (DispInc). (Sources: *Basic Petroleum Data Book,* published by the American Petroleum Institute, 2001, and *Economic Report of the President,* 2002)

   a. Regress GasUsed linearly versus CPIT, Cars, MPG, DispInc, and DefRPrice, where DefRPrice is the deflated retail price of gasoline (RPrice divided by CPI). What signs would you expect the coefficients to have? Do they have these signs? Which of the coefficients are statistically significant at the 0.05 level?
   b. Suppose the government makes the claim that for every 1 cent of tax on gasoline, there will be a $1 billion increase in tax revenue. Use the estimated equation in part **a** to support or refute the government's claim.

80. On October 30, 1995, the citizens of Quebec went to the polls to decide the future of their province. They were asked to vote "Yes" or "No" to whether Quebec, a predominantly French-speaking province, should secede from Canada and become a sovereign country. The "No" side was declared the winner, but only by a thin margin. Immediately following the vote, however, allegations began to surface that the result was closer than it should have been. [Source: Cawley and Sommers (1996)]. In particular, the ruling separatist Parti Québécois, whose job was to decide which ballots were rejected, was accused by the "No" voters of systematic electoral fraud by voiding thousands of "No" votes in the predominantly allophone and anglophone electoral divisions of Montreal. (An allophone refers to someone whose first language is neither English nor French. An anglophone refers to someone whose first language is English.)

Cawley and Sommers examined whether electoral fraud had been committed by running a regression, using data from the 125 electoral divisions in the October 1995 referendum. The dependent variable was REJECT, the percentage of rejected ballots in the electoral division. The explanatory variables were as follows:

   ■ ALLOPHONE: percentage of allophones in the electoral division
   ■ ANGLOPHONE: percentage of anglophones in the electoral division
   ■ REJECT94: percentage of rejected votes from that electoral division during a similar referendum in 1994
   ■ LAVAL: dummy variable equal to 1 for electoral divisions in the Laval region, 0 otherwise
   ■ LAV_ALL: interaction (i.e., product) of LAVAL and ALLOPHONE

The estimated regression equation (with *t*-values in parentheses) is

$$\text{Predicted REJECT} = 1.112 + 0.020 \text{ ALLOPHONE}$$
$$\qquad\qquad\qquad (5.68) \qquad\quad (4.34)$$

$$+ 0.001 \text{ ANGLOPHONE} + 0.223 \text{ REJECT94}$$
$$\quad (0.12) \qquad\qquad\qquad\qquad (2.64)$$

$$- 3.773 \text{ LAVAL} + 0.387 \text{ LAV\_ALL}$$
$$\quad (-8.61) \qquad\qquad\quad (15.62)$$

The R^2 value was 0.759. Based on this analysis, Cawley and Sommers state that, "The evidence presented here suggests that there were voting irregularities in the October 1995 Quebec referendum, especially in Laval." Discuss how they came to this conclusion.

81. Suppose we are trying to explain variations in salaries for technicians in a particular field of work. The file **P12_81.xlsx** contains annual salaries for 200 technicians. It also shows how many years of experience each technician has, as well as his or her education level. There are four education levels, as explained in the comment in cell D3. Three suggestions are put forth for the relationship between Salary and these two explanatory variables:

- We should regress Salary linearly versus the two given variables, YrsExper and EducLev.
- All that really matters in terms of education is whether the person got a college degree or not. Therefore, we should regress Salary linearly versus YrsExper and a dummy variable indicating whether he or she got a college degree.
- Each level of education might result in different jumps in salary. Therefore, we should regress

Salary linearly versus YrsExper and dummy variables for the different education levels.

a. Run the indicated regressions for each of these three suggestions. Then (i) explain what each equation is saying and how the three are different (focus here on the coefficients), (ii) which you prefer, and (iii) whether (or how) the regression results in your preferred equation contradict the average salary results shown in the PivTab sheet of the file.

b. Consider the four workers shown on the Predict sheet of the file. (These are four new workers, not among the original 200.) Using your preferred equation, calculate a predicted salary and a 95% prediction interval for each of these four workers.

c. It turns out (you don't have to check this) that the interaction between years of experience and education level is *not* significant for this data set. In general, however, argue why we might expect an interaction between them for salary data of technical workers. What form of interaction would you suspect? (There is not necessarily one right answer, but argue convincingly one way or the other, that is, for a positive or a negative interaction.)

The Artsy Corporation has been sued in the U.S. Federal Court on charges of sex discrimination in employment under Title VII of the Civil Rights Act of 1964.[10] The litigation at contention here is a class-action lawsuit brought on behalf of all females who were employed by the company, or who had applied for work with the company, between 1979 and 1987. Artsy operates in several states, runs four quite distinct businesses, and has many different types of employees. The allegations of the plaintiffs deal with issues of hiring, pay, promotions, and other "conditions of employment."

In such large class-action employment discrimination lawsuits, it has become common for statistical evidence to play a central role in the determination of guilt or damages. In an interesting twist on typical legal procedures, a precedent has developed in these cases that plaintiffs may make a prima facie case purely in terms of circumstantial statistical evidence. If that statistical evidence is reasonably strong, the burden of proof shifts to the defendants to rebut the plaintiffs' statistics with other data, other analyses of the same data, or nonstatistical testimony. In practice, statistical arguments often dominate the proceedings of such Equal Employment Opportunity (EEO) cases. Indeed, in this case the statistical data used as evidence filled numerous computer tapes, and the supporting statistical analysis comprised thousands of pages of printouts and reports. We work here with a typical subset that pertains to one contested issue at one of the company's locations.

The data in the file **Artsy Lawsuit.xlsx** relate to the pay of 256 employees on the hourly payroll at one of the company's production facilities. The data include an identification number (ID) that would permit us to identify the person by name or social security number; the person's gender (Gender), where 0 denotes female and 1 denotes male; the person's job grade in 1986 (Grade); the length of time (in years) the person had been in that job grade as of December 31, 1986 (TInGrade); and the person's weekly pay rate as of December 31, 1986 (Rate). These data permit a statistical examination of one of the issues in the case—fair pay for female employees. We deal with one of three pay classes of employees—those on the biweekly payroll, and at one of the company's locations at Pocahantus, Maine.

The plaintiffs' attorneys have proposed settling the pay issues in the case for this group of female employees for a "back pay" lump payment to female employees of 25% of their pay during the period 1979 to 1987. It is our task to examine the data statistically for evidence in favor of, or against, the charges. We are to advise the lawyers for the company on how to proceed. Consider the following issues as they have been laid out to us by the attorneys representing the firm:

1. Overall, how different is pay by gender? Are the differences in pay statistically significant? Does a statistical significance test have meaning in a case like this? If so, how should it be performed? Lay out as succinctly as possible the arguments that you anticipate the plaintiffs will make with this data set.

2. The company wishes to argue that a legitimate explanation of the pay rate differences may be the difference in job grades. (In this analysis, we will tacitly assume that each person's job grade is, in fact, appropriate for him or her, even though the plaintiffs' attorneys have charged that females have been unfairly kept in the lower grades. Other statistical data, not available here, are used in that analysis.) The lawyers ask, "Is there a relatively easy way to understand, analyze, and display the pay differences by job grade? Is it easy enough that it could be presented to an average jury without confusing them?" Again, use the data to anticipate the possible arguments of the plaintiffs. To what extent does job grade appear to explain the pay rate differences between the genders? Propose and carry out appropriate hypothesis tests or confidence intervals to check whether the difference in pay between genders is statistically significant within each of the grades.

[9]This case was contributed by Peter Kolesar from Columbia University.

[10]Artsy is an actual corporation, and the data given in this case are real, but the name has been changed to protect the firm's true identity.

3. In the actual case, the previous analysis suggested to the attorneys that differences in pay rates are due, at least in part, to differences in job grades. They had heard that in another EEO case, the dependence of pay rate on job grade had been investigated with regression analysis. Perform a simple linear regression of pay rate on job grade for them. Interpret the results fully. Is the regression significant? How much of the variability in pay does job grade account for? Carry out a full check of the quality of your regression. What light does this shed on the pay fairness issue? Does it help or hurt the company? Is it fair to the female employees?

4. It is argued that seniority within a job grade should be taken into account because the company's written pay policy explicitly calls for the consideration of this factor. How different are times in grade by gender? Are they enough to matter?

5. The Artsy legal team wants an analysis of the simultaneous influence of grade and time in grade on pay. Perform a multiple regression of pay rate versus grade and time in grade. Is the regression significant? How much of the variability in pay rates is explained by this model? Will this analysis help your clients? Could the plaintiffs effectively attack it? Consider residuals in your analysis of these issues.

6. Organize your analyses and conclusions in a brief report summarizing your findings for your client, the Artsy Corporation. Be complete but succinct. Be sure to advise them on the settlement issue. Be as forceful as you can be in arguing "the Artsy Case" without misusing the data or statistical theory. Apprise your client of the risks they face by developing the forceful and legitimate counterargument the female plaintiffs could make. ∎

Dupree Fuels Company is facing a difficult problem. Dupree sells heating oil to residential customers. Given the amount of competition in the industry, both from other home heating oil suppliers and from electric and natural gas utilities, the price of the oil supplied and the level of service are critical in determining a company's success. Unlike electric and natural gas customers, oil customers are exposed to the risk of running out of fuel. Home heating oil suppliers therefore have to guarantee that the customer's oil tank will not be allowed to run dry. In fact, Dupree's service pledge is, "50 free gallons on us if we let you run dry." Beyond the cost of the oil, however, Dupree is concerned about the perceived reliability of his service if a customer is allowed to run out of oil.

To estimate customer oil use, the home heating oil industry uses the concept of "degree days." A degree day is equal to the difference between the average daily temperature and 68 degrees Fahrenheit. So if the average temperature on a given day is 50, the degree days for that day will be 18. (If the degree day calculation results in a negative number, the degree days number is recorded as 0.) By keeping track of the number of degree days since the customer's last oil fill, by knowing the size of the customer's oil tank, and by estimating the customer's oil consumption as a function of the number of degree days, the oil supplier can estimate when the customer is getting low on fuel and then resupply the customer.

Dupree has used this scheme in the past but is disappointed with the results and the computational burdens it places on the company. First, the system requires that a consumption-per-degree-day figure be estimated for each customer to reflect that customer's consumption habits, size of home, quality of home insulation, and family size. Because Dupree has more than 1500 customers, the computational burden of keeping track of all of these customers is enormous. Second, the system is crude and unreliable. The consumption per degree day for each customer is computed by dividing the oil consumption during the preceding year by the degree days during

the preceding year. Customers have tended to use less fuel than estimated during the colder months and more fuel than estimated during the warmer months. This means that Dupree is making more deliveries than necessary during the colder months and customers are running out of oil during the warmer months.

Dupree wants to develop a consumption estimation model that is practical and more reliable. The following data are available in the file **Dupree Fuels.xlsx**:

- The number of degree days since the last oil fill and the consumption amounts for 40 customers.

- The number of people residing in the homes of each of the 40 customers. Dupree thinks that this might be important in predicting the oil consumption of customers using oil-fired hot water heaters because it provides an estimate of the hot-water requirements of each customer. Each of the customers in this sample uses an oil-fired hot water heater.

- An assessment, provided by Dupree sales staff, of the home type of each of these 40 customers. The home type classification, which is a number between 1 and 5, is a composite index of the home size, age, exposure to wind, level of insulation, and furnace type. A low index implies a lower oil consumption per degree day, and a high index implies a higher consumption of oil per degree day. Dupree thinks that the use of such an index will allow them to estimate a consumption model based on a sample data set and then to apply the same model to predict the oil demand of each of his customers.

Use regression to see whether a statistically reliable oil consumption model can be estimated from the data. ■

---

[11]Case Studies 12.2 through 12.4 are based on problems from *Advanced Management Accounting,* 2nd edition, by Robert S. Kaplan and Anthony A. Atkinson, Prentice Hall, 1989. We thank them for allowing us to adopt their problems.

The Gunderson Plant manufactures the industrial product line of FGT Industries. Plant management wants to be able to get a good, yet quick, estimate of the manufacturing overhead costs that can be expected each month. The easiest and simplest method to accomplish this task is to develop a flexible budget formula for the manufacturing overhead costs. The plant's accounting staff has suggested that simple linear regression be used to determine the behavior pattern of the overhead costs. The regression data can provide the basis for the flexible budget formula. Sufficient evidence is available to conclude that manufacturing overhead costs vary with direct labor hours. The actual direct labor hours and the corresponding manufacturing overhead costs for each month of the last 3 years have been used in the linear regression analysis.

The 3-year period contained various occurrences not uncommon to many businesses. During the first year, production was severely curtailed during 2 months due to wildcat strikes. In the second year, production was reduced in 1 month because of material shortages, and increased significantly (scheduled overtime) during 2 months to meet the units required for a one-time sales order. At the end of the second year, employee benefits were raised significantly as the result of a labor agreement. Production during the third year was not affected by any special circumstances. Various members of Gunderson's accounting staff raised some issues regarding the historical data collected for the regression analysis. These issues were as follows.

■ Some members of the accounting staff believed that the use of data from all 36 months would provide a more accurate portrayal of the cost behavior. While they recognized that any of the monthly data could include efficiencies and inefficiencies, they believed these efficiencies and inefficiencies would tend to balance out over a longer period of time.

■ Other members of the accounting staff suggested that only those months that were considered normal should be used so that the regression would not be distorted.

■ Still other members felt that only the most recent 12 months should be used because they were the most current.

■ Some members questioned whether historical data should be used at all to form the basis for a flexible budget formula.

The accounting department ran two regression analyses of the data—one using the data from all 36 months and the other using only the data from the last 12 months. The information derived from the two linear regressions is shown below (t-values shown in parentheses). The 36-month regression is

$$OH_t = 123,810 + 1.60\ DLH_t, \quad R^2 = 0.32$$
$$(1.64)$$

The 12-month regression is

$$OH_t = 109,020 + 3.00\ DLH_t, \quad R^2 = 0.48$$
$$(3.01)$$

Questions

1. Which of the two results (12 months versus 36 months) would you use as a basis for the flexible budget formula?

2. How would the four specific issues raised by the members of Gunderson's accounting staff influence your willingness to use the results of the statistical analyses as the basis for the flexible budget formula? Explain your answer. ■

Wagner Printers performs all types of printing including custom work, such as advertising displays, and standard work, such as business cards. Market prices exist for standard work, and Wagner Printers must match or better these prices to get the business. The key issue is whether the existing market price covers the cost associated with doing the work. On the other hand, most of the custom work must be priced individually. Because all custom work is done on a job-order basis, Wagner routinely keeps track of all the direct labor and direct materials costs associated with each job. However, the overhead for each job must be estimated. The overhead is applied to each job using a predetermined (normalized) rate based on estimated overhead and labor hours. Once the cost of the prospective job is determined, the sales manager develops a bid that reflects both the existing market conditions and the estimated price of completing the job.

In the past, the normalized rate for overhead has been computed by using the historical average of overhead per direct labor hour. Wagner has become increasingly concerned about this practice for two reasons. First, it hasn't produced accurate forecasts of overhead in the past. Second, technology has changed the printing process, so that the labor content of jobs has been decreasing, and the normalized rate of overhead per direct labor hour has steadily been increasing. The file **Wagner Printers.xlsx** shows the overhead data that Wagner has collected for its shop for the past 52 weeks. The average weekly overhead for the last 52 weeks is $54,208, and the average weekly number of labor hours worked is 716. Therefore, the normalized rate for overhead that will be used in the upcoming week is about $76 (= 54,208/716) per direct labor hour.

Questions

1. Determine whether you can develop a more accurate estimate of overhead costs.

2. Wagner is now preparing a bid for an important order that may involve a considerable amount of repeat business. The estimated requirements for this project are 15 labor hours, 8 machine hours, $150 direct labor cost, and $750 direct material cost. Using the existing approach to cost estimation, Wagner has estimated the cost for this job as $2040 (= 150 + 750 + (76 × 15)). Given the existing data, what cost would you estimate for this job? ∎

Time Series Analysis and Forecasting

©Mark Richards/Photo Edit, Inc.

FORECASTING LABOR REQUIREMENTS AT TACO BELL

How much quantitative analysis occurs at fast-food restaurants? At Taco Bell, a lot! An article by Huerter and Swart (1998) explains the approach to labor management that has occurred at Taco Bell restaurants over the past decade. Labor is a large component of costs at Taco Bell. Approximately 30% of every sales dollar goes to labor. However, the unique characteristics of fast-food restaurants make it difficult to plan labor utilization efficiently. In particular, the Taco Bell product—food—cannot be inventoried; it must be made fresh at the time the customer orders it. Because of shifting demand throughout any given day, where the lunch period accounts for approximately 52% of a day's sales and as much as 25% of a day's sales can occur during the busiest hour, labor requirements vary greatly throughout the day. If too many workers are on hand during slack times, they are paid for doing practically nothing. Worse than that, however, are the lost sales (and unhappy customers) that occur if too few workers are on hand during peak times. Before 1988, Taco Bell made very little effort to manage the labor problem in an efficient, centralized manner. The company simply allocated about 30% of each store's sales to the store managers and let them allocate it as best they could—not always with good results.

In 1988 Taco Bell initiated its "value meal" deals, where certain meals were priced as low as 59 cents. This increased demand to the point where management could no longer ignore the labor allocation problem. Therefore, in-store computers were installed, data from all stores were collected, and a team of analysts was assigned the task of developing a cost-efficient labor allocation system. This system, which has now been fully integrated into all Taco Bell stores since 1993, is composed of three subsystems: (1) a forecasting subsystem that, for each store, forecasts the arrival rate of customers by 15-minute interval by day of week; (2) a simulation subsystem that, for each store, simulates the congestion and number of lost customers that will occur for any customer arrival rate, given a specific number (and deployment) of workers; and (3) an optimization subsystem that, for each store, indicates the minimum cost allocation of workers, subject to various constraints, such as a minimum service level and a minimum shift length for workers. Although all three of these subsystems are important, the forecasting subsystem is where it all starts. Each store must have a reasonably accurate forecast of future customer arrival rates, broken down by small time intervals (such as 11:15 A.M. to 11:30 A.M. on Friday), before labor requirements can be predicted and labor allocations can be made in an intelligent manner. Like many real-world forecasting systems, Taco Bell's has two important characteristics: (1) it requires extensive data, which have been made available by the in-store computer systems, and (2) the eventual forecasting method used is mathematically a fairly simple one, namely, 6-week moving averages, which we study in this chapter.

Simple or not, the forecasts, as well as the other system components, have enabled Taco Bell to cut costs and increase profits considerably. In its first 4 years, 1993 to 1996, the labor management system is estimated to have saved Taco Bell approximately $40.34 million in labor costs. Because the number of Taco Bell stores is constantly increasing, the annual company-wide savings from the system will certainly grow in the future. In addition, the focus on quantitative analysis has produced other side benefits for Taco Bell. Its service is now better and more consistent across stores, with many fewer customers leaving because of slow service. Also, the quantitative models developed have enabled Taco Bell to evaluate the effectiveness of various potential productivity enhancements, including self-service drink islands, customer-activated touch screens for ordering, and smaller kitchen areas. So the next time you order food from Taco Bell, you can be assured that there is definitely a method to the madness! ■

13.1 INTRODUCTION

Many decision-making applications depend on a forecast of some quantity. Here are several examples.

Examples of Forecasting Applications

- When a service organization, such as a fast-food restaurant, plans its staffing over some time period, it must forecast the customer demand as a function of time. This might be done at a very detailed level, such as the demand in successive 15-minute periods, or at a more aggregate level, such as the demand in successive weeks.

- When a company plans its ordering or production schedule for a product it sells to the public, it must forecast the customer demand for this product so that it can stock appropriate quantities—neither too much nor too little.

- When an organization plans to invest in stocks, bonds, or other financial instruments, it typically attempts to forecast movements in stock prices and interest rates.

- When government representatives plan policy, they attempt to forecast movements in macroeconomic variables such as inflation, interest rates, and unemployment.

Unfortunately, forecasting is a very difficult task, both in the short run and in the long run. Typically, we base forecasts on historical data. We search for patterns or relationships in the historical data, and then we make forecasts. There are two problems with this approach. The first is that it is not always easy to uncover historical patterns or relationships. In particular, it is often difficult to separate the noise, or random behavior, from the underlying patterns. Some forecasts can even overdo it, by attributing importance to patterns that are in fact random variations and are unlikely to repeat themselves.

The second problem is that there are no guarantees that past patterns will continue in the future. A new war could break out somewhere in the world, a company's competitor could introduce a new product into the market, the bottom could fall out of the stock market, and so on. Each of these shocks to the system being studied could drastically alter the future in a highly unpredictable way. This partly explains why forecasts are almost always wrong. Unless they have inside information to the contrary, forecasters must assume that history will repeat itself. But we all know that history does *not* always repeat itself. Therefore, there are many famous forecasts that turned out to be way off the mark, even though the forecasters made reasonable assumptions and used standard forecasting techniques. Nevertheless, forecasts are required constantly, so fear of failure is no excuse for not giving it our best effort.

13.2 FORECASTING METHODS: AN OVERVIEW

There are many forecasting methods available, and all practitioners have their favorites. To say the least, there is little agreement among practitioners or theoreticians as to the best forecasting method. The methods can generally be divided into three groups: (1) *judgmental* methods, (2) *extrapolation* (or *time series*) methods, and (3) *econometric* (or *causal*) methods. The first of these is basically nonquantitative and will not be discussed here; the last two are quantitative. In this section we describe extrapolation and econometric methods in some generality. In the rest of the chapter, we go into more detail, particularly about the extrapolation methods.

13.2.1 Extrapolation Methods

Extrapolation methods are quantitative methods that use past data of a time series variable—and nothing else, except possibly time itself—to forecast future values of the variable. The idea is that we can use past movements of a variable, such as company sales or U.S. exports to Japan, to forecast its future values. Many extrapolation methods are available, including trend-based regression, exponential smoothing, moving averages, and autoregression. Some of these methods are relatively simple, both conceptually and in terms of the calculations required, whereas others are quite complex. Also, as the names imply, some of these methods use the same regression methods we discussed in the previous two chapters, whereas others do not.

All of these extrapolation methods search for *patterns* in the historical series and then extrapolate these patterns into the future. Some try to track long-term upward or downward trends and then project these. Some try to track the seasonal patterns (sales up in November and December, down in other months, for example) and then project these. Basically, the more complex the method, the more closely it tries to track historical patterns. Researchers have long believed that good forecasting methods should be able to track the ups and downs—the zigzags on a graph—of a time series. This has led to voluminous research and increasingly complex methods. But is complexity always better?

Surprisingly, empirical evidence shows that it is sometimes worse. This is documented in the quarter-century review article by Armstrong (1986) and the article by Schnarrs and Bavuso (1986). They document a number of empirical studies on literally thousands of time series forecasts where complex methods fared no better, and often worse, than simple methods. In fact, the Schnarrs and Bavuso article presents evidence that a naive forecast from a "random walk" model often outperforms all of the more sophisticated extrapolation methods. With this naive model we forecast that next period's value will be the same as this period's value. So if today's closing stock price is 51.375, we forecast that tomorrow's closing stock price will be 51.375. This method is certainly simple, and it sometimes works quite well. We discuss random walks in more detail in Section 13.5.

The evidence in favor of simpler models is not accepted by everyone, particularly not those who have spent years investigating complex models, and complex models continue to be studied and used. However, there is a very plausible reason why simple models might provide better forecasts. The whole idea behind extrapolation methods is to extrapolate historical patterns into the future. But it is often difficult to determine which patterns are real and which represent noise—random ups and downs that are not likely to repeat themselves. Also, if something important changes (a competitor introduces a new product or interest rates increase, for example), it is certainly possible that the historical patterns will change. A potential problem with complex methods is that they often track a historical series *too* closely. That is, they often track patterns that are really noise. Simpler methods, on the other hand, track only the most basic underlying patterns and therefore can be more flexible and accurate in forecasting the future.

13.2.2 Econometric Models

Econometric models, also called **causal** models, use regression to forecast a time series variable by using other explanatory time series variables. For example, a company might use a causal model to regress future sales on its advertising level, the population income level, the interest rate, and possibly others. In one sense, regression analysis involving time series variables is similar to the regression analysis discussed in the previous two chapters. We can still use the same least squares approach and the same multiple regression software in many time series regression models. In fact, several examples and problems in the previous two chapters used time series data.

However, causal regression models for time series data present new mathematical challenges that go well beyond the level of this book. To get a glimpse of the potential difficulties, suppose a company wants to use a causal regression model to forecast its monthly sales for some product, based on two other time series variables: its monthly advertising levels for the product and its main competitor's monthly advertising levels for a competing product. We could simply estimate a regression equation of the form

$$Y_t = \alpha + \beta_1 X_{1t} + \beta_2 X_{2t} \tag{13.1}$$

Here, Y_t is the company's sales in month t, and X_{1t} and X_{2t} are the company's and the competitor's advertising levels in month t. We might learn something useful from this regression model, but we should be aware of the following problems.

One problem is that we must decide on the appropriate "lags" for the regression equation. Do sales this month depend only on advertising levels *this* month, as specified in equation (13.1), or also on advertising levels in the previous month, the previous two months, and so on? A second problem is whether to include lags of the *sales* variable in the regression equation as explanatory variables. Presumably, sales in one month might depend on the level of sales in previous months (as well as on advertising levels). A third problem is that the two advertising variables can be *autocorrelated* and *cross-correlated*. Autocorrelation means, for example, that the company's advertising level in one month can depend on its advertising levels in previous months. Cross-correlation means, for example, that the company's advertising level in one month can be related to the competitor's advertising levels in previous months, or that the competitor's advertising in one month can be related to the company's advertising levels in previous months.

These are difficult issues, and the way in which they are addressed can make a big difference in the usefulness of the resulting regression model. We examine several regression-based models in this chapter, but we avoid situations such as the one just described, where one time series variable Y is regressed on one or more time series X's. [Pankratz (1991) is a good reference for these latter types of models.]

13.2.3 Combining Forecasts

There is one other general forecasting method that is worth mentioning. In fact, it has attracted a lot of attention in recent years, and many researchers believe that it has great potential for increasing forecast accuracy. The method is simple—we combine two or more forecasts to obtain the final forecast. The reasoning behind this method is also simple—the forecast errors from different forecasting methods might cancel one another. The forecasts that are combined can be of the same general type—extrapolation forecasts, for example—or they can be of different types, such as judgmental and extrapolation. The *number* of forecasts to combine and the *weights* to use in combining them have been the subject of several research studies.

Although the findings are not entirely consistent, it appears that the marginal benefit from each individual forecast after the first two or three is minor. Also, there is not much evidence to suggest that the simplest weighting scheme—weight each forecast equally, that is, average them—is any less accurate than more complex weighting schemes.

13.2.4 Components of Time Series Data

In Chapter 2 we discussed time series graphs, a useful graphical means of depicting time series data. We now use these time series graphs to help explain and identify four important components of a time series. These components are called the *trend* component, the *seasonal* component, the *cyclic* component, and the *random* (or *noise*) component.

Let's start by looking at a very simple time series. This is a time series where every observation is the same. Such a series is shown in Figure 13.1. The graph in this figure shows time (t) on the horizontal axis and the observation values (Y) on the vertical axis. We assume that Y is measured at regularly spaced intervals, usually days, weeks, months, quarters, or years, with Y_t being the value of the observation at time period t. As indicated in Figure 13.1, the individual observation points are usually joined by straight lines to make any patterns in the time series more apparent. Because all observations in this time series are equal, the resulting time series graph is a horizontal line. We refer to this time series as the *base* series. We will now illustrate more interesting time series built from this base series.

Figure 13.1

The Base Series

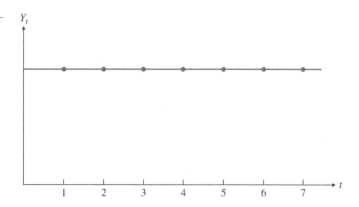

If the observations increase or decrease regularly through time, we say that the time series has a **trend**. The graphs in Figure 13.2 illustrate several possible trends. The *linear* trend in Figure 13.2a occurs if a company's sales, for example, increase by the same amount from period to period. This constant per period change is then the slope of the linear trend line. The curve in Figure 13.2b is an *exponential* trend curve. It occurs in a business such as the personal computer business, where sales have increased at a tremendous rate (at least in the 1990s, the boom years). For this type of curve, the *percentage* increase in Y_t from period to period remains constant. The curve in Figure 13.2c is an *S-shaped* trend curve. For example, this type of trend curve is appropriate for a new product that takes a while to catch on, then exhibits a rapid increase in sales as the public becomes aware of it, and finally tapers off to a fairly constant level. The curves in Figure 13.2 all represent *upward* trends. Of course, we could just as well have *downward* trends of the same types.

Figure 13.2   Series with Trends

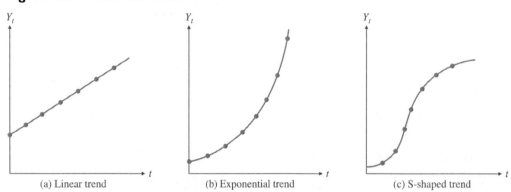

(a) Linear trend   (b) Exponential trend   (c) S-shaped trend

Many time series have a **seasonal** component. For example, a company's sales of swimming pool equipment increase every spring, then stay relatively high during the summer, and then drop off until next spring, at which time the yearly pattern repeats itself. An important aspect of the seasonal component is that it tends to be predictable from one year to the next. That is, the *same* seasonal pattern tends to repeat itself every year.

In Figure 13.3 we show two possible seasonal patterns. In Figure 13.3a there is nothing but the seasonal component. That is, if there were no seasonal variation, we would have the base series in Figure 13.1. In Figure 13.3b we show a seasonal pattern superimposed on a linear trend line.

Figure 13.3

Series with
Seasonality

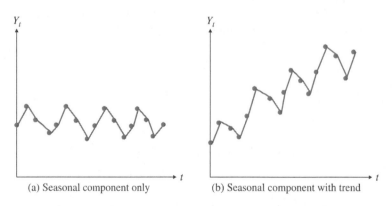

(a) Seasonal component only   (b) Seasonal component with trend

The third component of a time series is the **cyclic** component. By studying past movements of many business and economic variables, it becomes apparent that there are business cycles that affect many variables in similar ways. For example, during a recession housing starts generally go down, unemployment goes up, stock prices go down, and so on. But when the recession is over, all of these variables tend to move in the opposite direction. Unfortunately, the cyclic component is harder to predict than the seasonal component. The reason is that seasonal variation is much more regular. For example, swimming pool supplies sales *always* start to increase during the spring. Cyclic variation, on the other hand, is more irregular for the simple reason that the "business cycle" does not always have the same length. A further distinction is that the length of a seasonal cycle is generally one year; the length of a business cycle is generally much longer than one year.

The graphs in Figure 13.4 illustrate the cyclic component of a time series. In Figure 13.4a cyclic variation is superimposed on the base series in Figure 13.1. In Figure 13.4b this same cyclic variation is superimposed on the series in Figure 13.3b. The resulting graph has trend, seasonal variation, and cyclic variation.

Figure 13.4

Series with Cyclic Component

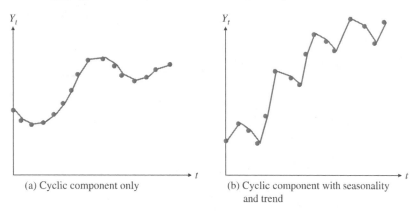

(a) Cyclic component only

(b) Cyclic component with seasonality and trend

The final component in a time series is called the **random** component, or simply **noise**. This unpredictable component gives most time series graphs their irregular, jagged-edge appearances. Usually, a time series can be determined only to a certain extent by its trend, seasonal, and cyclic components. Then other factors determine the rest. These other factors may be inherent randomness, unpredictable "shocks" to the system, the unpredictable behavior of human beings who interact with the system, and possibly others. These factors combine to create a certain amount of unpredictability in almost all time series.

Figures 13.5 and 13.6 show the effect that noise can have on a time series graph. The graph on the left of each figure shows the random component only, superimposed on the base series. Then on the right of each figure, the random component is superimposed on the trend-with-seasonal-component graph from Figure 13.3b. The difference between Figures 13.5 and 13.6 is the relative magnitude of the noise. When it is small, as in Figure 13.5, the other components emerge fairly clearly; they are not disguised by the noise. But if the noise is large in magnitude, as in Figure 13.6, the noise makes it very difficult to distinguish the other components.

Figure 13.5

Series with Noise

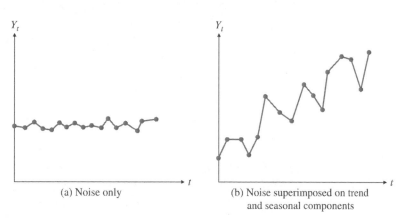

(a) Noise only

(b) Noise superimposed on trend and seasonal components

Figure 13.6

Series with
More Noise

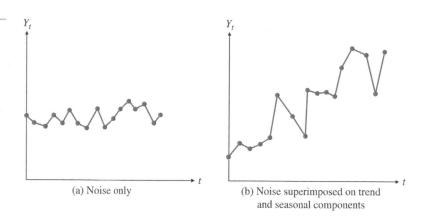

(a) Noise only   (b) Noise superimposed on trend
                             and seasonal components

13.2.5 General Notation and Formulas

We now introduce a bit of notation and discuss some aspects common to most forecasting methods. In general, we let Y denote the variable we want to forecast. Then Y_t denotes the observed value of Y at time t. Typically, the first observation (the most distant one) corresponds to period $t = 1$, and the last observation (the most recent one) corresponds to period $t = T$, so that T denotes the number of historical observations of Y. The periods themselves might be weeks, months, quarters, years, or any other convenient unit of time.

Suppose we have just observed Y_{t-k} and want to make a "k-period-ahead" forecast; that is, we want to use the information through time $t - k$ to forecast Y_t. Then we denote the resulting forecast by $F_{t-k,t}$. The first subscript denotes the period in which the forecast is made, and the second subscript denotes the period being forecasted. As an example, if the data are monthly and September 2004 corresponds to $t = 67$, then a forecast of Y_{69}, the value in November 2004, would be labeled $F_{67,69}$. The **forecast error** is the difference between the actual value and the forecast. It is denoted by E with appropriate subscripts. Specifically, the forecast error associated with $F_{t-k,t}$ is

$$E_{t-k,t} = Y_t - F_{t-k,t}$$

This double-subscript notation is necessary to specify when the forecast is being made and which period is being forecasted. However, the former is often clear from context. Therefore, to simplify the notation, we usually drop the first subscript and write F_t and E_t to denote the forecast of Y_t and the error in this forecast.

We first develop a model to fit the historical data. Then we use this model to forecast the future.

There are actually two steps in any forecasting procedure. The first step is to build a model that fits the historical data well. The second step is to use this model to forecast the future. Most of the work goes into the first step. For any trial model we see how well it "tracks" the known values of the time series. Specifically, we calculate the one-period-ahead forecasts, F_t (or more precisely, $F_{t-1,t}$), from the model and compare these to the known values, Y_t, for each t in the historical time period. We attempt to find a model that produces small forecast errors, E_t. We expect that if the model forecasts the *historical* data well, it will also forecast *future* data well.

Forecasting software packages typically report several summary measures of the forecast errors. The most important of these are MAE (mean absolute error), RMSE (root mean square error), and MAPE (mean absolute percentage error). These are defined in equations (13.2), (13.3), and (13.4). Fortunately, models that make any one of these measures small tend to make the others small, so that we can choose whichever measure we want to minimize. In the following formulas, N denotes the number of terms in each sum. This value is typically slightly less than T, the number of historical observations, because it is usually not possible to provide a forecast for each historical period.

> **Mean Absolute Error**
>
> $$\text{MAE} = \left(\sum_{t=1}^{N} |E_t| \right) / N \qquad \text{(13.2)}$$

> **Root Mean Square Error**
>
> $$\text{RMSE} = \sqrt{\left(\sum_{t=1}^{N} E_t^2 \right) / N} \qquad \text{(13.3)}$$

> **Mean Absolute Percentage Error**
>
> $$\text{MAPE} = 100\% \times \left(\sum_{t=1}^{N} |E_t / Y_t| \right) / N \qquad \text{(13.4)}$$

A model that makes any one of these error measures small tends to make the other two small as well.

RMSE is similar to a standard deviation in that the errors are squared; because of the square root, its units are the same as those of the forecasted variable. The MAE is similar to the RMSE, except that absolute values of errors are used instead of squared errors. The MAPE is probably the most easily understood measure because it does not depend on the units of the forecasted variable; it is always stated as a percentage. For example, the statement that the forecasts are off on average by 2% has a clear meaning, even if you do not know the units of the variable being forecasted.

Some forecasting software packages choose the best model from a given class (such as the best exponential smoothing model) by minimizing MAE, RMSE, or MAPE. However, small values of these measures guarantee only that the model forecasts the *historical* observations well. There is still no guarantee that the model will forecast *future* values accurately.

We now examine a number of useful forecasting models. You should be aware that more than one of these models can be appropriate for any particular time series data. For example, a random walk model and an autoregression model could be equally effective for forecasting stock price data. (Remember also that we can combine forecasts from more than one model to obtain a possibly better forecast.) We try to give some insights into choosing the best type of model for various types of time series data, but ultimately the choice depends on the experience of the forecaster.

13.3 TESTING FOR RANDOMNESS

All forecasting models we build have the general form shown in equation (13.5). The fitted value in this equation is the part we calculate from past data and any other available information (such as the season of the year), and it is used as a forecast for *Y*. The residual is the forecast error, the difference between the observed value of *Y* and its forecast:

$$Y_t = \text{Fitted Value} + \text{Residual} \qquad \text{(13.5)}$$

In a time series context the terms residual and forecast error are used interchangeably.

For time series data, there is a residual for each historical period, that is, for each value of *t*. We want this time series of residuals to be random "noise," as discussed in Section 13.2.4. The reason is that if this series of residuals is not noise, then it can be modeled further. For example, if the residuals trend upwardly, then we can refine our model to include this trend component in the *fitted* value. The point is that we want the fitted value to include all components of the original series that can possibly be forecasted, and we want the leftover residuals to be noise.

We now discuss ways to determine whether a time series of residuals is random noise (which we usually abbreviate to "random"). The simplest method, but not always a reliable one, is to examine time series graphs of residuals visually. This often enables us to detect nonrandom patterns. For example, the time series graphs in Figures 13.7 through 13.11 illustrate some common nonrandom patterns. In Figure 13.7, there is an upward trend. In Figure 13.8, the variance increases through time (larger zigzags to the right). Figure 13.9 exhibits seasonality, where observations in certain months are consistently larger than those in other months. There is a "meandering" pattern in Figure 13.10, where large observations tend to be followed by other large observations, and small observations tend to be followed by other small observations. Finally, the opposite behavior of Figure 13.10 is illustrated in Figure 13.11. Here, there are *too many* zigzags—large observations tend to follow small observations and vice versa. None of the time series in these figures can be considered random.

Figure 13.7

A Series with Trend

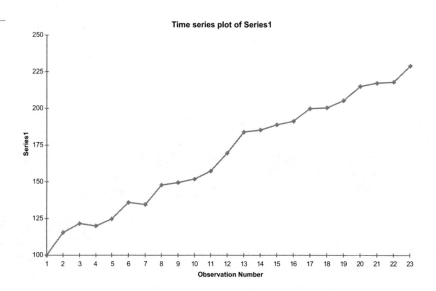

Figure 13.8

A Series with Increasing Variance Through Time

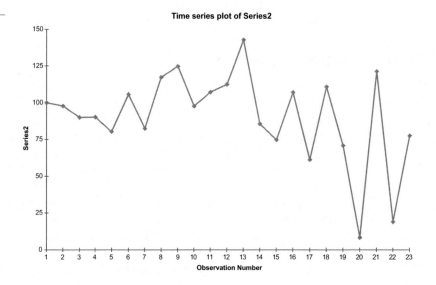

Figure 13.9

A Series with
Seasonality

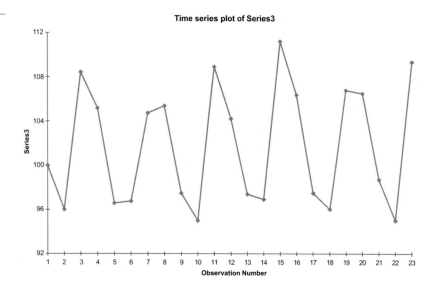

Figure 13.10

A Series That
Meanders

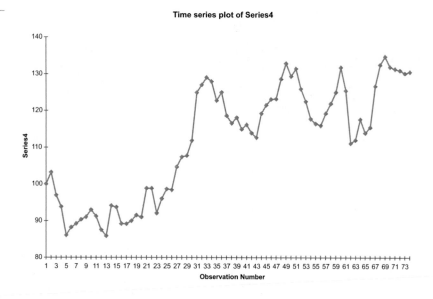

Figure 13.11

A Series That
Oscillates Frequently

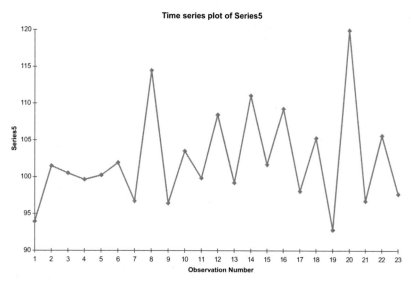

13.3.1 The Runs Test

It is not always easy to detect randomness or the lack of it from the visual inspection of a graph. Therefore, we discuss two quantitative methods of that test for randomness. The first is called the *runs test*. We first choose a base value, which could be the average value of the series, the median value, or even some other value. Then we define a **run** as a consecutive series of observations that remain on one side of this base level. For example, if the base level is 0 and we observe the series 1, 5, 3, −3, −2, −4, −1, 3, 2, then there are three runs: 1, 5, 3; −3, −2, −4, −1; and 3, 2. The idea behind the runs test is that a random series should have a number of runs that is neither too large nor too small. If the series has too few runs, then it could be trending (as in Figure 13.7) or it could be meandering (as in Figure 13.10). If the series has too many runs, then it is zigzagging too often (as in Figure 13.11).

This runs test can be used on any time series, not just a series of residuals.

> The **runs test** is a formal test of the null hypothesis of randomness. If there are too many or too few runs in the series, then we conclude that the series is not random.

We do not provide the mathematical details of the runs test, but we illustrate how it is implemented in StatTools in the following example.

EXAMPLE | **13.1 FORECASTING MONTHLY STEREO SALES**

Monthly sales for a chain of stereo retailers are listed in the file **Stereo Sales.xlsx**. They cover the period from the beginning of 2004 to the end of 2007, during which there was no upward or downward trend in sales and no clear seasonal peaks or valleys. This behavior is apparent in the time series graph of sales in Figure 13.12. Therefore, a simple forecast model of sales is to use the *average* of the series, 182.67, as a forecast of sales for each month. Do the resulting residuals represent random noise?

Figure 13.12

Time Series Graph of Stereo Sales

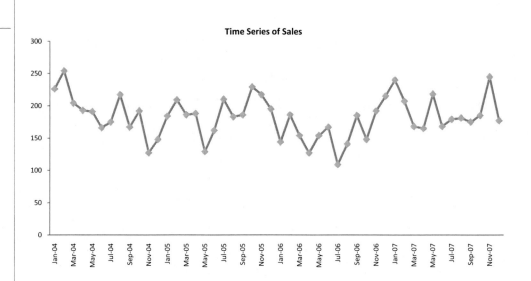

Objective To use StatTools's Runs Test procedure to check whether the residuals from this simple forecasting model represent random noise.

Solution

To obtain the residuals for this forecasting model, we subtract the average, 182.67, from each observation. Therefore, the plot of the residuals, shown in Figure 13.13, has exactly the same shape as the plot of sales. The only difference is that it is shifted down by 182.67 and has mean 0. We now use the runs test to check whether there are too many or too few runs around the base value of 0 in this residual plot. To do so, we select Runs Test for Randomness from the StatTools Time Series and Forecasting dropdown, choose Residual as the variable to analyze, and choose Mean of Series as the cutoff value. (This corresponds to the horizontal line at 0 in Figure 13.13.) This produces the output in shown in Figure 13.14.

Figure 13.13

Time Series Graph of Residuals

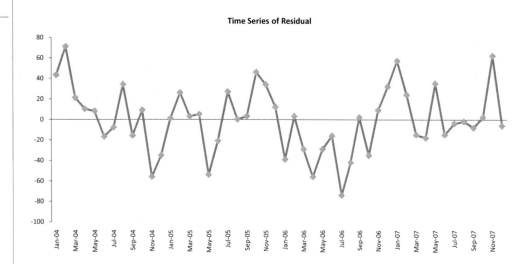

Figure 13.14

Runs Test for Randomness

	I	J
7		Residual
8	*Runs Test for Randomness*	Data Set #1
9	Observations	48
10	Below Mean	22
11	Above Mean	26
12	Number of Runs	20
13	Mean	0.00
14	E(R)	24.8333
15	StdDev(R)	3.4027
16	Z-Value	-1.4204
17	P-Value (two-tailed)	0.1555

The important elements of this output are the following:

- The number of observed runs is 20, in cell J12.

- The number of runs *expected* under an assumption of randomness is 24.833, in cell J14. Therefore, the series of residuals has too *few* runs. Positive values tend to follow positive values, and negative values tend to follow negative values.

A small p-value in the runs test provides evidence of nonrandomness.

- The z-value in cell J16, −1.42, indicates how many standard errors the observed number of runs is below the expected number of runs. The corresponding p-value indicates how extreme this z-value is. It can be interpreted just like other p-values for hypothesis tests. If it is small, say, less than 0.05, then we can reject the null hypothesis of randomness and conclude that the series of residuals is *not* random noise. However, the p-value for this example is only 0.1555. Therefore, there is not convincing evidence of nonrandomness in the residuals, and we can conclude that the residuals represent noise. ∎

13.3.2 Autocorrelation

Like the runs test, auto-correlations can be calculated for any time series, not just a series of residuals.

In this section we discuss another way to check for randomness of a time series of residuals—we examine its *autocorrelations*. The "auto" means that successive observations are correlated with one another. For example, in the most common form of autocorrelation, *positive* autocorrelation, large observations tend to follow large observations, and small observations tend to follow small observations. In this case the runs test is likely to pick it up because there will be fewer runs than expected. Another way to check for the same nonrandomness property is to calculate the autocorrelations of the time series.

> An **autocorrelation** is a type of correlation used to measure whether values of a time series are related to their own past values.

To understand autocorrelations it is first necessary to understand what it means to *lag* a time series. This concept is easy to illustrate in a spreadsheet. We again use the monthly stereo sales data in the **Stereo Sales.xlsx** file. To lag by 1 month, we simply "push down" the series by one row. See column D of Figure 13.15. Note that there is a blank cell at the top of the lagged series (in cell D2). We can continue to push the series down one row at a time to obtain other lags. For example, the lag 3 version of the series appears in column F. Now there are three missing observations at the top. Note that in December 2004, say, the first, second, and third lags correspond to the observations in November 2004, October 2004, and September 2004, respectively. That is, lags are simply previous observations, removed by a certain number of periods from the present time. These lagged columns can be obtained by copying and pasting the original series or by using Lag from the StatTools Utilities dropdown.

Figure 13.15

Lags for Stereo Sales

	A	B	C	D	E	F
1	Month	Sales	Residual	Lag1(Residual)	Lag2(Residual)	Lag3(Residual)
2	Jan-04	226	43.333			
3	Feb-04	254	71.333	43.333		
4	Mar-04	204	21.333	71.333	43.333	
5	Apr-04	193	10.333	21.333	71.333	43.333
6	May-04	191	8.333	10.333	21.333	71.333
7	Jun-04	166	-16.667	8.333	10.333	21.333
8	Jul-04	175	-7.667	-16.667	8.333	10.333
9	Aug-04	217	34.333	-7.667	-16.667	8.333
10	Sep-04	167	-15.667	34.333	-7.667	-16.667
11	Oct-04	192	9.333	-15.667	34.333	-7.667
12	Nov-04	127	-55.667	9.333	-15.667	34.333
13	Dec-04	148	-34.667	-55.667	9.333	-15.667
14	Jan-05	184	1.333	-34.667	-55.667	9.333
15	Feb-05	209	26.333	1.333	-34.667	-55.667
16	Mar-05	186	3.333	26.333	1.333	-34.667

Then the autocorrelation of lag k, for any integer k, is essentially the correlation between the original series and the lag k version of the series. For example, in Figure 13.15 the lag 1 autocorrelation is the correlation between the observations in columns C and D. Similarly, the lag 2 autocorrelation is the correlation between the observations in columns C and E.[1]

We have shown the lagged versions of Sales in Figure 13.15, and we have explained autocorrelations in terms of these lagged variables, to help motivate the concept of autocorrelation. However, we can use StatTools's Autocorrelation procedure directly, *without* forming the lagged variables, to calculate autocorrelations. This is illustrated in the following continuation of Example 13.1.

EXAMPLE	13.1 FORECASTING MONTHLY STEREO SALES (CONTINUED)

The runs test on the stereo sales data suggests that the pattern of sales is not random. Large values tend to follow large values, and small values tend to follow small values. Do autocorrelations support this conclusion?

Objective   To examine the autocorrelations of the residuals from the forecasting model for evidence of nonrandomness.

Solution

We use StatTools's Autocorrelation procedure, found under the StatTools Time Series and Forecasting dropdown. It requires us to specify the time series variable (Residual), the number of lags we want (we chose the StatTools default value), and whether we want a chart of the autocorrelations. This chart is called a **correlogram**. The resulting autocorrelations and correlogram appear in Figure 13.16. A typical autocorrelation of lag k indicates the relationship between observations k periods apart. For example, the autocorrelation of lag 3, 0.0814, indicates that there is very little relationship between residuals separated by 3 months.

How large is a "large" autocorrelation? Under the assumption of randomness, it can be shown that the standard error of any autocorrelation is approximately $1/\sqrt{T}$, in this case $1/\sqrt{48} = 0.1443$. (Recall that T denotes the number of observations in the series.) If the series is truly random, then only an occasional autocorrelation will be larger than 2 standard errors in magnitude. Therefore, any autocorrelation that *is* larger than 2 standard errors in magnitude is worth our attention. These significantly nonzero autocorrelations are boldfaced in the StatTools output. The only "large" autocorrelation for the residuals is the first, or lag 1, autocorrelation of 0.3492. The fact that it is *positive* indicates once again that there is some tendency for large residuals to follow large residuals and for small to follow small. The autocorrelations for other lags are less than two standard errors in magnitude and can be ignored.

---

[1]We ignore the exact details of the calculations here. Just be aware that the formula for autocorrelations that is usually used differs slightly from the correlation formula in Chapter 3. However, the difference is very slight and of little practical importance.

Figure 13.16

Correlogram and
Autocorrelations of
Residuals

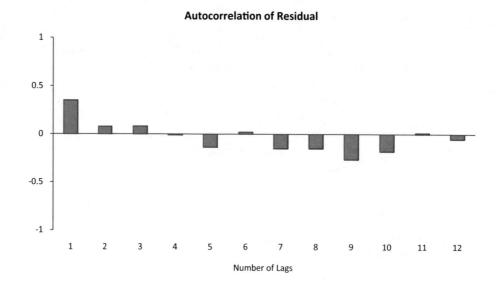

Autocorrelation Table	Residual Data Set #1
Number of Values	48
Standard Error	0.1443
Lag #1	**0.3492**
Lag #2	0.0772
Lag #3	0.0814
Lag #4	-0.0095
Lag #5	-0.1353
Lag #6	0.0206
Lag #7	-0.1494
Lag #8	-0.1492
Lag #9	-0.2626
Lag #10	-0.1792
Lag #11	0.0121
Lag #12	-0.0516

Typically, we can ask for autocorrelations up to as many lags as we like. However, there are several practical considerations to keep in mind. First, it is common practice to ask for no more lags than 25% of the number of observations. For example, if there are 48 observations, we should ask for no more than 12 autocorrelations (lags 1–12). (StatTools chooses this number of lags if you accept its "auto" setting.)

Second, the first few lags are typically the most important. Intuitively, if there is any relationship between successive observations, it is likely to be between nearby observations. The June 2007 observation is more likely to be related to the May 2007 observation than to the October 2006 observation. Sometimes there is a fairly large spike in the correlogram at some large lag, such as lag 9. However, this can often be ignored as a random "blip" unless there is some obvious reason for its occurrence. A similarly large autocorrelation at lag 1 or 2 is usually taken more seriously. The one exception to this is a *seasonal* lag. For example, for monthly data an autocorrelation at lag 12 corresponds to a relationship between observations a year apart, such as May 2007 and May 2006. If this autocorrelation is significantly large, it probably should not be ignored.

Autocorrelation analysis is somewhat advanced. However, it is the basis for many important forecasting methods.

We do not examine autocorrelations much further in this book. However, many advanced forecasting techniques are based largely on the examination of the autocorrelation structure of time series. This autocorrelation structure tells us how a series is related to its own past values through time, which can be very valuable information for forecasting *future* values.

Level A

1. The file **P13_01.xlsx** contains the monthly number of airline tickets sold by the CareFree Travel Agency. Is this time series *random*? Perform a runs test and compute a few autocorrelations to support your answer.

2. The file **P13_02.xlsx** contains the weekly sales at a local bookstore for each of the past 25 weeks. Is this time series *random*? Perform a runs test and compute a few autocorrelations to support your answer.

3. The number of employees on the payroll at a food-processing plant is recorded at the start of each month. These data are provided in the file **P13_03.xlsx**. Perform a runs test and compute a few autocorrelations to determine whether this time series is random.

4. The quarterly numbers of applications for home mortgage loans at a branch office of Northern Central Bank are recorded in the file **P13_04.xlsx**. Perform a runs test and compute a few autocorrelations to determine whether this time series is random.

5. The number of reported accidents at a manufacturing plant located in Flint, Michigan, was recorded at the start of each month. These data are provided in the file **P13_05.xlsx**. Is this time series *random*? Perform a runs test and compute a few autocorrelations to support your answer.

6. The file **P13_06.xlsx** contains the weekly sales at the local outlet of WestCoast Video Rentals for each of the past 36 weeks. Perform a runs test and compute a few autocorrelations to determine whether this time series is random.

Level B

7. Determine whether the RAND() function in Excel actually generates a random stream of numbers. Generate at least 100 random numbers to test their randomness with a runs test and with autocorrelations. Summarize your findings.

8. Use a runs test and calculate autorrelations to decide whether the random series explained in each part (**a–c**) are random. For each part, generate at least 100 random numbers in the series.
   a. A series of independent normally distributed values, each with mean 70 and standard deviation 5.
   b. A series where the first value is normally distributed with mean 70 and standard deviation 5, and each succeeding value is normally distributed with mean equal to the *previous* value and standard deviation 5. (For example, if the fourth value is 67.32, then the fifth value will be normally distributed with mean 67.32.)
   c. A series where the first value, Y_1, is normally distributed with mean 70 and standard deviation 5, and each succeeding value, Y_t, is normally distributed with mean $(1 + a_t)Y_{t-1}$ and standard deviation $5(1 + a_t)$, where the a_t's are independent, normally distributed values with mean 0 and standard deviation 0.2. (For example, if $Y_{t-1} = 67.32$ and $a_t = -0.2$, then Y_t will be normally distributed with mean $0.8(67.32) = 53.856$ and standard deviation $0.8(5) = 4$.)

13.4 REGRESSION-BASED TREND MODELS

Many time series follow a long-term trend except for random variation. This trend can be upward or downward. A straightforward way to model this trend is to estimate a regression equation for Y_t, using time t as the *single* explanatory variable. In this section we discuss the two most frequently used trend models, *linear* trend and *exponential* trend.

13.4.1 Linear Trend

A linear trend means that the time series variable changes by a constant *amount* each time period. The relevant equation is equation (13.6), where, as in previous regression equations, a is the intercept, b is the slope, and ϵ_t is an error term.

Linear Trend Model

$$Y_t = a + bt + \epsilon_t \qquad (13.6)$$

The interpretation of b is that it represents the expected change in the series from one period to the next. If b is positive, the trend is upward; if b is negative, the trend is downward. The intercept term a is less important. It literally represents the expected value of the series at time $t = 0$. If time t is coded so that the first observation corresponds to $t = 1$, then a is where we expect the series to have been one period before we started observing. However, it is possible that time is coded in another way. For example, we might have annual data that start in 1997. Then the first value of t might be entered as 1997, which means that the intercept a corresponds to a period 1997 years earlier! Clearly, we would not take its value literally in this case.

As always, a graph of the time series is a good place to start. It indicates whether a linear trend model is likely to provide a good fit. Generally, the graph should rise or fall at approximately a constant rate through time, without too much random variation. But even if there is a lot of random variation—a lot of zigzags—a linear trend to the data might be a good starting point. Then the *residuals* from this trend line, which should have no remaining trend, could possibly be modeled by some other method in this chapter.

EXAMPLE	13.2 QUARTERLY PHARMACEUTICAL SALES

The file **Pharmaceutical Sales.xlsx** contains quarterly sales data for a large pharmaceutical company from first quarter 1998 through fourth quarter 2007 (in millions of dollars). The time series graph of these data appears in Figure 13.17. Sales increase from $3062 million in the initial quarter to $8307 million in the final quarter. How well does a linear trend fit these data? Are the residuals from this fit random?

Figure 13.17

Time Series Graph of Pharmaceutical Sales

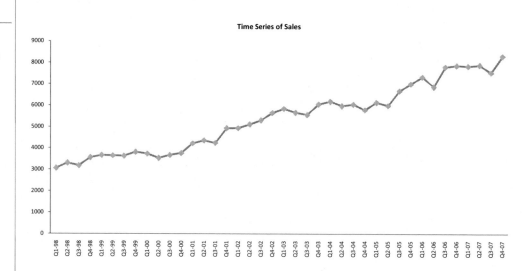

Objective To fit a linear trend line to quarterly sales and examine its residuals for randomness.

Solution

The graph in Figure 13.17 indicates a clear upward trend with little or no curvature. Therefore, a linear trend is certainly plausible. To estimate it with regression, we first need a *numeric* time variable—labels such as Q1-98 will not do. We construct this time variable in column C of the data set, using the consecutive values 1 through 40. We then run a simple regression of Sales versus Time, with the results shown in Figure 13.18. The estimated linear trend line is

$$\text{Forecasted Sales} = 2686.7 + 131.991\text{Time}$$

Figure 13.18

Regression Output for Linear Trend

Summary	Multiple R	R-Square	Adjusted R-Square	StErr of Estimate		
	0.9806	0.9615	0.9605	312.87		

ANOVA Table	Degrees of Freedom	Sum of Squares	Mean of Squares	F-Ratio	p-Value	
Explained	1	92856588.48	92856588.48	948.5801	< 0.0001	
Unexplained	38	3719823.497	97890.09201			

Regression Table	Coefficient	Standard Error	t-Value	p-Value	Confidence Interval 95% Lower	Upper
Constant	2686.72	100.82	26.6476	< 0.0001	2482.61	2890.83
Time	131.991	4.29	30.7990	< 0.0001	123.31	140.67

This equation implies that we expect sales to increase by $131.991 million per quarter. (The 2686.7 value in this equation is what we would predict sales to be at time 0—quarter 4 of 1997.) To use this equation to forecast future sales, we substitute later values of Time into the regression equation, so that each future prediction is $131.991 larger than the previous prediction. For example, the forecast for Q4 of 2008 is

$$\text{Forecasted Sales Q4-08} = 2686.7 + 131.991(44) = 8494.3$$

Excel provides an easier way to obtain this trend line. Once the graph in Figure 13.17 is constructed, we can use Excel's Trendline tool. (Select the chart and then select More Trendline Options from the Trendline dropdown on the Chart Tools Layout ribbon.) This gives us several types of trend lines to choose from, and we select the linear option for this example. We can also check the options to show the regression equation and its R^2 value on the chart, as we have done in Figure 13.19. This superimposed trend line indicates a reasonably good fit.

Figure 13.19

Time Series Graph with Linear Trend Superimposed

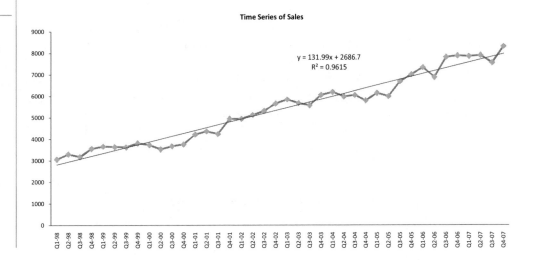

However, the fit is not perfect, as the plot of the residuals in Figure 13.20 indicates. These residuals tend to "meander," staying positive for a while, then negative, then positive, and so on. You can check that the runs test for these residuals produces a z-value of -3.074, with a corresponding p-value of 0.002, and that its first two autocorrelations are significantly positive. In short, these residuals are *not* random noise, and they could be modeled further. However, we do not pursue this analysis here.

Figure 13.20

Time Series Graph of Residuals

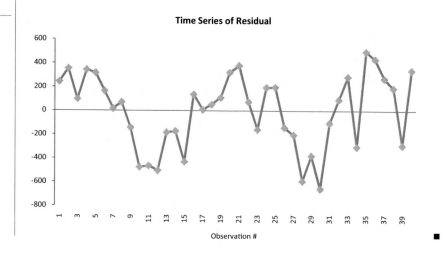

13.4.2 Exponential Trend

In contrast to a linear trend, an exponential trend is appropriate when the time series changes by a constant *percentage* (as opposed to a constant dollar amount) each period. Then the appropriate regression equation is equation (13.7), where c and b are constants, and u_t represents a *multiplicative* error term.

Exponential Trend Model

$$Y_t = ce^{bt}u_t \qquad \textbf{(13.7)}$$

An exponential trend for Y is equivalent to a linear trend for the logarithm of Y.

Equation (13.7) is useful for understanding how an exponential trend works, as we will discuss, but it is not useful for estimation. For that, we require a *linear* equation. Fortunately, we can achieve linearity by taking natural logarithms of both sides of equation (13.7). (The key, as usual, is that the logarithm of a product is the sum of the logarithms.) The result appears in equation (13.8), where $a = \ln(c)$ and $\epsilon_t = \ln(u_t)$. This equation represents a *linear* trend, but the dependent variable is now the logarithm of the original Y_t. This implies the following important fact: If a time series exhibits an exponential trend, then a plot of its logarithm should be approximately linear.

***Equivalent Linear Trend for Logarithm of* Y**

$$\ln(Y_t) = a + bt + \epsilon_t \qquad \textbf{(13.8)}$$

Because the computer does the calculations, our main responsibility is to interpret the final result. This is not too difficult. It can be shown that the coefficient b (expressed as a percentage) is approximately the percentage change per period. For example, if $b = 0.05$, then the series is increasing by approximately 5% per period.[2] On the other hand, if $b = -0.05$, then the series is decreasing by approximately 5% per period.

An exponential trend can be estimated with StatTools's Regression procedure, but only after the log transformation has been made on Y_t. We illustrate this in the following example.

EXAMPLE	13.3 QUARTERLY PC DEVICE SALES

The file **PC Device Sales.xlsx** contains quarterly sales data (in millions of dollars) for a large PC device manufacturer from the first quarter of 1993 through the fourth quarter of 2007. Are the company's sales growing exponentially through this entire period?

Objective   To estimate the company's exponential growth and to see whether it has been maintained during the entire period from 1993 until the end of 2007.

Solution

We first estimate and interpret an exponential trend for the years 1993 through 2003. Then we see how well the projection of this trend into the future fits the data after 2003. The time series graph through 2003 appears in Figure 13.21. We have used Excel's Trendline tool, with the Exponential option, to superimpose an exponential trend line and the corresponding equation on this plot. The fit is evidently quite good. Equivalently, Figure 13.22 illustrates the time series of log sales for this same period, with a *linear* trend line superimposed. Its fit is equally good.

Figure 13.21

Time Series Graph of Sales with Exponential Trend Superimposed

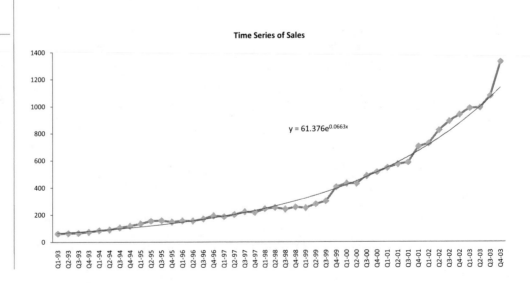

$y = 61.376e^{0.0663x}$

---

[2]More precisely, this percentage change is $e^b - 1$. For example, when $b = 0.05$, this is $e^b - 1 = 5.13\%$.

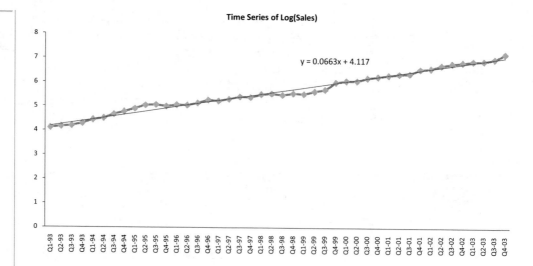

We can also use StatTools's Regression procedure to estimate this exponential trend, as shown in Figure 13.23. To produce this output, we must first add a time variable in column C (with values 1 through 44) and make a logarithmic transformation of Sales in column D. Then we regress Log(Sales) on Time (using the data through 2003 only) to obtain the regression output. Note that its two coefficients in cells B18 and B19 are the same as those shown for the linear trend in Figure 13.22. If we take the antilog of the constant 4.117 (with the formula = EXP(B18)), we obtain the constant *multiple* shown in Figure 13.21. It corresponds to the constant c in equation (13.7).

Figure 13.23

Regression Output
for Estimating
Exponential Trend

	A	B	C	D	E	F	G
7		Multiple	R-Square	Adjusted	StErr of		
8	Summary	R		R-Square	Estimate		
9		0.9922	0.9844	0.9840	0.1086		
10							
11		Degrees of	Sum of	Mean of			
12	ANOVA Table	Freedom	Squares	Squares	F-Ratio	p-Value	
13	Explained	1	31.21992793	31.21992793	2645.6403	< 0.0001	
14	Unexplained	42	0.495621782	0.011800519			
15							
16			Standard			Confidence Interval 95%	
17	Regression Table	Coefficient	Error	t-Value	p-Value	Lower	Upper
18	Constant	4.1170	0.0333	123.5616	< 0.0001	4.0498	4.1843
19	Time	0.0663	0.0013	51.4358	< 0.0001	0.0637	0.0689

What does it all mean? The estimated equation (13.7) is

$$\text{Forecasted Sales} = 61.376e^{0.0663t}$$

The most important constant in this equation is the coefficient of Time, $b = 0.0663$. Expressed as a percentage, this coefficient implies that the company's sales increased by approximately 6.63% per quarter throughout this 11-year period. (The constant multiple, $c = 61.376$, is our forecast of sales at time 0—in quarter 4 of 1992.) To use this equation for forecasting the future, we substitute later values of Time into the regression equation, so that each future forecast is about 6.63% larger than the previous forecast. For example, the forecast of the second quarter of 2004 is

$$\text{Forecasted Sales in Q2-04} = 61.376e^{0.0663(46)} = 1295.72$$

Has this exponential growth continued beyond 2003? It has *not*, due possibly to slumping sales in the computer industry or increased competition from other manufacturers. We checked this by creating the Forecast column in Figure 13.24 (by substituting into the regression equation for the entire period though Q4–07). We then used StatTools to create a time series graph of the two series Sales and Forecast, shown in Figure 13.25. It is clear that sales in the forecast period did not exhibit nearly the 6.63% growth observed in the estimation period. As the company clearly realizes, nothing that good lasts forever.

Figure 13.24

Creating Forecasts of Sales

	A	B	C	D	E
1	Quarter	Sales	Time	Log(Sales)	Forecast
2	Q1-93	61.14	1	4.1131663	65.58583
3	Q2-93	64.07	2	4.1599762	70.08398
4	Q3-93	66.18	3	4.1923783	74.89063
5	Q4-93	72.76	4	4.2871664	80.02694
6	Q1-94	84.70	5	4.4391156	85.51552
7	Q2-94	90.05	6	4.5003651	91.38053
8	Q3-94	106.06	7	4.664005	97.64778
9	Q4-94	118.21	8	4.7724627	104.3449
10	Q1-95	134.38	9	4.9006716	111.5013
11	Q2-95	154.67	10	5.0412938	119.1485
12	Q3-95	157.41	11	5.0588539	127.3202
13	Q4-95	147.16	12	4.9915204	136.0523

Figure 13.25 Time Series Graph of Forecasts Superimposed on Sales for the Entire Period

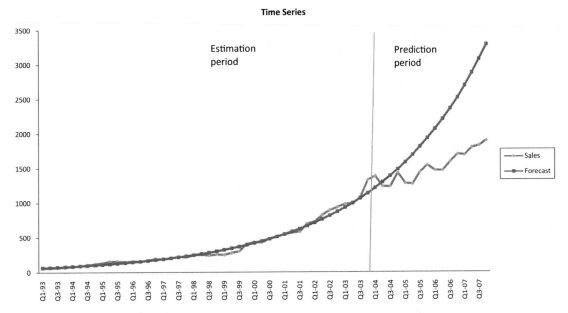

Before leaving this example, we comment briefly on the standard error of estimate shown in cell E9 of Figure 13.23. This value, 0.1086, is in *log* units, not original dollar units. Therefore, it is a totally misleading indicator of the forecast errors we might make from the exponential trend equation. To obtain more meaningful measures, we first obtain the forecasts of sales, as explained previously. Then we can easily obtain any of the three forecast error measures discussed previously in equations (13.2), (13.3), and (13.4). The results appear in Figure 13.26. The squared errors, absolute errors, and absolute percentage errors are first calculated with the formulas =(B2-E2)^2, =ABS(B2-E2), and =G2/B2 in cells F2, G2, and H2, which are then copied down. The error measures (for the data through 2003 only) then appear in cells K2, K3, and K4. The corresponding formulas for RMSE, MAE, and MAPE are straightforward. RMSE is the square root of the average of the squared errors in column F, and MAE and MAPE are the averages of the values in columns G and H, respectively. The latter is particularly simple to interpret. Forecasts for the 11-year estimate period were off, on average, by 7.86%. (Of course, as you can check, forecasts for the quarters *after* 2003 were off by much more!)

Figure 13.26

Measures of
Forecast Errors

	A	B	C	D	E	F	G	H	I	J	K	L
1	Quarter	Sales	Time	Log(Sales)	Forecast	SqError	AbsError	AbsPctError		Measures of forecast error		
2	Q1-93	61.14	1	4.1131663	65.58583	19.76541	4.445831	0.07271559		RMSE	41.86	
3	Q2-93	64.07	2	4.1599762	70.08398	36.16795	6.013979	0.09386576		MAE	25.44	
4	Q3-93	66.18	3	4.1923783	74.89063	75.87506	8.710629	0.13162027		MAPE	7.86%	
5	Q4-93	72.76	4	4.2871664	80.02694	52.8084	7.266939	0.09987547				
6	Q1-94	84.70	5	4.4391156	85.51552	0.66507	0.815518	0.00962831				
7	Q2-94	90.05	6	4.5003651	91.38053	1.770302	1.330527	0.01477542				
8	Q3-94	106.06	7	4.664005	97.64778	70.7654	8.412218	0.07931565				

Whenever we observe a time series that is increasing at an increasing rate (or decreasing at a decreasing rate), an exponential trend model is worth trying. The key to the analysis is to regress the *logarithm* of the time series variable versus time (or use Excel's Trendline tool). The coefficient of time, written as a percentage, is then the approximate percentage increase (if positive) or decrease (if negative) per period.

PROBLEMS

Level A

9. The file **P13_01.xlsx** contains the monthly number of airline tickets sold by the CareFree Travel Agency.
   a. Does a linear trend appear to fit these data well? If so, estimate and interpret the linear-trend model for this time series. Also, interpret the R^2 and s_e values.
   b. Provide an indication of the typical forecast error generated by the estimated model in part **a**.
   c. Is there evidence of some seasonal pattern in these sales data? If so, characterize the seasonal pattern.

10. The file **P13_10.xlsx** contains the daily closing prices of Wal-Mart stock for a 1-year period. Does a linear or exponential trend fit these data well? If so, estimate and interpret the best trend model for this time series. Also, interpret the R^2 and s_e values.

11. The file **P13_11.xlsx** contains annual data on the amount of life insurance in force in the United States.

Fit an exponential growth curve to these data. Write a short report to summarize your findings.

12. The file **P13_12.xlsx** contains 5 years of monthly data on sales (number of units sold) for a particular company. The company suspects that except for random noise, its sales are growing by a constant *percentage* each month and that they will continue to do so for at least the near future.
   a. Explain briefly whether the plot of the series visually supports the company's suspicion.
   b. Fit the appropriate regression model to the data. Report the resulting equation and state explicitly what it says about the percentage growth per month.
   c. What are the RMSE and MAPE for the forecast model in part **b**? In words, what do they measure? Considering their magnitudes, does the model seem to be doing a good job?
   d. In words, how does the model make forecasts for future months? Specifically, given the forecast

value for the last month in the data set, what simple arithmetic could you use to obtain forecasts for the next few months?

13. The file **P13_13.xlsx** contains quarterly data on GDP. (The data are expressed in billions of current dollars, they are seasonally adjusted, and they represent annualized rates.)
    a. Look at a time series plot of GDP. Does it suggest a linear relationship; an exponential relationship?
    b. Use regression to estimate a linear relationship between GDP and Time. Interpret the associated "constant" term and the "slope" term. Would you say that the fit is good?

Level B

14. The file **P13_14.xlsx** gives monthly exchange rates (dollars per unit of local currency) for 25 countries. Technical analysts believe that by charting past changes in exchange rates, it is possible to predict future changes of exchange rates. After analyzing the autocorrelations for these data, do you believe that technical analysis has potential?

15. The unit sales of a new drug for the first 25 months after its introduction to the marketplace are recorded in the file **P13_15.xlsx**.
    a. Estimate a linear trend equation using the given data. How well does the linear trend fit these data? Are the residuals from this linear trend model *random*?
    b. If the residuals from this linear trend model are *not* random, propose another regression-based trend model that more adequately explains the long-term trend in this time series. Estimate the alternative model(s) using the given data. Check the residuals from the model(s) for randomness. Summarize your findings.
    c. Given the best estimated model of the trend in this time series, interpret R^2 and s_e.

13.5 THE RANDOM WALK MODEL

Random series are sometimes building blocks for other time series models. The model we now discuss, the **random walk** model, is an example of this. In a random walk model the series itself is not random. However, its *differences*—that is, the changes from one period to the next—are random. This type of behavior is typical of stock price data (as well as various other time series data). For example, the graph in Figure 13.27 shows monthly closing prices for a tractor manufactor's stock from January 2001 through April 2007. (See the file **Tractor Closing Prices.xlsx**.) This series is not random, as can be seen from its gradual upward trend at the beginning and the general meandering behavior throughout. (Although the runs test and autocorrelations are not shown for the series itself, they confirm that the series is not random. There are significantly *fewer* runs than expected, and the autocorrelations are significantly *positive* for many lags.)

Figure 13.27

Time Series Graph of Tractor Stock Prices

If we were standing in April 2007 and were asked to forecast the company's prices for the next few months, it is intuitive that we would not use the average of the historical values as our forecast. This forecast would tend to be too low because of the upward trend. Instead, we might base our forecast on the most recent observation. This is exactly what the random walk model does.

Equation (13.9) for the random walk model is given in the box, where μ is a constant and ϵ_t is a random series (noise) with mean 0 and some standard deviation σ that remains *constant* through time.

Random Walk Model

$$Y_t = Y_{t-1} + \mu + \epsilon_t \qquad (13.9)$$

If we let $DY_t = Y_t - Y_{t-1}$, the change in the series from time t to time $t-1$ (where D stands for difference), then we can write the random walk model as in equation (13.10). This implies that the differences form a random series with mean μ and standard deviation σ. An estimate of μ is the average of the differences, labeled $\overline{Y}_D$, and an estimate of σ is the sample standard deviation of the differences, labeled s_D.

Difference Form of Random Walk Model

$$DY_t = \mu + \epsilon_t \qquad (13.10)$$

In words, a series that behaves according to this random walk model has random differences, and the series tends to trend upward (if $\mu > 0$) or downward (if $\mu < 0$) by an amount μ each period. If we are standing in period t and want to forecast Y_{t+1}, then a reasonable forecast is given by equation (13.11). That is, we add the estimated trend to the current observation to forecast the next observation.

One-Step-Ahead Forecast for Random Walk Model

$$F_{t+1} = Y_t + \overline{Y}_D \qquad (13.11)$$

We illustrate this method in the following example.

EXAMPLE | **13.4 RANDOM WALK MODEL OF STOCK PRICES**

The monthly closing prices of the tractor company's stock from January 2001 through April 2007, shown in Figure 13.27, indicate some upward trend. Does this series follow a random walk model with an upward trend? If so, how should future values of these stock prices be forecasted?

Objective To check whether the company's monthly closing prices follow a random walk model with an upward trend, and to see how future prices can be forecasted.

Solution

We have already seen that the closing price series itself is not random, due to the upward trend. To check for the adequacy of a random walk model, we need the *differenced* series. Each value in the differenced series is that month's closing price minus the previous month's closing price. This series can be calculated easily with an Excel formula, or it can be generated automatically with the Difference item on the StatTools Utilities dropdown. (When asked for the *number* of difference variables, we accept the default value of 1.) This differenced series appears in column C of Figure 13.28. This figure also shows the mean and standard deviation of the differences, 0.418 and 4.245, which are used in forecasting. Finally, Figure 13.28 shows several autocorrelations of the differences, only one of which is (barely) significant. A runs test for the differences, not shown here, has a large *p*-value, which supports the conclusion that the differences are random.

	A	B	C	D	E	F
						Diff1(Closing Price)
1	Month	Closing Price	Diff1(Closing Price)		One Variable Summary	Data Set #1
2	Jan-01	22.595			Mean	0.418
3	Feb-01	22.134	-0.461		Std. Dev.	4.245
4	Mar-01	24.655	2.521		Count	75
5	Apr-01	26.649	1.994			
6	May-01	26.303	-0.346			
7	Jun-01	27.787	1.484			Diff1(Closing Price)
8	Jul-01	32.705	4.918		Autocorrelation Table	Data Set #1
9	Aug-01	29.745	-2.96		Number of Values	75
10	Sep-01	26.741	-3.004		Standard Error	0.1155
11	Oct-01	24.852	-1.889		Lag #1	**-0.2435**
12	Nov-01	28.050	3.198		Lag #2	0.1348
13	Dec-01	27.847	-0.203		Lag #3	-0.0049
14	Jan-02	30.040	2.193		Lag #4	-0.0507
15	Feb-02	29.680	-0.36		Lag #5	0.0696
16	Mar-02	30.139	0.459		Lag #6	0.0009
17	Apr-02	29.276	-0.863		Lag #7	-0.0630
18	May-02	29.703	0.427		Lag #8	-0.0295
19	Jun-02	30.017	0.314		Lag #9	0.0496
20	Jul-02	29.687	-0.33		Lag #10	-0.1728
21	Aug-02	31.765	2.078		Lag #11	-0.0334
22	Sep-02	33.788	2.023		Lag #12	-0.0554
23	Oct-02	30.942	-2.846			
24	Nov-02	38.526	7.584			
25	Dec-02	34.099	-4.427			

The plot of the differences appears in Figure 13.29. A visual inspection of the plot also supports the conclusion of random differences, although these differences do not vary around a mean of 0. Rather, they vary around a mean of 0.418. This positive value measures the upward trend—the closing prices increase, on average, by 0.418 per month. Finally, the variability in this figure is fairly constant (except for the two wide swings in 2005). Specifically, the zigzags do not tend to get appreciably wider through time. Therefore, we can conclude that the random walk model with an upward drift fits these data quite well.

To forecast future closing prices, we add the number of months ahead being forecasted times the mean difference to the final closing price (53.947 in April 2007). For example, a forecast of the closing price for September 2007 is as follows:

$$\text{Forecasted Closing Price for 9/07} = 53.947 + 0.418(5) = 56.037$$

As a rough measure of the accuracy of this forecast, we can use the standard deviation of the differences, 4.245. Specifically, it can be shown that the standard error for forecasting *k* periods ahead is the standard deviation of the differences multiplied by the square root of *k*. In this case, the standard error is 9.492. As usual, we can be 95% confident that the actual closing price in September will be no more than 2 standard errors from the forecast. Unfortunately, this results in a wide interval—from about 37 to 75. This reflects the fact that it is very difficult to make accurate forecasts for a series with this much variability.

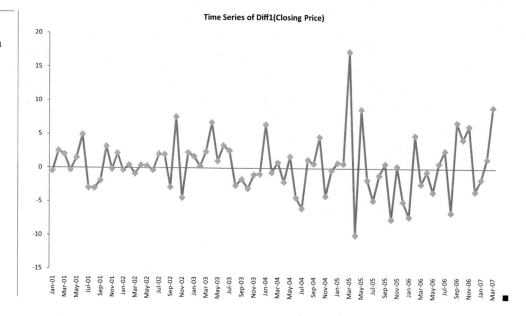

Figure 13.29

Time Series Graph of Differences

PROBLEMS

Level A

16. The file **P13_16.xlsx** contains the daily closing prices of American Express stock for a 1-year period.
    a. Use the random walk model to forecast the closing price of this stock on the next trading day.
    b. We can be about 95% certain that the forecast made in part **a** is off by no more than how many dollars?

17. The closing value of the AMEX Airline Index for each trading day during a 1-year period, is given in the file **P13_17.xlsx**.
    a. Use the random walk model to forecast the closing price of this stock on the next trading day.
    b. We can be about 68% certain that the forecast made in part **a** is off by no more than how many dollars?

18. The file **P13_18.xlsx** contains the daily closing prices of ChevronTexaco stock for a 1-year period.
    a. Use the random walk model to forecast the closing price of this stock on the next trading day.
    b. We can be about 99.7% certain that the forecast made in part **a** is off by no more than how many dollars?

19. The closing value of the Dow Jones Industrial Average for each trading day for a 1-year period is provided in the file **P13_19.xlsx**.
    a. Use the random walk model to forecast the closing price of this index on the next trading day.
    b. Would it be wise to use the random walk model to forecast the closing price of this index for a trading

day approximately *one month* after the next trading day? Explain why or why not.

20. Continuing the previous problem, consider the differences between consecutive closing values of the Dow Jones Industrial Average for the given set of trading days. Do these differences form a random series? Demonstrate why or why not.

21. The closing price of a share of JPMorgan's stock for each trading day during a 1-year period is recorded in the file **P13_21.xlsx**.
    a. Use the random walk model to forecast the closing price of this stock on the next trading day.
    b. We can be about 68% certain that the forecast made in part **a** is off by no more than how many dollars?

22. The purpose of this problem is to get you used to the concept of autocorrelation in a time series. You could do it with any time series, but here you should use the series of Wal-Mart daily stock prices in the file **P13_10.xlsx**.
    a. First, do it the "easy" way. Use the Autocorrelation procedure in StatTools to get a list of autocorrelations and a corresponding correlogram of the closing prices. You can choose the number of lags.
    b. Now do it the "hard" way. Create columns of lagged versions of the Close variable—3 or 4 lags will suffice. Next, look at scatterplots of Close versus its first few lags. If the autocorrelations are large, you should see fairly tight scatters—that's

what autocorrelation is all about. Also, generate a correlation matrix to see the correlations between Close and its first few lags. These should be approximately the same as the autocorrelations from part **a**. (Autocorrelations are calculated slightly differently than regular correlations, which accounts for any slight discrepancies you might notice, but these discrepancies should be minor.)

c. Create the first differences of Close in a new column. (You can do this manually with formulas, or you can use StatTools's Difference procedure under Data Utilities.) Now repeat parts **a** and **b** with the differences instead of the original closing prices—that is, examine the autocorrelations of the differences. They should be small, and the scatterplots of the differences versus lags of the differences should be "swarms." This illustrates what happens when the differences of a time series variable have "insignificant" autocorrelations.

d. Write a short report of your findings.

Level B

23. Consider a random walk model with the following equation: $Y_t = Y_{t-1} + 500 + \epsilon_t$, where ϵ_t is a normally distributed random series with mean 0 and standard deviation 10.

a. Use Excel to simulate a time series that behaves according to this random walk model.

b. Use the time series you constructed in part **a** to forecast the next observation.

24. The file **P13_24.xlsx** contains the daily closing prices of Procter & Gamble stock for a one-year period. Use only the data from 2003 to estimate the trend component of the random walk model. Next, use the estimated random walk model to forecast the behavior of the time series for the 2004 dates in the series. Comment on the accuracy of the generated forecasts over this period. How could you improve the forecasts as you progress through the 2004 trading days?

13.6 AUTOREGRESSION MODELS[3]

We now discuss a regression-based extrapolation method that regresses the current value of the time series on past (lagged) values. This is called **autoregression**, where the "auto" means that the explanatory variables in the equation are lagged values of the dependent variable, so that we are regressing the dependent variable on lagged versions of itself. This procedure is fairly straightforward on a spreadsheet. We first create lags of the dependent variable and then use a regression procedure to regress the original column on the lagged columns. Some trial and error is generally required to see how many lags are useful in the regression equation. The following example illustrates the procedure.

EXAMPLE | **13.5 FORECASTING HAMMER SALES**

A retailer has recorded its weekly sales of hammers (units purchased) for the past 42 weeks. (See the file **Hammer Sales.xlsx**.) A graph of this time series appears in Figure 13.30. It reveals a "meandering" behavior. The values begin high and stay high awhile, then get lower and stay lower awhile, then get higher again. (This behavior could be caused by any number of things, including the weather, increases and decreases in building projects, and possibly others.) How useful is autoregression for modeling these data and how can it be used for forecasting?

[3]This section can be omitted without any loss of continuity.

Objective   To use autoregression, with an appropriate number of lagged terms, to forecast hammer sales.

Solution

It is generally best to begin with plenty of lags and then delete the higher numbered lags that aren't necessary.

A good place to start is with the autocorrelations of the series. These indicate whether the Sales variable is linearly related to any of its lags. The first six autocorrelations are shown in Figure 13.31. The first three of them are significantly positive, and then they decrease. Based on this information, we create three lags of Sales and run a regression of Sales versus these three lags. The output from this regression appears in Figure 13.32. We see that R^2 is fairly high, about 57%, and that s_e is about 15.7. However, the p-values for lags 2 and 3 are both quite large. It appears that once the first lag is included in the regression equation, the other two are not really needed.

Figure 13.30   Time Series Graph of Sales of Hammers

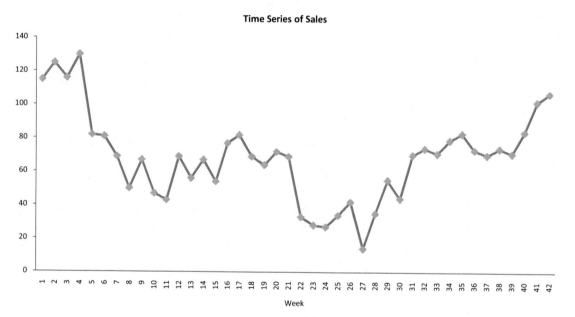

Figure 13.31

Autocorrelations for Hammer Sales Data

	A	B
27		**Sales**
28	*Autocorrelation Table*	**Data Set #1**
29	Number of Values	42
30	Standard Error	0.1543
31	Lag #1	**0.7523**
32	Lag #2	**0.5780**
33	Lag #3	**0.4328**
34	Lag #4	0.2042
35	Lag #5	0.1093
36	Lag #6	-0.0502

Figure 13.32 Autoregression Output with Three Lagged Variables

	A	B	C	D	E	F	G
7		Multiple	R-Square	Adjusted	StErr of		
8	*Summary*	R		R-Square	Estimate		
9		0.7573	0.5736	0.5370	15.7202		
10							
11		Degrees of	Sum of	Mean of	F-Ratio	p-Value	
12	*ANOVA Table*	Freedom	Squares	Squares			
13	Explained	3	11634.19978	3878.066594	15.6927	< 0.0001	
14	Unexplained	35	8649.38996	247.1254274			
15							
16		Coefficient	Standard	t-Value	p-Value	Confidence Interval 95%	
17	*Regression Table*		Error			Lower	Upper
18	Constant	15.4986	7.8820	1.9663	0.0572	-0.5027	31.5000
19	Lag1(Sales)	0.6398	0.1712	3.7364	0.0007	0.2922	0.9874
20	Lag2(Sales)	0.1523	0.1987	0.7665	0.4485	-0.2510	0.5556
21	Lag3(Sales)	-0.0354	0.1641	-0.2159	0.8303	-0.3686	0.2977

The two curves in this figure look pretty close to one another. However, a comparison of the vertical distances between pairs of points indicates that they are not so close after all.

Therefore, we reran the regression with only the first lag included. (Actually, we first omitted only the third lag. But the resulting output showed that the second lag was still insignificant.) The regression output with only the first lag included appears in Figure 13.33. In addition, a graph of the dependent and fitted variables, that is, the original Sales variable and its forecasts, appears in Figure 13.34. (This latter graph was formed from the Week, Sales, and Fitted columns.) The estimated regression equation is

$$\text{Forecasted Sales}_t = 13.763 + 0.793\text{Sales}_{t-1}$$

The associated R^2 and s_e values are approximately 65% and 15.4. The R^2 value is a measure of the reasonably good fit we see in Figure 13.34, whereas s_e is a measure of the likely forecast error for short-term forecasts. It implies that a short-term forecast could easily be off by as much as 2 standard errors, or about 31 hammers.

Figure 13.33 Autoregression Output with a Single Lagged Variable

	A	B	C	D	E	F	G
7		Multiple	R-Square	Adjusted	StErr of		
8	*Summary*	R		R-Square	Estimate		
9		0.8036	0.6458	0.6367	15.4476		
10							
11		Degrees of	Sum of	Mean of	F-Ratio	p-Value	
12	*ANOVA Table*	Freedom	Squares	Squares			
13	Explained	1	16969.97657	16969.97657	71.1146	< 0.0001	
14	Unexplained	39	9306.511237	238.6284932			
15							
16		Coefficient	Standard	t-Value	p-Value	Confidence Interval 95%	
17	*Regression Table*		Error			Lower	Upper
18	Constant	13.7634	6.7906	2.0268	0.0496	0.0281	27.4988
19	Lag1(Sales)	0.7932	0.0941	8.4329	< 0.0001	0.6029	0.9834

Figure 13.34 Forecasts from Autoregression

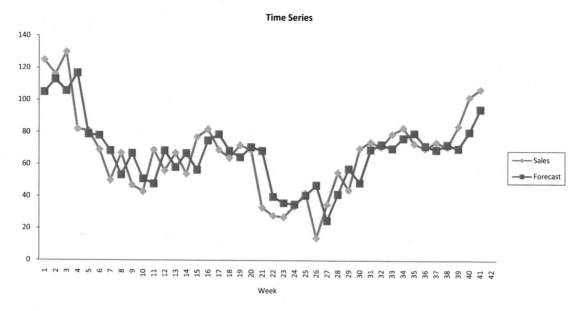

To forecast, substitute known values of Y into the regression equation if they are available. Otherwise, substitute forecasted values.

To use the regression equation for forecasting *future* sales values, we substitute known or forecasted sales values in the right-hand side of the equation. Specifically, the forecast for week 43, the first week after the data period, is

$$\text{Forecasted Sales}_{43} = 13.763 + 0.793\text{Sales}_{42} = 13.763 + 0.793(107) \simeq 98.6$$

Here we use the *known* value of sales in week 42. However, the forecast for week 44 requires the *forecasted* value of sales in week 43:

$$\text{Forecasted Sales}_{44} = 13.763 + 0.793\text{Forecasted Sales}_{43}$$

$$\text{Forecasted Sales}_{44} = 13.763 + 0.793(98.6) \simeq 92.0$$

Perhaps these two forecasts of future sales values are on the mark, and perhaps they are not. The only way we will know for certain is by observing future sales values. However, it is interesting that in spite of the *upward* movement in the series in the last 3 weeks, the forecasts for weeks 43 and 44 are for *downward* movements. This is a combination of two properties of the regression equation. First, the coefficient of Sales_{t-1}, 0.793, is positive. Therefore, the equation forecasts that large sales will be followed by large sales, that is, positive autocorrelation. Second, however, this coefficient is less than 1, and this provides a dampening effect. The equation forecasts that a large will follow a large, but not *that* large. ■

Sometimes an autoregression model can be virtually equivalent to another forecasting model. As an example, suppose we find that the following equation adequately models a time series variable Y:

$$Y_t = 75.65 + 0.976Y_{t-1}$$

The coefficient of the lagged term, 0.976, is nearly equal to 1. If this coefficient were 1, we could subtract the lagged term from both sides of the equation and write that the *difference* series is a constant—that is, we would have a random walk model. As you can see, a random walk model is a special case of an autoregression model. However, autoregression models are much more general. Unfortunately, a more thorough study of them would take us into the realm of econometrics, which is well beyond the level of this book.

PROBLEMS

Level A

25. Consider the Consumer Price Index (CPI), which provides the annual percentage change in consumer prices. The data are in the file **P02_26.xlsx**.
  a. Compute the first six autocorrelations of this time series.
  b. Use the results of part **a** to specify one or more "promising" autoregression models. Estimate each model with the available data. Which model provides the best fit to the given data?
  c. Use the best autoregression model from part **b** to produce a forecast of the CPI in the next year. Also, provide a measure of the likely forecast error.

26. The Consumer Confidence Index (CCI) attempts to measure people's feelings about general business conditions, employment opportunities, and their own income prospects. The file **P02_28.xlsx** contains the annual average values of the CCI.
  a. Compute the first six autocorrelations of this time series.
  b. Use the results of part **a** to specify one or more "promising" autoregression models. Estimate each model with the available data. Which model provides the best fit to the given data?
  c. Use the best autoregression model from part **b** to produce a forecast of the CCI in the next year. Also, provide a measure of the likely forecast error.

27. Consider the proportion of Americans under the age of 18 living below the poverty level. The data are in the file **P02_29.xlsx**.
  a. Compute the first six autocorrelations of this time series.
  b. Use the results of part **a** to specify one or more "promising" autoregression models. Estimate each model with the available data. Which model provides the best fit to the given data?
  c. Use the best autoregression model from part **b** to produce a forecast of the proportion of American

children living below the poverty level in the next year. Also, provide a measure of the likely forecast error.

28. Examine the trend in the annual average values of the discount rate. The data are in the file **P02_30.xlsx**.
  a. Specify one or more "promising" autoregression models based on autocorrelations of this time series. Estimate each model with the available data. Which model provides the best fit to given data?
  b. Use the best autoregression model from part **a** to produce forecasts of the discount rate in the next 2 years.

29. The file **P02_34.xlsx** contains time series data on the percentage of the resident population in the United States who completed four or more years of college.
  a. Specify one or more "promising" autoregression models based on autocorrelations of this time series. Estimate each model with the available data. Which model provides the best fit to the given data?
  b. Use the best autoregression model from part **a** to produce forecasts of higher education attainment (i.e., completion of four or more years of college) in the United States in the next 3 years.

30. Consider the average annual interest rates on 30-year fixed mortgages in the United States. The data are recorded in the file **P02_35.xlsx**.
  a. Specify one or more "promising" autoregression models based on autocorrelations of this time series. Estimate each model with the available data. Which model provides the best fit to the given data?
  b. Use the best autoregression model from part **a** to produce forecasts of the average annual interest rates on 30-year fixed mortgages in the next 3 years.

31. The file **P13_31.xlsx** lists the monthly unemployment rates for several years. A common way to forecast time series is by using regression with lagged variables.

a. Predict future monthly unemployment rates using some combination of the unemployment rates for the last 4 months. For example, you might use last month's unemployment rate and the unemployment rate from 3 months ago as explanatory variables. Make sure all variables that you finally decide to keep in your equation are significant at the 0.15 level.

b. Do the residuals in your equation exhibit any autocorrelation?

c. Predict the next month's unemployment rate.

d. There is a 5% chance that the next month's unemployment rate will be less than what value?

e. What is the probability the next month's unemployment rate will be less than 6%?

Level B

32. The unit sales of a new drug for the first 25 months after its introduction to the marketplace are recorded in the file **P13_15.xlsx**. Specify one or more "promising" autoregression models based on autocorrelations of this time series. Estimate each model with the available data. Which model provides the best fit to the given data? Use the best autoregression model you found to forecast the sales of this new drug in the 26th month.

33. The file **P13_02.xlsx** contains the weekly sales at a local bookstore for each of the past 25 weeks.

a. Specify one or more "promising" autoregression models based on autocorrelations of this time series. Estimate each model with the available data. Which model provides the best fit to the given data?

b. What general result emerges from your analysis in part **a**? In other words, what is the most appropriate autoregression model for any given *random* time series?

c. Use the best autoregression model from part **a** to produce forecasts of the weekly sales at this bookstore for the next 3 weeks.

34. The file **P13_24.xlsx** contains the daily closing prices of Procter & Gamble stock for a one-year period.

a. Use only the data from 2003 to estimate an appropriate autoregression model.

b. Next, use the estimated autoregression model from part **a** to forecast the behavior of this time series for the 2004 dates of the series. Comment on the accuracy of the generated forecasts over this period.

c. How well does the autoregression model perform in comparison to the random walk model with respect to the accuracy of these forecasts? Explain any significant differences between the forecasting abilities of the two models.

13.7 MOVING AVERAGES

Perhaps the simplest and one of the most frequently used extrapolation methods is the method of **moving averages**. To implement the moving averages method, we first choose a **span**, the number of terms in each moving average. Let's say the data are monthly and we choose a span of 6 months. Then the forecast of next month's value is the average of the values of the last 6 months. For example, we average January to June to forecast July, we average February to July to forecast August, and so on. This procedure is the reason for the term *moving* averages.

> A **moving average** is the average of the observations in the past few periods, where the number of terms in the average is the **span**.

A moving averages model with a span of 1 is a random walk model with a mean trend of 0.

The role of the span is important. If the span is large—say, 12 months—then many observations go into each average, and extreme values have relatively little effect on the forecasts. The resulting series of forecasts will be much smoother than the original series. (For this reason, the moving average method is called a *smoothing* method.) In contrast, if the span is small—say, 3 months—then extreme observations have a larger effect on the forecasts, and the forecast series will be much less smooth. In the extreme, if the span is 1, there is no smoothing effect at all. The method simply forecasts next month's value to be the same as the current month's value. This is often called the **naive** forecasting model. It is a special case of the random walk model we discussed previously, with the mean difference equal to 0.

What span should we use? This requires some judgment. If we believe the ups and downs in the series are random noise, then we don't want future forecasts to react too quickly to these ups and downs, and we should use a relatively large span. But if we want to track every little zigzag—under the belief that each up or down is predictable—then we should use a smaller span. We shouldn't be fooled, however, by a plot of the (smoothed) forecast series superimposed on the original series. This graph will almost always look better when a small span is used, because the forecast series will appear to track the original series better. Does this mean it will always provide better future forecasts? Not necessarily. There is little point in tracking random ups and downs closely if they represent unpredictable noise.

The following example illustrates the use of moving averages.

EXAMPLE | **13.6 HOUSES SOLD IN THE MIDWEST**

The file **House Sales.xlsx** contains monthly data on the number of houses sold in the Midwest (in thousands) from January 1994 through May 2001. (These data are seasonally adjusted.)[4] A time series graph of the data appears in Figure 13.35. Does a moving averages model fit this data set well? What span should be used?

Figure 13.35   Time Series Plot of Monthly House Sales

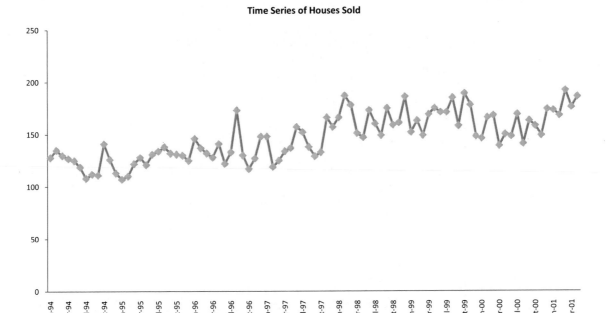

Objective   To see whether a moving averages model with an appropriate span fits the housing sales data, and to see how StatTools implements this method.

[4]We discuss seasonal adjustment in Section 13.9. Government data are often reported in seasonally adjusted form, with the seasonality removed, to make any trends more apparent.

Solution

Although the moving averages method is quite easy to implement in Excel—we just form an average of the appropriate span and copy it down—it can be tedious. Therefore, we call on the forecasting procedure of StatTools. Actually, this procedure is fairly general in that it allows us to forecast with several methods, either with or without taking seasonality into account. Because this is our first exposure to this procedure, we go through it in some detail in this example. In later examples, we mention some of its other capabilities.

To use the StatTools Forecasting procedure, select Forecast from the StatTools Time Series and Forecasting dropdown. This brings up the dialog box in Figure 13.36, which has three tabs in its bottom section. The Time Scale tab, shown in Figure 13.36, allows us to select the time period. The Forecast Settings tab, shown in Figure 13.37, allows us to select a forecasting method. Finally, the Graphs to Display tab, not shown here, allows us to select several optional time series graphs. For now, fill out the dialog box sections as shown and select the Forecast Overlay option in the Graphs to Display tab. In particular, note from Figure 13.37 that we are using the moving averages method with a span of 3, and we are asking for forecasts of the next 12 months.

Figure 13.36

Forecast Dialog Box with Time Scale Tab Visible

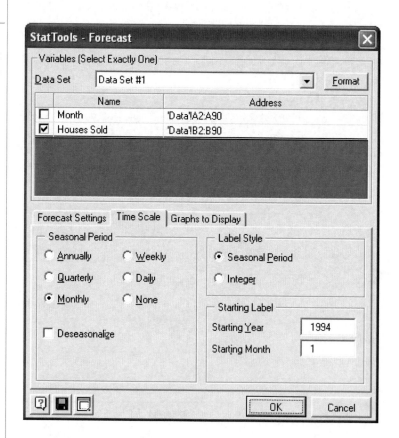

Another option in Figure 13.37 is that we can elect to "hold out" a subset of the data for validation purposes. If we hold out several periods at the end of the data set for validation, then any model that is built is estimated only for the nonholdout observations, and summary measures are reported for the nonholdout and holdout subsets separately. For now, we are not using a holdout period.

Figure 13.37

Forecast Dialog Box with Forecast Settings Tab Visible

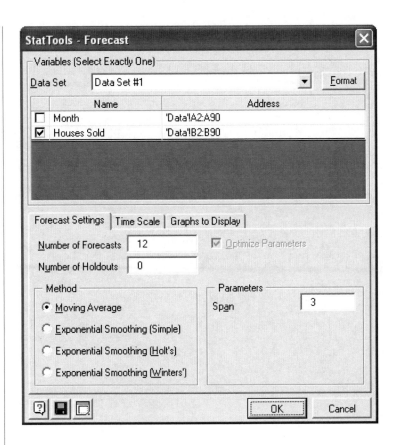

The output consists of several parts, as shown in Figures 13.38 through 13.41. We actually ran the analysis twice, once for a span of 3 and once for a span of 12. These figures show the comparison. (We also obtained output for a span of 6, with results similar to those for a span of 12.) First, the summary measures MAE, RMSE, and MAPE of the forecast errors are shown in Figure 13.38. As we see, both spans produce similar magnitudes of forecast errors. For example, they are both off, on average, by slightly more than 8%.

Figure 13.38 Moving Averages Summary Output

	A	B	C	D	E	F	G	H
8	*Forecasting Constant*						*Forecasting Constant*	
9	Span	3					Span	12
10					Moving averages method			
11					with spans 3 and 12			
12	*Moving Averages*						*Moving Averages*	
13	Mean Abs Err	12.26					Mean Abs Err	12.43
14	Root Mean Sq Err	14.96					Root Mean Sq Err	15.62
15	Mean Abs Per% Err	8.37%					Mean Abs Per% Err	8.07%

Figure 13.39 Moving Averages Detailed Output

	A	B	C	D	E	F	G	H	I	J
40	*Forecasting Data*	**Houses Sold**	**Forecast**	**Error**			*Forecasting Data*	**Houses Sold**	**Forecast**	**Error**
41	Jan-1994	128.0000					Jan-1994	128.0000		
42	Feb-1994	135.0000					Feb-1994	135.0000		
43	Mar-1994	130.0000					Mar-1994	130.0000		
44	Apr-1994	127.0000	131.00	-4.00			Apr-1994	127.0000		
45	May-1994	125.0000	130.67	-5.67			May-1994	125.0000		
46	Jun-1994	119.0000	127.33	-8.33			Jun-1994	119.0000		
47	Jul-1994	108.0000	123.67	-15.67			Jul-1994	108.0000		
48	Aug-1994	112.0000	117.33	-5.33			Aug-1994	112.0000		
49	Sep-1994	111.0000	113.00	-2.00			Sep-1994	111.0000		
50	Oct-1994	141.0000	110.33	30.67			Oct-1994	141.0000		
51	Nov-1994	126.0000	121.33	4.67			Nov-1994	126.0000		
52	Dec-1994	113.0000	126.00	-13.00			Dec-1994	113.0000		
53	Jan-1995	107.0000	126.67	-19.67			Jan-1995	107.0000	122.92	-15.92
54	Feb-1995	110.0000	115.33	-5.33			Feb-1995	110.0000	121.17	-11.17
55	Mar-1995	122.0000	110.00	12.00			Mar-1995	122.0000	119.08	2.92
56	Apr-1995	128.0000	113.00	15.00			Apr-1995	128.0000	118.42	9.58
126	Feb-2001	168.0000	165.33	2.67			Feb-2001	168.0000	158.17	9.83
127	Mar-2001	192.0000	171.67	20.33			Mar-2001	192.0000	158.33	33.67
128	Apr-2001	176.0000	177.67	-1.67			Apr-2001	176.0000	160.33	15.67
129	May-2001	186.0000	178.67	7.33			May-2001	186.0000	163.42	22.58
130	Jun-2001		184.67				Jun-2001		166.42	
131	Jul-2001		182.22				Jul-2001		167.95	
132	Aug-2001		184.30				Aug-2001		167.86	
133	Sep-2001		183.73				Sep-2001		170.10	
134	Oct-2001		183.42				Oct-2001		170.69	
135	Nov-2001		183.81				Nov-2001		171.75	
136	Dec-2001		183.65				Dec-2001		173.65	
137	Jan-2002		183.63				Jan-2002		173.62	
138	Feb-2002		183.70				Feb-2002		173.67	
139	Mar-2002		183.66				Mar-2002		174.14	
140	Apr-2002		183.66				Apr-2002		172.66	
141	May-2002		183.67				May-2002		172.38	

Figure 13.40

Moving Averages Forecasts with Span 3

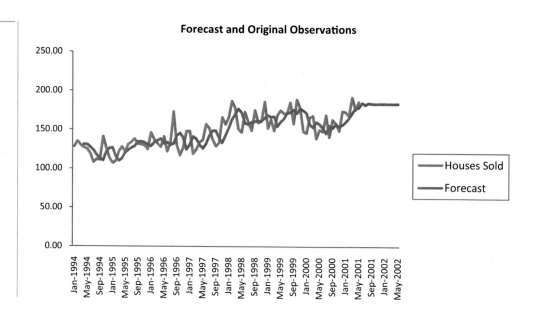

Forecast and Original Observations

Figure 13.41

Moving Averages
Forecasts with
Span 12

Forecast and Original Observations

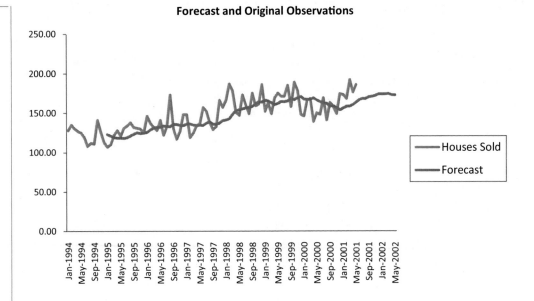

The essence of the forecasting method is very simple and is captured in column C of Figure 13.39 (for a span of 3). Each value in the historical period in this column is an average of the three preceding values in column B. The forecast errors are then just the differences between columns B and C. For the future periods, the forecast formulas in column C use observations when they are available. If they are not available, previous forecasts are used. For example, the value in cell C131, the forecast for July 2001, is the average of the *observed* values in April and May and the *forecasted* value in June.

The graphs in Figures 13.40 and 13.41 show the behavior of the forecasts. The forecasted series with span 3 follows the ups and downs of the actual series fairly closely, whereas the forecasted series with span 12 is much smoother and doesn't react nearly as much to these ups and downs. Which of these is better? The error summary measures indicate that it is a virtual toss-up. The MAPE with span 12 is slightly lower, but the RMSE with span 3 is slightly lower. Note that the *future* forecasts are considerably lower with span 12 than with span 3.

At this point, how to proceed is up to the judgment of the forecaster, who presumably has some knowledge of the housing sales market in the Midwest. If she believes that the ups and downs in the original series are largely unpredictable noise, then she will probably trust the smooth forecasts from a span of 12. Otherwise, she might use a span of 3 (or some other intermediate span, such as 6). ∎

The moving average method we have presented is the simplest of a group of moving average methods used by professional forecasters. We *smoothed* exactly once; that is, we took moving averages of several observations at a time and used these as forecasts. More complex methods smooth more than once, basically to get rid of random noise. They take moving averages, then moving averages of these moving averages, and so on for several stages. This can become quite complex, but the objective is quite simple—to smooth the data so that we can see underlying patterns.

Level A

35. The file **P13_16.xlsx** contains the daily closing prices of American Express stock for a 1-year period.
  a. Using a span of 3 days, forecast the price of this stock for the next trading day with the moving average method. How well does this method with span 3 forecast the known observations in this data set?
  b. Repeat part **a** with a span of 10.
  c. Which of these two spans appears to be more appropriate? Explain your choice.

36. The closing value of the AMEX Airline Index for each trading day during a 1-year period is given in the file **P13_17.xlsx**.
  a. How well does the moving average method track this series when the span is 4 days; when the span is 12 days?
  b. Using the more appropriate span, forecast the closing value of this index on the next trading day with the moving average method.

37. The closing value of the Dow Jones Industrial Average for each trading day during a 1-year period is provided in the file **P13_19.xlsx**.
  a. Using a span of 2 days, forecast the price of this index on the next trading day with the moving average method. How well does the moving average method with span 2 forecast the known observations in this data set?
  b. Repeat part **a** with a span of 5 days; with a span of 15 days.
  c. Which of these three spans appears to be most appropriate? Explain your choice.

38. The file **P13_10.xlsx** contains the daily closing prices of Wal-Mart stock during a 1-year period. Use the moving average method with a carefully chosen span to forecast this time series for the next 3 trading days. Defend your choice of the span used.

39. The Consumer Confidence Index (CCI) attempts to measure people's feelings about general business conditions, employment opportunities, and their own income prospects. The file **P02_28.xlsx** contains the annual average values of the CCI. Use the moving average method with a carefully chosen span to forecast this time series in the next 2 years. Defend your choice of the span used here.

Level B

40. Consider the file **P02_37.xlsx**, which contains total monthly U.S. retail sales data. While retaining the final 6 months of observations for validation purposes, use the method of moving averages with a carefully chosen span to forecast U.S. retail sales in the next year. Comment on the performance of your model. What makes this time series more challenging to forecast?

41. Consider a random walk model with the following equation: $Y_t = Y_{t-1} + \epsilon_t$, where ϵ_t is a random series with mean 0 and standard deviation 1. Specify a moving average model that is equivalent to this random walk model. In particular, what is the appropriate size of the span in the equivalent moving average model? Describe the smoothing effect of this span choice.

13.8 EXPONENTIAL SMOOTHING

There are two possible criticisms of the moving averages method. First, it puts equal weight on each value in a typical moving average when making a forecast. Many people would argue that if next month's forecast is to be based on the previous 12 months' observations, then more weight ought to be placed on the more recent observations. The second criticism is that the moving averages method requires a lot of data storage. This is particularly true for companies that routinely make forecasts of hundreds or even thousands of items. If 12-month moving averages are used for 1000 items, then 12,000 values are needed for next month's forecasts. This may or may not be a concern considering today's inexpensive computer storage capabilities.

Exponential smoothing is a method that addresses both of these criticisms. It bases its forecasts on a weighted average of past observations, with more weight put on the more recent observations, and it requires very little data storage. In addition, it is not difficult for most business people to understand, at least conceptually. Therefore, this method finds widespread use in the business world, particularly when frequent and automatic forecasts of many items are required.

There are many versions of exponential smoothing. The simplest is appropriately called *simple* exponential smoothing. It is relevant when there is no pronounced trend or seasonality in the series. If there is a trend but no seasonality, then *Holt's* method is applicable. If, in addition, there is seasonality, then *Winters'* method can be used. This does not exhaust the list of exponential smoothing models—researchers have invented many other variations—but these three models will suffice for us.

Exponential Smoothing Models

Simple exponential smoothing is appropriate for a series with no pronounced trend or seasonality. **Holt's** method is appropriate for a series with trend but no seasonality. **Winters'** method is appropriate for a series with seasonality (and possibly trend).

In this section we examine simple exponential smoothing and Holt's model for trend. Then in the next section we examine Winters' model when we focus on seasonal models in general.

13.8.1 Simple Exponential Smoothing

The level is where we think the series would be if it were not for random noise.

We now examine simple exponential smoothing in some detail. We first introduce two new terms. Every exponential model has at least one **smoothing constant**, which is always between 0 and 1. Simple exponential smoothing has a single smoothing constant denoted by α. (Its role is discussed shortly.) The second new term is L_t, called the **level** of the series at time t. This value is not observable but can only be estimated. Essentially, it is where we think the series would be at time t if there were no random noise. Then the simple exponential smoothing method is defined by the following two equations, where F_{t+k} is the forecast of Y_{t+k} made at time t:

Simple Exponential Smoothing Formulas

$$L_t = \alpha Y_t + (1 - \alpha)L_{t-1} \qquad \text{(13.12)}$$

$$F_{t+k} = L_t \qquad \text{(13.13)}$$

Even though you usually won't have to substitute into these equations manually, you should understand what they say. Equation (13.12) shows how to update the estimate of the level. It is a weighted average of the current observation, Y_t, and the previous level, L_{t-1}, with respective weights α and $1 - \alpha$. Equation (13.13) shows how forecasts are made. It says that the k-period-ahead forecast, F_{t+k}, made of Y_{t+k} in period t is the most recently estimated level, L_t. This is the *same* for any value of $k \geq 1$. The idea is that in simple exponential smoothing, we believe that the series is not really going anywhere. So as soon as we estimate where the series ought to be in period t (if it weren't for random noise), we forecast that this is where it will also be in any future period.

The smoothing constant α is analogous to the span in moving averages. There are two ways to see this. The first way is to rewrite equation (13.12), using the fact that the forecast error, E_t, made in forecasting Y_t at time $t - 1$ is $Y_t - F_t = Y_t - L_{t-1}$. A bit of algebra then gives equation (13.14).

Equivalent Formula for Simple Exponential Smoothing

$$L_t = L_{t-1} + \alpha E_t \qquad \text{(13.14)}$$

This equation says that the next estimate of the level is adjusted from the previous estimate by adding a multiple of the most recent forecast error. This makes sense. If our previous forecast was too high, then E_t is negative, and we adjust the estimate of the level downward. The opposite is true if our previous forecast was too low. However, equation (13.14) says that we do not adjust by the entire magnitude of E_t, but only by a fraction of it. If α is small, say, $\alpha = 0.1$, then the adjustment is minor; if α is close to 1, the adjustment is large. So if we want to react quickly to movements in the series, we choose a large α; otherwise, we choose a small α.

Another way to see the effect of α is to substitute recursively into the equation for L_t. If you are willing to go through some algebra, you can verify that L_t satisfies equation (13.15), where the sum extends back to the first observation at time $t = 1$.

> **Another Equivalent Formula for Simple Exponential Smoothing**
> $$L_t = \alpha Y_t + \alpha(1 - \alpha)Y_{t-1} + \alpha(1 - \alpha)^2 Y_{t-2} + \alpha(1 - \alpha)^3 Y_{t-3} + \cdots \quad \textbf{(13.15)}$$

Equation (13.15) shows how the exponentially smoothed forecast is a weighted average of previous observations. Furthermore, because $1 - \alpha$ is less than 1, the weights on the Y's decrease from time t backward. Therefore, if α is close to 0, then $1 - \alpha$ is close to 1 and the weights decrease very slowly. In other words, observations from the distant past continue to have a large influence on the next forecast. This means that the graph of the forecasts will be relatively smooth, just as with a large span in the moving averages method. But when α is close to 1, the weights decrease rapidly, and only very recent observations have much influence on the next forecast. In this case forecasts react quickly to sudden changes in the series.

Small smoothing constants provide forecasts that respond slowly to changes in the data. Large smoothing constants do the opposite.

What value of α should we use? There is no universally accepted answer to this question. Some practitioners recommend always using a value around 0.1 or 0.2. Others recommend experimenting with different values of α until a measure such as RMSE or MAPE is minimized. Some packages even have an optimization feature to find this optimal value of α. (This is the case with StatTools.) But just as we discussed in the moving averages section, the value of α that tracks the historical series most closely does not necessarily guarantee the most accurate *future* forecasts.

EXAMPLE | 13.6 HOUSES SOLD IN THE MIDWEST (CONTINUED)

Previously, we used the moving averages method to forecast monthly housing sales in the Midwest. (See the **House Sales.xlsx** file.) How well does simple exponential smoothing work with this data set? What smoothing constant should we use?

Objective To see how well a simple exponential smoothing model, with an appropriate smoothing constant, fits the housing sales data, and to see how StatTools implements this method.

Solution

We use StatTools to implement the simple exponential smoothing model, specifically equations (13.12) and (13.13). We do this again with the Forecast item from StatTools Time Series and Forecasting dropdown. We then fill in the forecast dialog box essentially like we did with moving averages, except that we select the exponential smoothing options in the Forecast Settings tab (see Figure 13.42). That is, we select the simple exponential smoothing option, choose a smoothing constant (0.1 was chosen here, but any other value could be chosen), and elect not to optimize.

Figure 13.42

Forecast Settings for
Exponential
Smoothing

Figure 13.42

Forecast Settings for
Exponential
Smoothing

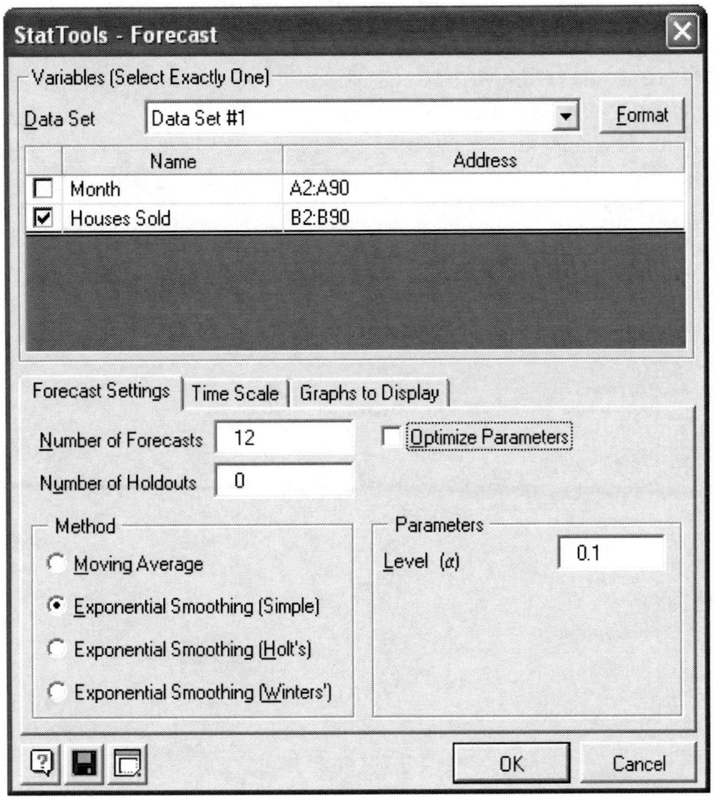

The results appear in Figures 13.43 and 13.44. The heart of the method takes place in columns C, D, and E of Figure 13.43. Column C calculates the smoothed levels (L_t) from equation (13.12), column D calculates the forecasts (F_t) from equation (13.13), and column E calculates the forecast errors (E_t) as the observed values minus the forecasts. Although we do not list the Excel formulas here, you can examine them in the StatTools output.

Every exponential smoothing method requires *initial* values, in this case the initial smoothed level in cell C41. There is no way to calculate this value, L_1, from equation (13.12) because the *previous* value, L_0, is unknown. Different implementations of exponential smoothing initialize in different ways. We have simply set L_1 equal to Y_1 (in cell B41). The effect of initializing in different ways is usually minimal because any effect of early data is usually washed out as we forecast into the future. In the present example, data from 1994 have little effect on forecasts of 2001 and beyond.

Note that the 12 future forecasts (rows 130 down) are all equal to the last calculated smoothed level, the one for May 2001 in cell C129. The fact that these remain constant is a consequence of the assumption behind *simple* exponential smoothing, namely, that the series is not really going anywhere. Therefore, the last smoothed level is the best indication of future values of the series we have.

Figure 13.44 shows the forecast series superimposed on the original series. We see the obvious smoothing effect of a relatively small α level. The forecasts don't track the series very well, but if the various zigzags in the original series are really random noise, then perhaps we don't want the forecasts to track these random ups and downs too closely. Perhaps we instead prefer a forecast series that emphasizes the basic underlying pattern.

We see several summary measures of the forecast errors in Figure 13.43. The RMSE and MAE indicate that the forecasts from this model are typically off by a magnitude of about 12 to 15 thousand, and the MAPE indicates that they are off by about 7.9%. (These

In the next subsection we use Holt's method on this series to see whether it captures the trend better than simple exponential smoothing.

are similar to the errors we obtained with moving averages.) These imply fairly sizable errors. One way to reduce the errors is to use a different smoothing method. We try this in the next subsection with Holt's method. Another way to reduce the errors is to use a different smoothing constant. There are two methods you can use. First, you can simply enter different values in the smoothing constant cell in the Forecast sheet. All formulas, including those for MAE, RMSE, and MAPE, will update automatically.

Figure 13.43

Simple Exponential Smoothing Output

	A	B	C	D	E
7					
8	*Forecasting Constant*				
9	Level (Alpha)	0.100			
10					
11					
12	*Simple Exponential*				
13	Mean Abs Err	11.93			
14	Root Mean Sq Err	15.08			
15	Mean Abs Per% Err	7.91%			
39					
40	*Forecasting Data*	Houses Sold	Level	Forecast	Error
41	Jan-1994	128.0000	128.00		
42	Feb-1994	135.0000	128.70	128.00	7.00
43	Mar-1994	130.0000	128.83	128.70	1.30
44	Apr-1994	127.0000	128.65	128.83	-1.83
123	Nov-2000	149.0000	157.82	158.80	-9.80
124	Dec-2000	174.0000	159.44	157.82	16.18
125	Jan-2001	173.0000	160.80	159.44	13.56
126	Feb-2001	168.0000	161.52	160.80	7.20
127	Mar-2001	192.0000	164.56	161.52	30.48
128	Apr-2001	176.0000	165.71	164.56	11.44
129	May-2001	186.0000	167.74	165.71	20.29
130	Jun-2001			167.74	
131	Jul-2001			167.74	
132	Aug-2001			167.74	
133	Sep-2001			167.74	
134	Oct-2001			167.74	
135	Nov-2001			167.74	
136	Dec-2001			167.74	
137	Jan-2002			167.74	
138	Feb-2002			167.74	
139	Mar-2002			167.74	
140	Apr-2002			167.74	
141	May-2002			167.74	

Second, you can check the Optimize Parameters option in Figure 13.42. This automatically runs an optimization algorithm (not Solver, by the way) to find the smoothing constant that minimizes RMSE. (StatTools is programmed to minimize RMSE. However, you could try minimizing MAPE, say, by using Excel's Solver add-in.) We did this for the housing data and obtained the forecasts in Figure 13.45 (from a smoothing constant of 0.295). The corresponding MAE, RMSE, and MAPE are 11.4, 14.1, and 7.7%, respectively—slightly better than before. This larger smoothing constant produces a less smooth forecast curve and slightly better error measures. However, there is no guarantee that *future* forecasts made with this optimal smoothing constant will be any better than with a smoothing constant of 0.1.

Figure 13.44

Graph of Forecasts
from Simple
Exponential
Smoothing

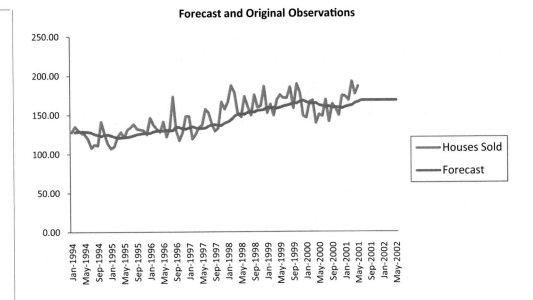

Figure 13.45

Graph of Forecasts
with an Optimal
Smoothing Constant

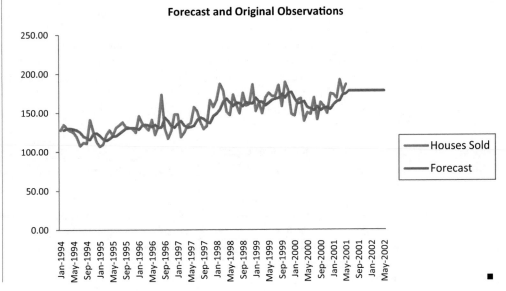

13.8.2 Holt's Model for Trend

The trend term in Holt's method estimates the change from one period to the next.

The simple exponential smoothing model generally works well if there is no obvious trend in the series. But if there is a trend, then this method consistently lags behind it. For example, if the series is constantly increasing, simple exponential smoothing forecasts will be consistently low. Holt's method rectifies this by dealing with trend explicitly. In addition to the level of the series, L_t, Holt's method includes a trend term, T_t, and a corresponding smoothing constant β. The interpretation of L_t is exactly as before. The interpretation of T_t is that it represents an estimate of the change in the series from one period to the next. The equations for Holt's model are as follows.

Formula's for Holt's Exponential Smoothing Method

$$L_t = \alpha Y_t + (1 - \alpha)(L_{t-1} + T_{t-1}) \qquad \textbf{(13.16)}$$

$$T_t = \beta(L_t - L_{t-1}) + (1 - \beta)T_{t-1} \qquad \textbf{(13.17)}$$

$$F_{t+k} = L_t + kT_t \qquad \textbf{(13.18)}$$

These equations are not as bad as they look. (And don't forget that the computer typically does all of the calculations for you.) Equation (13.16) says that the updated level is a weighted average of the current observation and the previous level plus the estimated change. Equation (13.17) says that the updated trend term is a weighted average of the difference between two consecutive levels and the previous trend term. Finally, equation (13.18) says that the k-period-ahead forecast made in period t is the estimated level plus k times the estimated change per period.

Everything we said about α for simple exponential smoothing applies to both α and β in Holt's model. The new smoothing constant β controls how quickly the method reacts to perceived changes in the trend. If β is small, the method reacts slowly. If it is large, the method reacts more quickly. Of course, there are now two smoothing constants to select. Some practitioners suggest using a small value of α (0.1 to 0.2, say) and setting β equal to α. Others suggest using an optimization option (available in StatTools) to select the "best" smoothing constants. We illustrate the possibilities in the following continuation of the housing sales example.

EXAMPLE | **13.6 HOUSES SOLD IN THE MIDWEST (CONTINUED)**

We again examine the monthly data on housing sales in the Midwest. In the previous subsection, we saw that simple exponential smoothing, even with an optimal smoothing constant, does only a "fair" job of forecasting housing sales. Given that there is an upward trend in housing sales over this period, we might expect Holt's method to perform better. Does it? What smoothing constants are appropriate?

Objective   To see whether Holt's method, with appropriate smoothing constants, captures the trend in the housing sales data better than simple exponential smoothing (or moving averages).

Solution

We implement Holt's method in StatTools almost exactly like we did for simple exponential smoothing. The only difference is that we can now choose *two* smoothing constants, as shown in Figure 13.46. They can have different values, although we have chosen them to be their default values of 0.1.

Figure 13.46

Dialog Box for Holt's Method

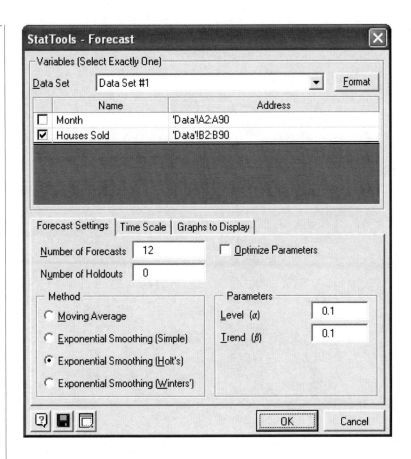

The StatTools outputs in Figures 13.47 and 13.48 are also very similar to the simple exponential smoothing outputs. The only difference is that there is now a trend column, column D, in the numerical output. You can check that the formulas in columns C, D, and E implement equations (13.16), (13.17), and (13.18). As before, there is an initialization problem in row 42. These require values of L_1 and T_1 to get the method started. Different implementations of Holt's method obtain these initial values in slightly different ways, but the effect is fairly minimal in most cases. (You can check cells C42 and D42 to see how StatTools does it.)

Somewhat surprisingly, the error measures for this implementation of Holt's method are no better than for simple exponential smoothing, even though this series exhibits a gradual upward trend. Perhaps this is because 0.1 and 0.1 are not the *optimal* smoothing constants. Therefore, we ran Holt's method a second time, checking the Optimize Parameters option. This resulted in somewhat better results and the forecasts shown in Figure 13.49. The optimal smoothing constants are $\alpha = 0.251$ and $\beta = 0.000$, and the MAE, RMSE, and MAPE values were 11.2, 13.9, and 7.7%—almost identical to simple exponential smoothing with an optimal smoothing constant.[5]

---

[5]The fact that β is 0 does not mean there is no trend. It simply means that we never update our initial estimate of trend, which is positive.

Figure 13.47 Output from Holt's Method

	A	B	C	D	E	F
7						
8	*Forecasting Constants*					
9	Level (Alpha)	0.100				
10	Trend (Beta)	0.100				
11						
12						
13	*Holt's Exponential*					
14	Mean Abs Err	12.05				
15	Root Mean Sq Err	15.08				
16	Mean Abs Per% Err	8.23%				
17						
41	Forecasting Data	Houses Sold	Level	Trend	Forecast	Error
42	Jan-1994	128.0000	128.00	0.65		
43	Feb-1994	135.0000	129.29	0.72	128.65	6.35
44	Mar-1994	130.0000	130.00	0.72	130.00	0.00
45	Apr-1994	127.0000	130.35	0.68	130.72	-3.72
46	May-1994	125.0000	130.42	0.62	131.02	-6.02
47	Jun-1994	119.0000	129.83	0.50	131.04	-12.04
125	Dec-2000	174.0000	160.52	-0.60	159.02	14.98
126	Jan-2001	173.0000	161.22	-0.47	159.91	13.09
127	Feb-2001	168.0000	161.47	-0.40	160.75	7.25
128	Mar-2001	192.0000	164.17	-0.09	161.07	30.93
129	Apr-2001	176.0000	165.27	0.03	164.08	11.92
130	May-2001	186.0000	167.37	0.23	165.30	20.70
131	Jun-2001				167.60	
132	Jul-2001				167.84	
133	Aug-2001				168.07	
134	Sep-2001				168.31	
135	Oct-2001				168.54	
136	Nov-2001				168.78	
137	Dec-2001				169.01	
138	Jan-2002				169.25	
139	Feb-2002				169.48	
140	Mar-2002				169.72	
141	Apr-2002				169.95	
142	May-2002				170.19	

You should not conclude from this example that Holt's method is never superior to simple exponential smoothing. Holt's method is often able to react quickly to a sudden upswing or downswing in the data, whereas simple exponential smoothing typically has a delayed reaction to such a change. It just happened in this example that the trend was gradual, so that both methods were able to react to it in equivalent ways.

Figure 13.48

Forecasts from
Holt's Method
with Nonoptimal
Smoothing
Constants

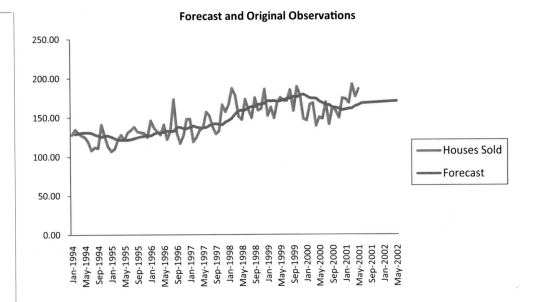

Forecast and Original Observations

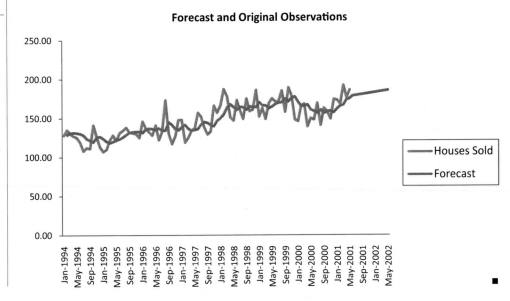

Forecast and Original Observations

PROBLEMS

Level A

42. Consider the airline ticket data in the file **P13_01.xlsx**.
    a. Create a time series chart of the data. Based on what you see, which of the exponential smoothing models do you think should be used for forecasting? Why?
    b. Use simple exponential smoothing to forecast these data, using no holdout period and requesting 12 months of future forecasts. Use the default smoothing constant of 0.1.
    c. Repeat part **b**, optimizing the smoothing constant. Does it make much of an improvement?
    d. Write a short report to summarize your results.

43. Consider the applications for home mortgages data in the file **P13_04.xlsx**.
    a. Create a time series chart of the data. Based on what you see, which of the exponential smoothing models do you think should be used for forecasting? Why?
    b. Use simple exponential smoothing to forecast these data, using no holdout period and requesting 4 quarters of future forecasts. Use the default smoothing constant of 0.1.
    c. Repeat part **b**, optimizing the smoothing constant. Does it make much of an improvement?
    d. Write a short report to summarize your results.

44. Consider the American Express closing price data in the file **P13_16.xlsx**. Focus only on the closing prices.
    a. Create a time series chart of the data. Based on what you see, which of the exponential smoothing models do you think should be used for forecasting? Why? (*Note*: The data are currently sorted from most recent to most distant in the past. Sort them in the opposite order first.)
    b. Use Holt's exponential smoothing to forecast these data, using no holdout period and requesting 20 days of future forecasts. Use the default smoothing constants of 0.1.
    c. Repeat part **b**, optimizing the smoothing constants. Does it make much of an improvement?
    d. Repeat parts **a** and **b**, this time using a holdout period of 50 days.
    e. Write a short report to summarize your results.

45. Consider the poverty level data in the file **P02_29.xlsx**. Focus only on the Percent variable.
    a. Create a time series chart of the data. Based on what you see, which of the exponential smoothing models do you think should be used for forecasting? Why?

    b. Use simple exponential smoothing to forecast these data, using no holdout period and requesting 3 years of future forecasts. Use the default smoothing constants of 0.1.
    c. Repeat part **b**, optimizing the smoothing constant. Make sure you request a chart of the series with the forecasts superimposed. Does the optimal smoothing constant make much of an improvement?
    d. Write a short report to summarize your results. Considering the chart in part **c**, would you say the forecasts are "good"?

Problems 46 through 48 ask you to apply the exponential smoothing formulas. These do not require StatTools. In fact, they do not even require Excel. You can do them with a hand calculator (or with Excel).

46. TOD Chevy is using Holt's method to forecast weekly car sales. Currently, the level is estimated to be 50 cars per week, and the trend is estimated to be 6 cars per week. During the current week, 30 cars are sold. After observing the current week's sales, forecast the number of cars 3 weeks from now. Use $\alpha = \beta = 0.3$.

47. You have been assigned to forecast the number of aircraft engines ordered each month by Commins Engine Company. At the end of February, the forecast is that 100 engines will be ordered during April. Then during March, 120 engines are actually ordered.
    a. Using $\alpha = 0.3$, determine a forecast (at the end of March) for the number of orders placed during April; during May. Use simple exponential smoothing.
    b. Suppose MAE = 16 at the end of March. At the end of March, Commins can be 68% sure that April orders will be between what two values, assuming normally distributed forecast errors? (*Hint*: It can be shown that the standard deviation of forecast errors is approximately 1.25 times MAE.)

48. Simple exponential smoothing with $\alpha = 0.3$ is being used to forecast sales of radios at Lowland Appliance. Forecasts are made on a monthly basis. After August radio sales are observed, the forecast for September is 100 radios.
    a. During September, 120 radios are sold. After observing September sales, what do we forecast for October radio sales? For November radio sales?
    b. It turns out that June sales were recorded as 10 radios. Actually, however, 100 radios were sold in June. After correcting for this error, develop a forecast for October radio sales.

Level B

49. Holt's method assumes an additive trend. For example, a trend of 5 means that the level will increase by 5 units per period. Suppose there is actually a **multiplicative trend**. For example, if the current estimate of the level is 50 and the current estimate of the trend is 1.2, we would predict demand to increase by 20% per period. So we would forecast the next period's demand to be 50(1.2) and forecast the demand 2 periods in the future to be $50(1.2)^2$. If we want to use a multiplicative trend in Holt's method, we should use the following equations:

$$L_t = \alpha Y_t + (1 - \alpha)(I)$$
$$T_t = \beta(II) + (1 - \beta)T_{t-1}$$

  a. What should (*I*) and (*II*) be?

  b. Suppose we are working with monthly data and month 12 is December, month 13 is January, and so on. Also suppose that $L_{12} = 100$ and $T_{12} = 1.2$. Suppose $Y_{13} = 200$. At the end of month 13, what is the prediction for Y_{15}? Assume $\alpha = \beta = 0.5$ and a multiplicative trend.

50. A version of simple exponential smoothing can be used to predict the outcome of sporting events. To illustrate, consider pro football. We first assume that all games are played on a neutral field. Before each day of play, we assume that each team has a rating. For example, if the rating for the Bears is +10 and the rating for the Bengals is +6, we predict the Bears to beat the Bengals by $10 - 6 = 4$ points. Suppose that the Bears play the Bengals and win by 20 points. For this game, we "underpredicted" the Bears' performance by $20 - 4 = 16$ points. Assuming that the best α for pro football is $\alpha = 0.10$, we would increase the Bears' rating by $16(0.1) = 1.6$ and decrease the Bengals' rating by 1.6 points. In a rematch, the Bears would then be favored by $(10 + 1.6) - (6 - 1.6) = 7.2$ points.

  a. How does this approach relate to the equation $L_t = L_{t-1} + \alpha e_t$?

  b. Suppose that the home field advantage in pro football is 3 points; that is, home teams tend to outscore visiting teams by an average of 3 points a game. How could the home field advantage be incorporated into this system?

  c. How might we determine the *best* α for pro football?

  d. How might we determine ratings for each team at the beginning of the season?

  e. Suppose we apply this method to predict pro football (16-game schedule), college football (11-game schedule), college basketball (30-game schedule), and pro basketball (82-game schedule). Which sport do you think would have the smallest optimal α; the largest optimal α? Why?

  f. Why might this approach yield poor forecasts for major league baseball?

13.9 SEASONAL MODELS

So far we have said practically nothing about seasonality. Seasonality is the consistent month-to-month (or quarter-to-quarter) differences that occur each year. For example, there is seasonality in beer sales—high in the summer months, lower in other months. Toy sales are also seasonal, with a huge peak in the months preceding Christmas. In fact, if you start thinking about time series variables that you are familiar with, the majority of them probably have some degree of seasonality.

How do we know whether there is seasonality in a time series? The easiest way is to check whether a graph of the time series has a *regular* pattern of ups and/or downs in particular months or quarters. Although random noise can sometimes obscure such a pattern, the seasonal pattern is usually fairly obvious.

Some time series software packages have special types of graphs for spotting seasonality, but we don't discuss these here.

There are basically three methods for dealing with seasonality. First, we can use Winters' exponential smoothing model. It is similar to simple exponential smoothing and Holt's method, except that it includes another component (and smoothing constant) to capture seasonality. Second, we can *deseasonalize* the data, then use any of our forecasting methods to model the deseasonalized data, and finally "reseasonalize" these forecasts. Finally, we can use multiple regression with dummy variables for the seasons. We discuss all three of these methods in this section.

As we saw with the housing sales data, government agencies often perform part of the second method for us—that is, they deseasonalize the data.

Seasonal models are usually classified as *additive* or *multiplicative*. Suppose that we have monthly data, and that the average of the 12 monthly values for a typical year is 150. An **additive** model finds seasonal indexes, one for each month, that we *add* to the monthly average, 150, to get a particular month's value. For example, if the index for March is 22, then we expect a typical March value to be $150 + 22 = 172$. If the seasonal index for September is -12, then we expect a typical September value to be $150 - 12 = 138$. A **multiplicative** model also finds seasonal indexes, but we *multiply* the monthly average by these indexes to get a particular month's value. Now if the index for March is 1.3, we expect a typical March value to be $150(1.3) = 195$. If the index for September is 0.9, then we expect a typical September value to be $150(0.9) = 135$. These models are summarized here.

> In an **additive** seasonal model, we add an appropriate seasonal index to a "base" forecast. These indexes, one for each season, typically average to 0.

> In a **multiplicative** seasonal model, we multiply a "base" forecast by an appropriate seasonal index. These indexes, one for each season, typically average to 1.

Either an additive or a multiplicative model can be used to forecast seasonal data. However, because multiplicative models are somewhat easier to interpret (and have worked well in applications), we focus on them. Note that the seasonal index in a multiplicative model can be interpreted as a percentage. Using the figures in the previous paragraph as an example, March tends to be 30% above the monthly average, whereas September tends to be 10% below it. Also, the seasonal indexes in a multiplicative model should average to 1. Computer packages typically ensure that this happens.

13.9.1 Winters' Exponential Smoothing Model

We now turn to Winters' exponential smoothing model. It is very similar to Holt's model—it again has level and trend terms and corresponding smoothing constants α and β—but it also has seasonal indexes and a corresponding smoothing constant γ (gamma). This new smoothing constant γ controls how quickly the method reacts to perceived changes in the pattern of seasonality. If γ is small, the method reacts slowly. If it is large, the method reacts more quickly. As with Holt's model, there are equations for updating the level and trend terms, and there is one extra equation for updating the seasonal indexes. For completeness, we list these equations in the accompanying box, but they are clearly too complex for hand calculation and are best left to the computer. In equation (13.21), S_t refers to the multiplicative seasonal index for period t. In equations (13.19), (13.21), and (13.22), M refers to the number of seasons ($M = 4$ for quarterly data, $M = 12$ for monthly data).

Formulas for Winters' Exponential Smoothing Model

$$L_t = \alpha \frac{Y_t}{S_{t-M}} + (1 - \alpha)(L_{t-1} + T_{t-1}) \tag{13.19}$$

$$T_t = \beta(L_t - L_{t-1}) + (1 - \beta)T_{t-1} \tag{13.20}$$

$$S_t = \gamma \frac{Y_t}{L_t} + (1 - \gamma)S_{t-M} \tag{13.21}$$

$$F_{t+k} = (L_t + kT_t)S_{t+k-M} \tag{13.22}$$

To see how the forecasting in equation (13.22) works, suppose we have observed data through June and want a forecast for the coming September, that is, a 3-month-ahead forecast. (In this case t refers to June and $t + k = t + 3$ refers to September.) Then we first add 3 times the current trend term to the current level. This gives a forecast for September that would be appropriate if there were no seasonality. Next, we multiply this forecast by the most recent estimate of September's seasonal index (the one from the previous September) to get the forecast for September. Of course, the computer does all of the arithmetic, but this is basically what it is doing. We illustrate the method in the following example.

| EXAMPLE | 13.7 QUARTERLY SOFT DRINK SALES |

The data in the **Soft Drink Sales.xlsx** file represent quarterly sales (in millions of dollars) for a large soft drink company from quarter 1 of 1992 through quarter 1 of 2007. As we might expect, there has been an upward trend in sales during this period, and there is also a fairly regular seasonal pattern, as shown in Figure 13.50. Sales in the warmer quarters, 2 and 3, are consistently higher than in the colder quarters, 1 and 4. How well can Winters' method track this upward trend and seasonal pattern?

Figure 13.50 Time Series Graph of Soft Drink Sales

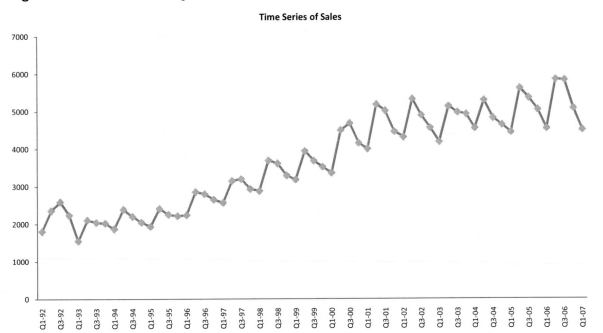

Objective To see how well Winters' method, with appropriate smoothing constants, can forecast the company's seasonal soft drink sales.

Solution

To use Winters' method with StatTools, we proceed exactly as with any of the other exponential smoothing methods. However, for a change (and because we have so many years of data), we use StatTools's option of holding out some of the data for validation. Specifically, we fill out the Time Scale tab in the Forecast dialog box as shown in Figure 13.51. Then we fill in the Forecast Settings tab of this dialog box as shown in Figure 13.52, selecting Winters' method, basing the model on the data through quarter 1, 2003, holding out 8 quarters of data (quarter 2,

2003, through quarter 1, 2005), and forecasting 4 quarters into the future. Note that when we choose Winters' method in Figure 13.52, the Deseasonalize option in Figure 13.51 is automatically disabled. It wouldn't make sense to deseasonalize *and* use Winters' method; we do one or the other. Also, we have elected to optimize the smoothing constants, but this is optional.

Figure 13.51

Time Scale Settings for Soft Drink Sales

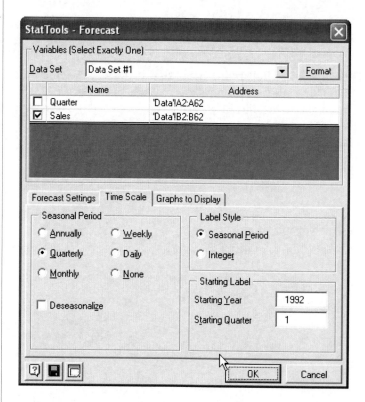

Figure 13.52

Forecast Settings for Soft Drink Sales

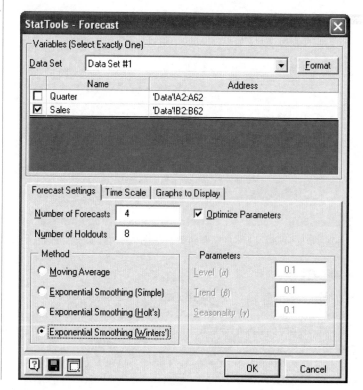

You can check that if we hold out 3 years of data, the MAPE for the holdout period increases quite a lot. It is common for the fit to be considerably better in the estimation period than in the holdout period.

Parts of the output are shown in Figure 13.53. The following points are worth noting: (1) The optimal smoothing constants (those that minimize RMSE) are $\alpha = 1.0$, $\beta = 0.0$, and $\gamma = 0.0$. Intuitively, these mean that we react right away to changes in level, but we never react to changes in trend or the seasonal pattern. (2) If we ignore seasonality, the series is trending upward at a rate of 56.05 per quarter (see column D). This is our initial estimate of trend and, because $\beta = 0$, it never changes. (3) The seasonal pattern stays constant throughout this 10-year period. The seasonal indexes, shown in column E, are 0.88, 1.10, 1.05, and 0.96. For example, quarter 1 is 12% below the yearly average, and quarter 2 is 10% above the yearly average. (4) The forecast series tracks the actual series quite well during the nonholdout period. For example, MAPE is 3.98%, meaning that on average our forecasts are off by about 4% on average. Surprisingly, MAPE for the holdout period is even lower, at 2.20%.

Figure 13.53 Output from Winters' Method for Soft Drink Sales

	A	B	C	D	E	F	G
7							
8	*Forecasting Constants (Optimized)*						
9	Level (Alpha)	1.000					
10	Trend (Beta)	0.000					
11	Season (Gamma)	0.000					
12							
13		Estimation	Holdouts				
14	*Winters' Exponential*	Period	Period				
15	Mean Abs Err	125.59	108.31				
16	Root Mean Sq Err	168.81	148.94				
17	Mean Abs Per% Err	3.98%	2.20%				
18							
41							
42	*Forecasting Data*	Sales	Level	Trend	Season	Forecast	Error
43	Q1-1992	1807.3700	2046.27	56.05	0.88		
44	Q2-1992	2355.3200	2140.57	56.05	1.10	2313.24	42.08
45	Q3-1992	2591.8300	2463.29	56.05	1.05	2311.24	280.59
46	Q4-1992	2236.3900	2319.32	56.05	0.96	2429.27	-192.88
47	Q1-1993	1549.1400	1753.91	56.05	0.88	2098.05	-548.91
48	Q2-1993	2105.7900	1913.79	56.05	1.10	1991.54	114.25
49	Q3-1993	2041.3200	1940.09	56.05	1.05	2072.63	-31.31
50	Q4-1993	2021.0100	2095.95	56.05	0.96	1924.76	96.25
92	Q2-2004	5284.7100	4802.87	56.05	1.10	5720.69	-435.98
93	Q3-2004	4817.4300	4578.52	56.05	1.05	5112.46	-295.03
94	Q4-2004	4634.5000	4806.36	56.05	0.96	4468.86	165.64
95	Q1-2005	4431.3600	5017.10	56.05	0.88	4294.73	136.63
96	Q2-2005	5602.2100				5582.11	20.10
97	Q3-2005	5349.8500				5396.85	-47.00
98	Q4-2005	5036.0000				4999.85	36.15
99	Q1-2006	4534.6100				4629.40	-94.79
100	Q2-2006	5836.1700				5828.82	7.35
101	Q3-2006	5818.2800				5632.76	185.52
102	Q4-2006	5070.4200				5216.05	-145.63
103	Q1-2007	4497.4700				4827.43	-329.96
104	Q2-2007					6075.52	
105	Q3-2007					5868.67	
106	Q4-2007					5432.24	
107	Q1-2008					5025.47	

The plot of the forecasts superimposed on the original series, shown in Figure 13.54, indicates that Winters' method clearly picks up the seasonal pattern and the upward trend and projects both of these into the future. In later examples, we investigate whether other seasonal forecasting methods can do this well.

Figure 13.54

Graph of Forecasts
from Winters'
Method

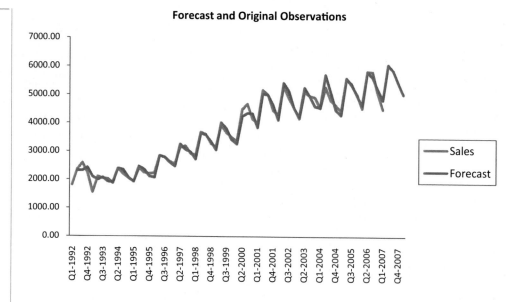

Forecast and Original Observations

One final comment is that we are not obligated to find the *optimal* smoothing constants. Some analysts might suggest using more "typical" values such as $\alpha = \beta = 0.2$ and $\gamma = 0.5$. (We often choose γ larger than α and β because each season's seasonal index gets updated only once per year.) To see how these smoothing constants affect the results, we can simply substitute their values in the range B9:B11 of Figure 13.53. As we would expect, MAE, RMSE, and MAPE all get somewhat worse (they increase to 184, 237, and 5.89%, respectively, for the estimation period), but a plot of the forecasts superimposed on the original sales data still indicates a very good fit. ∎

The three exponential smoothing methods we have examined are not the only ones available. For example, there are linear and quadratic models available in some software packages. These are somewhat similar to Holt's model except that they use only a single smoothing constant. There are also adaptive exponential smoothing models, where the smoothing constants themselves are allowed to change through time. Although these more complex models have been studied thoroughly in the academic literature and are used by some practitioners, they typically offer only marginal gains in forecast accuracy over the models we have examined.

13.9.2 Deseasonalizing: The Ratio-to-Moving-Averages Method

You have probably seen references to time series data that have been *deseasonalized*. In this section we discuss why this is done and how it is done. We also see how it can be used to forecast seasonal time series. First, data are often published in deseasonalized form so that readers can spot trends more easily. For example, if we see a time series of sales that has not been deseasonalized, and it shows a large increase from November to December, we might not be sure whether this represents a real increase in sales or a seasonal phenomenon (Christmas sales). However, if this increase is really just a seasonal effect, then the deseasonalized version of the series will show no such increase in sales.

Government economists and statisticians have a variety of sophisticated methods for deseasonalizing time series data, but they are typically variations of the **ratio-to-moving-averages** method described here. This method is applicable when we believe that seasonality is multiplicative, as described in the previous section. Our job is to find the seasonal indexes, which can then be used to deseasonalize the data. For example, if we estimate the index for June to be 1.3, this means that June's values are typically about 30% larger than the average for all months. Therefore, to deseasonalize a June value, we *divide* it by 1.3 (to make it smaller). Similarly, if February's index is 0.85, then February's values are 15% below the average for all months. So to deseasonalize a February value, we divide it by 0.85 (to make it larger).

> To **deseasonalize** an observation (assuming a multiplicative model of seasonality), *divide* it by the appropriate seasonal index.

To find the seasonal index for June 2005 (or any other month) in the first place, we essentially divide June's observation by the average of the 12 observations surrounding June. (This is the reason for the term "ratio" in the name of the method.) There is one minor problem with this approach. June 2005 is not exactly in the middle of any 12-month sequence. If we use the 12 months from January 2005 to December 2005, June 2005 is in the *first* half of the sequence; if we use the 12 months from December 2004 to November 2005, June 2005 is in the *last* half of the sequence. Therefore, we compromise by averaging the January-to-December and December-to-November averages. This is called a **centered** average. Then the seasonal index for June is June's observation divided by this centered average. The following equation shows more specifically how it works.

$$\text{Jun2005 index} = \frac{\text{Jun2005}}{\left(\frac{\text{Dec2004} + \cdots + \text{Nov2005}}{12} + \frac{\text{Jan2005} + \cdots + \text{Dec2005}}{12}\right)/2}$$

The only remaining question is how to combine all of the indexes for any specific month such as June. After all, if we have data for several years, the above procedure produces several June indexes, one for each year. The usual way to combine them is simply to average them. This single average index for June is then used to deseasonalize *all* of the June observations.

Once the seasonal indexes are obtained, we divide each observation by its seasonal index to deseasonalize the data. The deseasonalized data can then be forecasted by *any* of the methods we have described (other than Winters' method, which wouldn't make much sense). For example, we could use Holt's method or the moving averages method to forecast the deseasonalized data. Finally, we "reseasonalize" the forecasts by *multiplying* them by the seasonal indexes.

As this description suggests, the method is not meant for hand calculations! However, it is straightforward to implement in StatTools, as we illustrate in the following example.

| EXAMPLE | 13.7 QUARTERLY SOFT DRINK SALES (CONTINUED) |

We return to the soft drink sales data. (See the file **Soft Drink Sales.xlsx**.) Is it possible to obtain the same forecast accuracy with the ratio-to-moving-averages method as we obtained with Winters' method?

Objective To use the ratio-to-moving-averages method to deseasonalize the soft drink data and then forecast the deseasonalized data.

Solution

The answer to this question depends on which forecasting method we use to forecast the *deseasonalized* data. The ratio-to-moving-averages method only provides a means for deseasonalizing the data and providing seasonal indexes. Beyond this, any method can be used to forecast the deseasonalized data, and some methods obviously work better than others. For this example, we compared two possibilities: the moving averages method with a span of 4 quarters, and Holt's exponential smoothing method optimized. However, we show the results only for the latter. Because the deseasonalized series still has a clear upward trend, we would expect Holt's method to do well, and we would expect the moving averages forecasts to lag behind the trend. This is exactly what occurred. For example, the values of MAPE for the two methods are 8.33% (moving averages) and 3.98% (Holt's). (To make a fair comparison with the Winters' method output for these data, we again held out 8 quarters. The MAPE values reported are for the nonholdout period.)

To implement this latter method in StatTools, we proceed exactly as before, but this time we check the Deseasonalize option in the Time Scale tab of the Forecast dialog box. (See Figure 13.55.) Note that when the Holt's option is checked, this Deseasonalize option is enabled. When we check this option, we get a larger selection of optional charts in the Graphs to Display tab. We can see charts of the deseasonalized data and/or the original "reseasonalized" data.

Figure 13.55

Checking the
Deseasonalizing
Option

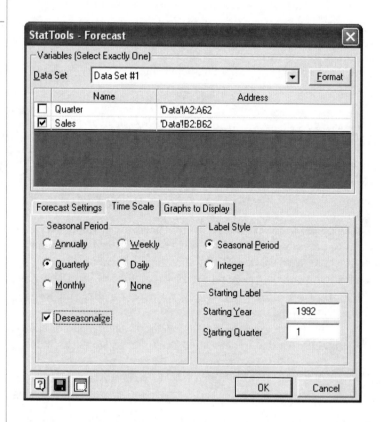

Selected outputs are shown in Figures 13.56 through 13.59. Figures 13.56 and 13.57 show the numerical output. In particular, Figure 13.57 shows the seasonal indexes from the ratio-to-moving averages method in column C. These are virtually identical to the seasonal indexes we found using Winters' method, although the methods are mathematically different. Column D contains the deseasonalized sales (column B divided by column C), columns E through H implement Holt's method on the deseasonalized data, and columns I and J are the "reseasonalized" forecasts and errors.

Figure 13.56

Summary Measures
for Forecast Errors

	A	B	C	D	E
8	**Forecasting Constants (Optimized)**				
9	Level (Alpha)	1.000			
10	Trend (Beta)	0.000			
11					
12		Estimation	Holdouts	Deseason	Deseason
13	**Holt's Exponential**	Period	Period	Estimate	Holdouts
14	Mean Abs Err	125.59	108.31	126.66	114.42
15	Root Mean Sq Err	168.81	148.94	171.57	161.54
16	Mean Abs Per% Err	3.98%	2.20%	3.98%	2.20%

Figure 13.57 Ratio-to-Moving-Averages Output

	A	B	C	D	E	F	G	H	I	J
61			Season	Deseason	Deseason	Deseason	Deseason	Deseason	Season	Season
62	Forecasting Data	Sales	Index	Sales	Level	Trend	Forecast	Errors	Forecast	Errors
63	Q1-1992	1807.3700	0.88	2046.27	2046.27	56.05				
64	Q2-1992	2355.3200	1.10	2140.57	2140.57	56.05	2102.32	38.25	2313.24	42.08
65	Q3-1992	2591.8300	1.05	2463.29	2463.29	56.05	2196.62	266.67	2311.24	280.59
66	Q4-1992	2236.3900	0.96	2319.32	2319.32	56.05	2519.35	-200.03	2429.27	-192.88
67	Q1-1993	1549.1400	0.88	1753.91	1753.91	56.05	2375.37	-621.47	2098.05	-548.91
68	Q2-1993	2105.7900	1.10	1913.79	1913.79	56.05	1809.96	103.83	1991.54	114.25
69	Q3-1993	2041.3200	1.05	1940.09	1940.09	56.05	1969.84	-29.76	2072.63	-31.31
70	Q4-1993	2021.0100	0.96	2095.95	2095.95	56.05	1996.14	99.81	1924.76	96.25
112	Q2-2004	5284.7100	1.10	4802.87	4802.87	56.05	5199.09	-396.23	5720.69	-435.98
113	Q3-2004	4817.4300	1.05	4578.52	4578.52	56.05	4858.92	-280.40	5112.46	-295.03
114	Q4-2004	4634.5000	0.96	4806.36	4806.36	56.05	4634.58	171.78	4468.86	165.64
115	Q1-2005	4431.3600	0.88	5017.10	5017.10	56.05	4862.41	154.69	4294.73	136.63
116	Q2-2005	5602.2100	1.10	5091.42			5073.15	18.27	5582.11	20.10
117	Q3-2005	5349.8500	1.05	5084.54			5129.20	-44.67	5396.85	-47.00
118	Q4-2005	5036.0000	0.96	5222.75			5185.26	37.49	4999.85	36.15
119	Q1-2006	4534.6100	0.88	5133.99			5241.31	-107.32	4629.40	-94.79
120	Q2-2006	5836.1700	1.10	5304.05			5297.36	6.68	5828.82	7.35
121	Q3-2006	5818.2800	1.05	5529.74			5353.42	176.32	5632.76	185.52
122	Q4-2006	5070.4200	0.96	5258.44			5409.47	-151.03	5216.05	-145.63
123	Q1-2007	4497.4700	0.88	5091.95			5465.52	-373.58	4827.43	-329.96
124	Q2-2007		1.10				5521.58		6075.52	
125	Q3-2007		1.05				5577.63		5868.67	
126	Q4-2007		0.96				5633.68		5432.24	
127	Q1-2008		0.88				5689.74		5025.47	

Figure 13.58

Forecast Graph of
Deseasonalized
Series

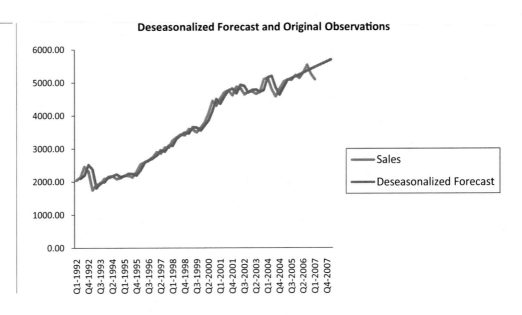

Deseasonalized Forecast and Original Observations

— Sales
— Deseasonalized Forecast

Figure 13.59

Forecast Graph of
Reseasonalized
(Original) Series

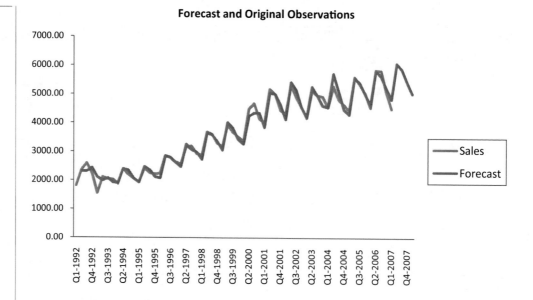

Forecast and Original Observations

The deseasonalized data, with forecasts superimposed, appear in Figure 13.58. Here we see only the smooth upward trend with no seasonality, which Holt's method is able to track very well. Then Figure 13.59 shows the results of reseasonalizing. Again, the forecasts track the actual sales data very well. In fact, we see that the summary measures of forecast errors (in Figure 13.56, range B14:B16) are quite comparable to those from Winters' method. The reason is that both arrive at virtually the same seasonal pattern. ■

13.9.3 Estimating Seasonality with Regression

We now examine a regression approach to forecasting seasonal data that uses dummy variables for the seasons. Depending on how we write the regression equation, we can create either an additive or a multiplicative seasonal model.

As an example, suppose that the data are quarterly data with a possible linear trend. Then we can introduce dummy variables Q_1, Q_2, and Q_3 for the first three quarters (using quarter 4 as the reference quarter) and estimate the additive equation

$$\hat{Y}_t = a + bt + b_1Q_1 + b_2Q_2 + b_3Q_3$$

Then the coefficients of the dummy variables, b_1, b_2 and b_3, indicate how much each quarter differs from the reference quarter, quarter 4, and the coefficient b represent the trend.

For example, if the estimated equation is

$$\hat{Y}_t = 130 + 25t + 15Q_1 + 5Q_2 - 20Q_3$$

then the average increase from one quarter to the next is 25 (the coefficient of t). This is the trend effect. However, quarter 1 averages 15 units higher than quarter 4, quarter 2 averages 5 units higher than quarter 4, and quarter 3 averages 20 units lower than quarter 4. These coefficients indicate the seasonality effect.

As discussed in Chapter 11, it is also possible to estimate a *multiplicative* model using dummy variables for seasonality (and possibly time for trend). Then we would estimate the equation

$$\hat{Y}_t = ae^{bt}e^{b_1Q_1}e^{b_2Q_2}e^{b_3Q_3}$$

or, after taking logs,

$$\ln \hat{Y}_t = \ln a + bt + b_1Q_1 + b_2Q_2 + b_3Q_3$$

One advantage of this approach is that it provides a model with *multiplicative* seasonal factors. It is also fairly easy to interpret the regression output, as illustrated in the following continuation of the soft drink sales example.

EXAMPLE | **13.7 QUARTERLY SOFT DRINK SALES (CONTINUED)**

Returning to the soft drink sales data (see the file **Soft Drink Sales.xlsx**), does a regression approach provide forecasts that are as accurate as those provided by the other seasonal methods in this chapter?

Objective To use a multiplicative regression equation, with dummy variables for seasons and a time variable for trend, to model soft drink sales.

Solution

We illustrate the multiplicative approach, although an additive approach is also possible. Figure 13.60 illustrates the data setup. Besides the Sales and Time variables, we need dummy variables for three of the four quarters (we created these manually), and a Log(Sales) variable. We then use multiple regression, with Log(Sales) as the dependent variable, and Time, Q1, Q2, and Q3 as the explanatory variables.

Figure 13.60

Data Setup for Multiplicative Model with Dummies

	A	B	C	D	E	F	G
1	Quarter	Sales	Time	Q1	Q2	Q3	Log(Sales)
2	Q1-92	1807.37	1	1	0	0	7.499628
3	Q2-92	2355.32	2	0	1	0	7.7644319
4	Q3-92	2591.83	3	0	0	1	7.8601195
5	Q4-92	2236.39	4	0	0	0	7.7126182
6	Q1-93	1549.14	5	1	0	0	7.3454552
7	Q2-93	2105.79	6	0	1	0	7.652446
8	Q3-93	2041.32	7	0	0	1	7.6213519
9	Q4-93	2021.01	8	0	0	0	7.6113527
10	Q1-94	1870.46	9	1	0	0	7.5339397
11	Q2-94	2390.56	10	0	1	0	7.7792829
12	Q3-94	2198.03	11	0	0	1	7.6953168
13	Q4-94	2046.83	12	0	0	0	7.6240475
14	Q1-95	1934.19	13	1	0	0	7.5674439
15	Q2-95	2406.41	14	0	1	0	7.7858913

The regression output appears in Figure 13.61. (Again, to make a fair comparison with previous methods, we base the regression only on the data through quarter 1 of 2005. That is, we again hold out the last 8 quarters. This means that the StatTools data set should be redefined so that it extends only through row 54.) Of particular interest are the coefficients of the explanatory variables. Recall that for a log dependent variable, these coefficients can be interpreted as *percentage* changes in the original sales variable. Specifically, the coefficient of Time means that deseasonalized sales increase by about 2.1% per quarter. Also, the coefficients of Q1, Q2, and Q3 mean that sales in quarters 1, 2, and 3 are, respectively, about 8.4% below, 14.0% above, and 8.9% above sales in the reference quarter, quarter 4. This pattern is quite comparable to the pattern of seasonal indexes we saw in previous models for these data.

Figure 13.61 Regression Output for Multiplicative Model

	A	B	C	D	E	F	G
7		Multiple	R-Square	Adjusted	StErr of		
8	Summary	R		R-Square	Estimate		
9		0.9660	0.9332	0.9276	0.0945		
10							
11		Degrees of	Sum of	Mean of			
12	ANOVA Table	Freedom	Squares	Squares	F-Ratio	p-Value	
13	Explained	4	5.9813	1.4953	167.6184	< 0.0001	
14	Unexplained	48	0.4282	0.0089			
15							
16			Standard			Confidence Interval 95%	
17	Regression Table	Coefficient	Error	t-Value	p-Value	Lower	Upper
18	Constant	7.4689	0.0354	211.1359	< 0.0001	7.3977	7.5400
19	Time	0.0214	0.0008	25.1710	< 0.0001	0.0197	0.0231
20	Q1	-0.0836	0.0364	-2.2973	0.0260	-0.1568	-0.0104
21	Q2	0.1402	0.0371	3.7806	0.0004	0.0656	0.2148
22	Q3	0.0894	0.0371	2.4122	0.0197	0.0149	0.1639

To compare the forecast accuracy of this method with earlier models, we must go through several steps manually. (See Figure 13.62 for reference.) We first calculate the forecasts in column H by entering the formula

=EXP(Regression!$B$18+MMULT(Data!C2:F2,Regression!$B$19:$B$22))

in cell H2 and copying it down. (This formula assumes the regression output is in a sheet named Regression. It uses Excel's MMULT function to sum the products of explanatory values and regression coefficients. You can replace this by "writing out" the sum of products if you like. The formula then takes EXP of the resulting sum to convert the log sales value back to the original sales units.) Next, we calculate the absolute errors, squared errors, and absolute percentage errors in columns I, J, and K, and we summarize them in the usual way, both for the estimation period and the holdout period, in columns N and O.

Note that these summary measures are considerably larger for this regression model than for the previous seasonality models, especially in the holdout period. We can get some idea why the holdout period does so poorly by looking at the plot of observations versus forecasts in Figure 13.63. The multiplicative regression model with Time included really implies *exponential* growth (as in Section 13.4.2), with seasonality superimposed. However, this company's sales growth tapered off in the last couple of years and did not keep up with the exponential growth curve. In short, the dummy variables do a good job of tracking seasonality, but the underlying exponential trend curve outpaces actual sales. We conclude that this regression model is *not* as good for forecasting this company's sales as Winters' method or Holt's method on the deseasonalized data.

Figure 13.62 Forecast Errors and Summary Measures

	A	B	C	D	E	F	G	H	I	J	K	L	M	N	O
1	Quarter	Sales	Time	Q1	Q2	Q3	Log(Sales)	Forecast	SqError	AbsError	PctAbsError		Error measures		
2	Q1-92	1807.37	1	1	0	0	7.499628	1646.863	25762.59	160.5073	0.0888071			Estimation	Holdout
3	Q2-92	2355.32	2	0	1	0	7.7644319	2104.437	62942.35	250.8831	0.10651764		RMSE	319.38	1035.32
4	Q3-92	2591.83	3	0	0	1	7.8601195	2043.366	300812.4	548.4637	0.21161252		MAE	244.81	1010.96
5	Q4-92	2236.39	4	0	0	0	7.7126182	1909.004	107181.4	327.3857	0.14639024		MAPE	7.28%	19.71%
6	Q1-93	1549.14	5	1	0	0	7.3454552	1793.833	59874.7	244.6931	0.15795414				
7	Q2-93	2105.79	6	0	1	0	7.652446	2292.242	34764.48	186.4524	0.08854271				
8	Q3-93	2041.32	7	0	0	1	7.6213519	2225.722	34004	184.4017	0.09033455				
9	Q4-93	2021.01	8	0	0	0	7.6113527	2079.369	3405.764	58.35892	0.02887612				
10	Q1-94	1870.46	9	1	0	0	7.5339397	1953.919	6965.484	83.45947	0.04461976				
11	Q2-94	2390.56	10	0	1	0	7.7792829	2496.808	11288.66	106.2481	0.04444486				
12	Q3-94	2198.03	11	0	0	1	7.6953168	2424.351	51221.2	226.321	0.10296538				
13	Q4-94	2046.83	12	0	0	0	7.6240475	2264.937	47570.79	218.1073	0.10655858				
14	Q1-95	1934.19	13	1	0	0	7.5674439	2128.292	37675.74	194.1024	0.10035333				

Figure 13.63 Graph of Forecasts for Multiplicative Model

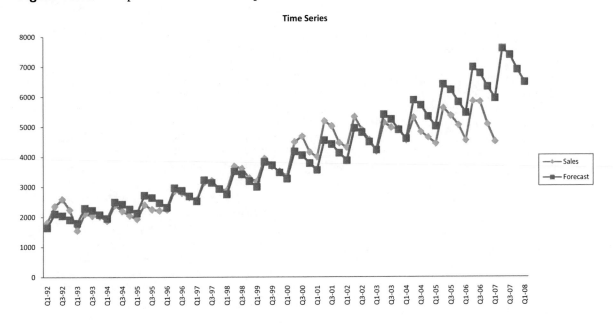

This method of detecting seasonality by using dummy variables in a regression equation is always an option. The other variables included in the regression equation could be time t, lagged versions of Y_t, and/or current or lagged versions of other independent variables. These variables would capture any time series behavior other than seasonality. Just remember that there is always one less dummy variable than the number of seasons. If the data are quarterly, then three dummies are needed; if the data are monthly, then 11 dummies are needed. If the coefficients of any of these dummies turn out to be statistically insignificant, they can be omitted from the equation. Then the omitted terms are effectively combined with the reference season. For example, if the Q_1 term were omitted, then quarters 1 and 4 would essentially be combined and treated as the reference season, and the other two seasons would be compared to them through their dummy variable coefficients. ■

PROBLEMS

Level A

51. The University Credit Union is open Monday through Saturday. Winters' method is being used (with $\alpha = \beta = \gamma = 0.5$) to predict the number of customers entering the bank each day. After incorporating the arrivals of 16 October, $L_t = 200$, $T_t = 1$, and the "seasonalities" are as follows: Monday, 0.90; Tuesday, 0.70; Wednesday, 0.80; Thursday, 1.1; Friday, 1.2; Saturday, 1.3. For example, the number of customers entering the bank on a typical Monday is 90% of the number of customers entering the bank on an average day. On Tuesday, 17 October, 182 customers enter the bank. At the close of business on 17 October, forecast the number of customers who will enter the bank on 25 October.

52. Last National Bank is using Winters' method (with $\alpha = 0.2$, $\beta = 0.1$, and $\gamma = 0.5$) to forecast the number of customers served each day. The bank is open Monday through Friday. At present, the following "seasonalities" have been estimated: Monday, 0.80; Tuesday, 0.90; Wednesday, 0.95; Thursday, 1.10; Friday, 1.25. A seasonality of 0.80 for Monday means that on a Monday, the number of customers served by the bank tends to be 80% of the average daily value. Currently, the level is estimated to be 20 customers, and the trend is estimated to equal 1 customer. After observing that 30 customers are served by the bank on Monday, forecast the number of customers who will be served by the bank on Wednesday.

53. Suppose that Winters' method is used to forecast quarterly U.S. retail sales (in billions of dollars). At the end of the first quarter of 2006, $L_t = 300$, $T_t = 30$, and the seasonal indexes are as follows: quarter 1, 0.90; quarter 2, 0.95; quarter 3, 0.95; quarter 4, 1.20. During the second quarter of 2006, retail sales are $360 billion. Assume $\alpha = 0.2$, $\beta = 0.4$, and $\gamma = 0.5$.
   a. At the end of the second quarter of 2006, develop a forecast for retail sales during the fourth quarter of 2006.
   b. At the end of the second quarter of 2006, develop a forecast for the second quarter of 2007.

54. The file **P02_38.xlsx** contains monthly retail sales of U.S. liquor stores.

   a. Is seasonality present in these data? If so, characterize the seasonality pattern and then deseasonalize this time series using the ratio-to-moving-average method.
   b. If you decided to deseasonalize this time series in part **a**, forecast the deseasonalized data for each month of the next year using the moving average method with an appropriate span.
   c. Does Holt's exponential smoothing method, with optimal smoothing constants, outperform the moving average method employed in part **b**? Demonstrate why or why not.

55. Continuing the previous problem, how do your responses to the questions change when you employ Winters' method to handle seasonality in this time series? Explain. Which forecasting method do you prefer, Winters' method or a method used in the previous problem? Defend your choice.

56. The file **P02_39.xlsx** contains monthly time series data for total U.S. retail sales of building materials (which includes retail sales of building materials, hardware and garden supply stores, and mobile home dealers).
   a. Is seasonality present in these data? If so, characterize the seasonality pattern and then deseasonalize this time series using the ratio-to-moving-average method.
   b. If you decided to deseasonalize this time series in part **a**, forecast the deseasonalized data for each month of the next year using the moving average method with an appropriate span.
   c. Does Holt's exponential smoothing method, with optimal smoothing constants, outperform the moving average method employed in part **b**? Demonstrate why or why not.

57. The file **P02_40.xlsx** consists of the monthly retail sales levels of U.S. gasoline service stations.
   a. Is there a seasonal pattern in these data? If so, how do you explain this seasonal pattern? Also, if necessary, deseasonalize these data using the ratio-to-moving-average method.
   b. Forecast this time series for the first 4 months of the next year using the most appropriate method for these data. Defend your choice of forecasting method.

58. The number of employees on the payroll at a food processing plant is recorded at the start of each month. These data are provided in the file **P13_03.xlsx**.
   a. Is there a seasonal pattern in these data? If so, how do you explain this seasonal pattern? Also, if necessary, deseasonalize these data using the ratio-to-moving-average method.
   b. Forecast this time series for the first 4 months of the next year using the most appropriate method. Defend your choice of forecasting method.

59. Consider the file **P02_37.xlsx**, which contains total monthly U.S. retail sales data. Compare the effectiveness of Winters' method with that of the ratio-to-moving-average method in deseasonalizing this time series. Using the deseasonalized time series generated by each of these two methods, forecast U.S. retail sales with the most appropriate method. Defend your choice of forecasting method.

60. Suppose that a time series consisting of 6 years (2000–2005) of quarterly data exhibits definite seasonality. In fact, assume that the seasonal indexes turn out to be 0.75, 1.45, 1.25, and 0.55.
   a. If the last four observations of the series (the four quarters of 2005) are 2502, 4872, 4269, and 1924, calculate the deseasonalized values for the four quarters of 2005.
   b. Suppose that a plot of the deseasonalized series shows an upward linear trend, except for some random noise. Therefore, a linear regression of this series versus time is estimated, and it produces the equation

Predicted deseasonalized value
$$= 2250 + 51\text{Quarter}$$

Here the time variable "Quarter" is coded so that Quarter = 1 corresponds to first quarter 2000, Quarter = 24 corresponds to fourth quarter 2005, and the others fall in between. Forecast the actual (not deseasonalized) values for the four quarters of 2006.

61. The file **P13_61.xlsx** contains monthly data on federal receipts of taxes. There are two variables: IndTax (taxes from individuals) and CorpTax (corporate taxes). For this problem, work only with IndTax.
   a. What evidence is there that seasonality is important in this series? Find seasonal indexes (by any method you like) and state briefly what they mean.
   b. Forecast the next 12 months by using a linear trend on the seasonally adjusted data. State briefly the steps you use to get this type of forecast, give the final RMSE, MAPE, and forecast for the next month. Then show numerically how you could replicate this forecast (i.e., show on paper how the package uses its estimated model to get the next month forecast). (Substitute in specific numbers, and do the arithmetic.)

62. Quarterly sales for a department store over a 6-year period are given in the file **P13_62.xlsx**.
   a. Use multiple regression to develop a model that can be used to predict future quarterly sales. (*Hint*: Use dummy variables and an explanatory variable for the quarter number, 1–24.)
   b. Letting Y_t be the sales during quarter number t, discuss how to fit the following model to these data.

$$Y_t = \alpha\beta^t{}_1\beta_2{}^{X_1}\beta_3{}^{X_2}\beta_4{}^{X_3}$$

Here $X_1 = 1$ if t is a first quarter, 0 otherwise; $X_2 = 1$ if t is a second quarter, 0 otherwise; and $X_3 = 1$ if t is a third quarter, 0 otherwise.
   a. Interpret the answer to part **b**.
   b. Which model appears to yield better predictions for sales, the one in part **a** or the one in part **b**?

63. Confederate Express Service is attempting to determine how its shipping costs for a month depend on the number of units shipped during a month. The number of units shipped and total shipping cost for the last 15 months are given in the file **P13_63.xlsx**.
   a. Determine a relationship between units shipped and monthly shipping cost.
   b. Plot the errors for the predictions in order of time sequence. Is there any unusual pattern?
   c. We have been told that there was a trucking strike during months 11 through 15, and we believe that this might have influenced shipping costs. How could the answer to part **a** be modified to account for the effect of the strike? After accounting for this effect, does the unusual pattern in part **b** disappear?

Level B

64. In our discussion of Winters' method, a monthly seasonality of 0.80 for January, say, means that during January, air conditioner (AC) sales are expected to be 80% of the sales during an average month. An alternative approach to modeling seasonality, called an **additive model**, is to let the seasonality factor for each month represent how far above average AC sales will be during the current month. For instance, if $S_{\text{Jan}} = -50$, then AC sales during January are expected to be 50 fewer than AC sales during an average month. (This is 50 ACs, not 50%.) If $S_{\text{July}} = 90$, then AC sales during July are expected to be 90 more than AC sales during an average month. Let

S_t = Seasonality for month t after observing month t demand

L_t = Estimate of level after observing month t demand

T_t = Estimate of trend after observing month t demand

Then the Winters' method equations given in the text should be modified as follows:

$$L_t = \alpha(I) + (1 - \alpha)(L_{t-1} + T_{t-1})$$

$$T_t = \beta(L_t - L_{t-1}) + (1 - \beta)T_{t-1}$$
$$S_t = \gamma(II) + (1 - \gamma)S_{t-12}$$

a. What should (*I*) and (*II*) be?

b. Suppose that month 13 is January, $L_{12} = 30$, $T_{12} = -3$, $S_1 = -50$, and $S_2 = -20$. Let $\alpha = \gamma = \beta = 0.5$. Suppose 12 ACs are sold during month 13. At the end of month 13, what is the prediction for AC sales during month 14 using this additive model?

65. Winters' method assumes a multiplicative seasonality but an additive trend. For example, a trend of 5 means that the level will increase by 5 units per period. Suppose that there is actually a *multiplicative* trend. Then (ignoring seasonality) if the current estimate of the level is 50 and the current estimate of the trend is 1.2, we would predict demand to increase by 20% per period. So we would forecast the next period's demand to be 50(1.2) and forecast the demand 2 periods in the future to be $50(1.2)^2$. If we want to use a multiplicative trend in Winters' method, we should use the following equations (assuming a period is a month):

$$L_t = \alpha\left(\frac{Y_t}{S_{t-12}}\right) + (1 - \alpha)(I)$$

$$T_t = \beta(II) + (1 - \beta)\,T_{t-1}$$

$$S_t = \gamma\left(\frac{Y_t}{L_t}\right) + (1 - \gamma)S_{t-12}$$

a. What should (*I*) and (*II*) be?

b. Suppose that we are working with monthly data and month 12 is December, month 13 is January, and so on. Also suppose that $L_{12} = 100$, $T_{12} = 1.2$, $S_1 = 0.90$, $S_2 = 0.70$, and $S_3 = 0.95$. Also, suppose $Y_{13} = 200$. At the end of month 13, what is the prediction for Y_{15} using $\alpha = \beta = \gamma = 0.5$ and a multiplicative trend?

66. Consider the file **P02_37.xlsx**, which contains total monthly U.S. retail sales data. Does a regression approach for estimating seasonality provide forecasts that are as accurate as those provided by (a) Winters' method and (b) the ratio-to-moving-average method? Compare the summary measures of forecast errors associated with each method for deseasonalizing the given time series. Summarize your findings after performing these comparisons.

67. The file **P02_39.xlsx** contains monthly time series data for total U.S. retail sales of building materials (which includes retail sales of building materials, hardware and garden supply stores, and mobile home dealers). Does a regression approach for estimating seasonality provide forecasts that are as accurate as those provided by (a) Winters' method and (b) the ratio-to-moving-average method? Compare the summary measures of forecast errors associated with each method for deseasonalizing the given time series. Summarize your findings after performing these comparisons.

13.10 CONCLUSION

We have covered a lot of ground in this chapter. Because forecasting is such an important activity in business, it has received a tremendous amount of attention by both academicians and practitioners. All of the methods discussed in this chapter—and more—are actually used, often on a day-to-day basis. There is really no point in arguing which of these methods is best. All of them have their strengths and weaknesses. The most important point is that when they are applied properly, they have all been found to be useful in real business situations.

Summary of Key Terms

Term	Explanation	Excel	Page	Equation Number
Extrapolation methods	Forecasting methods where only past values of a variable (and possibly time itself) are used to forecast future values		715	
Causal (or econometric) methods	Forecasting methods based on regression, where other time series variables are used as explanatory variables		716	
Trend	A systematic increase or decrease of a time series variable through time		718	

(continued)

Term	Explanation	Excel	Page	Equation Number
Seasonality	A regular pattern of ups and downs based on the season of the year, typically months or quarters		718	
Cyclic variation	An irregular pattern of ups and downs caused by business cycles		718	
Noise (or random variation)	The unpredictable ups and downs of a time series variable		719	
Mean absolute error (MAE)	The average of the absolute forecast errors	StatTools/ Time Series & Forecasting/Forecast	721	13.2
Root mean square error (RMSE)	The square root of the average of the squared forecast errors	StatTools/ Time Series & Forecasting/Forecast	721	13.3
Mean absolute percentage error (MAPE)	The average of the absolute percentage forecast errors	StatTools/ Time Series & Forecasting/Forecast	721	13.4
Runs test	A test of whether the forecast errors are random noise	StatTools/ Time Series & Forecasting/ Runs Test for Randomness	724	
Autocorrelations of residuals	Correlations of forecast errors with themselves, used to check whether they are random noise	StatTools/ Time Series & Forecasting/ Autocorrelation	726	
Correlogram	A bar chart of autocorrelations at different lags	StatTools/ Time Series & Forecasting/ Autocorrelation	727	
Linear trend model	A regression model where a time series variable changes by a constant amount each time period	StatTools/ Regression & Classification/ Regression	729	13.6
Exponential trend model	A regression model where a time series variable changes by a constant percentage each time period	StatTools/ Regression & Classification/ Regression	732	13.7
Random walk model	A model indicating that the differences between adjacent observations of a time series variable are constant except for random noise		738	13.9–13.11
Autoregression model	A regression model where the only explanatory variables are lagged values of the dependent variable	StatTools/ Regression & Classification/ Regression	741	
Moving averages model	A forecasting model where the average of several past observations is used to forecast the next observation	StatTools/ Time Series & Forecasting/ Forecast	746	

(continued)

Term	Explanation	Excel	Page	Equation Number
Span	The number of observations in each average of a moving averages model	StatTools/ Time Series & Forecasting/ Forecast	746	
Exponential smoothing models	A class of forecasting models where forecasts are based on weighted averages of previous observations, giving more weight to more recent observations	StatTools/ Time Series & Forecasting/ Forecast	753	
Smoothing constants	Constants between 0 and 1 that prescribe the weight attached to previous observations and hence the smoothness of the series of forecasts	StatTools/ Time Series & Forecasting/ Forecast	753	
Simple exponential smoothing	An exponential smoothing model useful for time series with no prominent trend or seasonality	StatTools/ Time Series & Forecasting/ Forecast	753	13.12–13.15
Holt's method	An exponential smoothing model useful for time series with trend but no seasonality	StatTools/ Time Series & Forecasting/ Forecast	753	13.16–13.18
Winters' method	An exponential smoothing model useful for time series with seasonality (and possibly trend)	StatTools/ Time Series & Forecasting/ Forecast	753	13.19–13.22
Deseasonalizing	A method for removing the seasonal component from time series data	StatTools/ Time Series & Forecasting/ Forecast	768	
Ratio-to-moving-averages method	A method for deseasonalizing a time series, so that some other method can then be used to forecast the deseasonalized series	StatTools/ Time Series & Forecasting/ Forecast	768	
Dummy variables for seasonality	A regression-based method for forecasting seasonality, where dummy variables are used for the seasons	StatTools/ Regression & Classification/ Regression	772	

PROBLEMS

Conceptual Exercises

C.1. "A truly random series will likely have a very small number of runs." Is this statement true or false? Explain your choice.

C.2. Distinguish between a *correlation* and an *autocorrelation.* How are these measures similar? How are these measures different?

C.3. What is the relationship between the random walk model and the autoregression model?

C.4. Under what conditions would you prefer a simple exponential smoothing model to the moving averages method for forecasting a time series?

C.5. Is it more appropriate to use an *additive* or a *multiplicative* model to forecast seasonal data? Summarize the difference(s) between these two types of seasonal models.

Level A

68. The file **P13_68.xlsx** contains quarterly revenues of Toys "R" Us. Discuss the seasonal and trend components of the growth of Toys "R" Us revenues. Also, use any reasonable forecasting method to forecast quarterly revenues for the next year. Explain your choice of forecasting method.

69. The file **P13_69.xlsx** contains quarterly revenues and earnings per share (EPS) for the following companies: Mattel, McDonald's, Eli Lilly, General Motors, Microsoft, AT&T, Nike, GE, Coca-Cola, and Ford.
  a. For each company, use a regression model with trend and seasonal components to forecast revenues and EPS.
  b. For each company, use Winters' method to forecast revenues and EPS.
  c. For each company, which method appears to be more accurate?

70. The file **P13_70.xlsx** contains the sales in (millions of dollars) for Sun Microsystems.
  a. Use these data to predict the company's sales for the next 2 years. You need consider only a linear and exponential trend, but you should justify the equation you choose.
  b. In words, how do your predictions of sales increase from year to year?
  c. Are there any outliers?

71. The file **P13_71.xlsx** contains the sales in (millions of dollars) for Procter & Gamble.
  a. Use these data to predict Procter & Gamble sales for the next 2 years. You need consider only a linear and exponential trend, but you should justify the equation you choose.
  b. Use your answer from part **a** to explain how your predictions of Procter & Gamble sales increase from year to year.
  c. Are there any outliers?
  d. We can be approximately 95% sure that Procter & Gamble sales in the year following next year will be between what two values?

72. The file **P13_72.xlsx** lists the sales of Nike. Forecast sales in the next 2 years with a linear or exponential trend. Are there any outliers in your predictions for the observed period?

73. The file **P12_44.xlsx** contains data on pork sales. Price is in dollars per hundred pounds sold, quantity sold is in billions of pounds, per capita income is in dollars, U.S. population is in millions, and GNP is in billions of dollars.
  a. Use these data to develop a regression equation that could be used to predict the quantity of pork sold during future periods. Is autocorrelation, heteroscedasticity, or multicollinearity a problem?

b. Suppose that during each of the next two quarters, price is $45, U.S. population is 240, GNP is 2620, and per capita income is $10,000. (All of these are expressed in the units described above.) Predict the quantity of pork sold during each of the next 2 quarters.
  c. We expect our prediction of pork sales to be accurate within what value 68% of the time?
  d. Use Winters' method to develop a forecast of pork sales during the next 2 quarters.

74. The file **P13_74.xlsx** contains data on a motel chain's revenue and advertising.
  a. Use these data and multiple regression to make predictions of the motel chain's revenues during the next 4 quarters. Assume that advertising during each of the next 4 quarters is $50,000. (*Hint*: Try using advertising, lagged by 1 quarter, as an explanatory variable.)
  b. Use simple exponential smoothing to make predictions for the motel chain's revenues during the next 4 quarters.
  c. Use Holt's method to make forecasts for the motel chain's revenues during the next 4 quarters.
  d. Use Winters' method to determine predictions for the motel chain's revenues during the next 4 quarters.
  e. Which of these forecasting methods would you expect to be the most reliable for these data?

75. The file **P13_75.xlsx** contains data on monthly U.S. housing sales (in thousands of houses).
  a. Using Winters' method, find values of α, β, and γ that yield an RMSE as small as possible.
  b. Although we have not discussed autocorrelation for smoothing methods, good forecasts derived from smoothing methods should exhibit no autocorrelation. Do the forecast errors for this problem exhibit autocorrelation?
  c. At the end of the observed period, what is the forecast of housing sales during the next few months?

76. Let Y_t be the sales during month t (in thousands of dollars) for a photography studio, and let P_t be the price charged for portraits during month t. The data are in the file **P12_45.xlsx**. Use regression to fit the following model to these data:

$$Y_t = \alpha + \beta_1 Y_{t-1} + \beta_2 P_t + \epsilon_t$$

This equation indicates that last month's sales and the current month's price are explanatory variables. The last term, ϵ_t, is an error term.
  a. If the price of a portrait during month 21 is $10, what would we predict for sales in month 21?
  b. Does there appear to be a problem with autocorrelation, heteroscedasticity, or multicollinearity?

77. The file **P13_77.xlsx** gives quarterly auto sales, GNP, interest rates and unemployment rates.

a. With all but the most recent 2 years of data, use regression to forecast auto sales. Interpret the coefficients in your final equation.

b. Use all but the most recent 2 years of data to develop an exponential smoothing model to forecast future auto sales.

c. To *validate* your model, determine which model does the best job of forecasting for the most recent 2 years of data. It is usually recommended to hold out some of your data to validate any forecast model. This helps avoid "overfitting."

Level B

78. The file **P13_78.xlsx** contains monthly time series data on corporate bond yields. These are averages of daily figures, and each is expressed as an annual rate. The variables are:

- YieldAAA: average yield on AAA bonds
- YieldBAA: average yield on BAA bonds

If you examine either Yield variable, you will notice that the autocorrelations of the series are not only large for many lags, but that the lag 1 autocorrelation of the *differences* is significant. This is very common. It means that the series is not a random walk and that it is probably possible to provide a better forecast than the "naive" forecast from the random walk model. Here is the idea. The large lag 1 autocorrelation of the differences means that the differences are related to the first lag of the differences. This relationship can be estimated by creating the difference variable and a lag of it, then regressing the former on the latter, and finally using this information to forecast the original Yield variable.

a. Verify that the autocorrelations are as described, and form the difference variable and the first lag of it. Call these DYield and L1DYield (where D is for difference, L1 is for first lag).

b. Run a regression with DYield as the dependent variable and L1DYield as the single explanatory variable. In terms of the original variable Yield, this equation can be written as

$$\text{Yield}_t - \text{Yield}_{t-1} = a + b(\text{Yield}_{t-1} - \text{Yield}_{t-2})$$

Solving for Yield_t is equivalent to the following equation that can be used for forecasting:

$$\text{Yield}_t = a + (1 + b)\text{Yield}_{t-1} - b\text{Yield}_{t-2}$$

Try it—that is, try forecasting the next month from the known last 2 months' values. How might you forecast values 2 or 3 months from the last observed month? (*Hint*: If you do not have an *observed* value to use in the right side of the equation, use a forecasted value.)

c. The autocorrelation structure led us to the equation in part **b**. That is, the autocorrelations of the original series took a long time to die down, so we

looked at the autocorrelations of the differences, and the large spike at lag 1 led to regressing DYield on L1DYield. In turn, this led ultimately to an equation for Yield$_t$ in terms of its first two lags. Now see what you would have obtained if you had tried regressing Yield$_t$ on its first two lags in the first place—that is, if you had used regression to estimate the equation

$$\text{Yield}_t = a + b_1 \text{Yield}_{t-1} + b_2 \text{Yield}_{t-2}$$

When you use multiple regression to estimate this equation, do you get the same equation as in part **b**?

79. The file **P13_79.xlsx** contains 5 years of monthly data for a particular company. The first variable is Time (1–60). The second variable, Sales1, has data on sales of a product. Note that Sales1 increases linearly throughout the period, with only a minor amount of "noise." (The third variable, Sales2, is discussed and used in the next problem.) For this problem use the Sales1 variable to see how the following forecasting methods are able to track a linear trend.

a. Forecast this series with the moving average method with various spans such as 3, 6, and 12. What can you conclude?

b. Forecast this series with simple exponential smoothing with various smoothing constants such as 0.1, 0.3, 0.5, and 0.7. What can you conclude?

c. Now repeat part **b** with Holt's exponential smoothing method, again for various smoothing constants. Can you do significantly better than in parts **a** and **b**?

d. What can you conclude from your findings in parts **a**, **b**, and **c** about forecasting this type of series?

80. The Sales2 variable in the file from the previous problem was created from the Sales1 variable by multiplying by monthly seasonal factors. Basically, the summer months are high and the winter months are low. This might represent the sales of a product that has a linear trend and seasonality.

a. Repeat parts **a**, **b**, and **c** from the previous problem to see how well these forecasting methods can deal with trend *and* seasonality.

b. Now use Winters' method, with various values of the three smoothing constants, to forecast the series. Can you do much better? Which smoothing constants work well?

c. Use the ratio-to-moving-average method, where you first do the seasonal decomposition and then forecast (by any appropriate method) the deseasonalized series. Does this do as well as, or better than, Winters' method?

d. What can you conclude from your findings in parts **a**, **b**, and **c** about forecasting this type of series?

81. The file **P13_81.xlsx** contains monthly time series data on federal expenditures in various categories. All values are in billions of current dollars. The variables are:

- Defense: expenditures on national defense
- Science: expenditures on science, space, and technology
- Energy: expenditures on energy
- Environ: expenditures on natural resources and environment
- Trans: expenditures on transportation

Analyze the Science variable by (a) simple exponential smoothing, (b) Holt's method, (c) simple exponential smoothing on the trend-adjusted data (the residuals from regressing linearly versus time), and (d) moving averages on the adjusted or unadjusted data. Experiment with the smoothing constants [or span in (d)], or use the optimize feature. Do any of these methods produce significantly better fits than the others as measured by RMSE or MAPE?

82. The data in the file **P13_82.xlsx** represent annual changes in the average surface air temperature of the earth. (The source doesn't say exactly how this was measured.) A look at the time series shows a gradual upward trend, starting with negative values and ending with (mostly) positive values. This might be used to support the theory of global warming.

a. Is this series a random walk? Explain.
b. Regardless of your answer in part **a**, use a random walk model to forecast the next value of the series. What is your forecast, and what is an approximate 95% forecast interval?
c. Forecast the series in three ways: (i) simple exponential smoothing ($\alpha = 0.35$), (ii) Holt's method ($\alpha = 0.5$, $\beta = 0.1$), and (iii) simple exponential smoothing ($\alpha = 0.3$) on trend-adjusted data, that is, the residuals from regressing linearly versus time. (These smoothing constants are close to "optimal.") For each of these, list the MAPE, the RMSE, and the forecast for next year. Also, comment on any "problems" with forecast errors from any of these three approaches. Finally, compare the "qualitative" features of the three forecasts (for example, how do their short-run or longer-run forecasts differ?). Is any one of the methods clearly superior to the others?
d. Does your analysis predict convincingly that global warming would occur during the observed years? Explain.

The Indiana University Credit Union Eastland Plaza Branch was having trouble getting the correct staffing levels to match customer arrival patterns. On some days, the number of tellers was too high relative to the customer traffic, so that tellers were often idle. On other days, the opposite occurred. Long customer waiting lines formed because the relatively few tellers could not keep up with the number of customers. The credit union manager, James Chilton, knew that there was a problem, but he had little of the quantitative training he believed would be necessary to find a better staffing solution. James figured that the problem could be broken down into three parts. First, he needed a reliable forecast of each day's number of customer arrivals. Second, he needed to translate these forecasts into staffing levels that would make an adequate trade-off between teller idleness and customer waiting. Third, he needed to translate these staffing levels into individual teller work assignments—who should come to work when.

The last two parts of the problem require analysis tools (queueing and scheduling) that we have not covered. However, you can help James with the first part—forecasting. The file **Credit Union Arrivals.xlsx** lists the number of customers entering this credit union branch each day of the past year. It also lists other information: the day of the week, whether the day was a staff or faculty payday, and whether the day was the day before or after a holiday. Use this data set to develop one or more forecasting models that James could use to help solve his problem. Based on your model(s), make any recommendations about staffing that appear reasonable. ∎

Amanta Appliances sells two styles of refrigerators at more than 50 locations in the Midwest. The first style is a relatively expensive model, whereas the second is a standard, less expensive model. Although weekly demand for these two products is fairly stable from week to week, there is enough variation to concern management at Amanta. There have been relatively unsophisticated attempts to forecast weekly demand, but they haven't been very successful. Sometimes demand (and the corresponding sales) are lower than forecasted, so that inventory costs are high. Other times the forecasts are too low. When this happens and on-hand inventory is not sufficient to meet customer demand, Amanta requires expedited shipments to keep customers happy—and this nearly wipes out Amanta's profit margin on the expedited units.[6] Profits at Amanta would almost certainly increase if demand could be forecasted more accurately.

Data on weekly sales of both products appear in the file **Amanta Sales.xlsx**. A time series chart of the two sales variables indicates what Amanta management expected—namely, there is no evidence of any upward or downward trends or of any seasonality. In fact, it might appear that each series is an unpredictable sequence of random ups and downs. But is this really true? Is it possible to forecast either series, with some degree of accuracy, with an extrapolation method (where only past values of *that* series are used to forecast current and future values)? What method appears to be best? How accurate is it? Also, is it possible, when trying to forecast sales of one product, to somehow incorporate current or past sales of the *other* product in the forecast model? After all, these products might be "substitute" products, where high sales of one go with low sales of the other, or they might be complementary products, where sales of the two products tend to move in the *same* direction. ∎

---

[6]Because Amanta uses expediting when necessary, its sales each week are equal to its customer demands. Therefore, we use the terms *demand* and *sales* interchangeably.